The
HANDBOOK *of*
ENVIRONMENTAL
COMPLIANCE *in*
ONTARIO

*To Cynthia, my wife, and the rest of my
family for their love and support*
—J.-D.P.

*To my parents for their unfailing support
and to Debra for her patience
and encouragement*
—B.G.I.

The
HANDBOOK *of* ENVIRONMENTAL COMPLIANCE *in* ONTARIO

John-David Phyper

Brett Ibbotson

McGraw-Hill Ryerson
Toronto   Montreal

First published in 1991 by
McGraw-Hill Ryerson Limited
330 Progress Avenue
Scarborough, Ontario M1P 2Z5

Acquisitions Editor: *Glen Ellis*

ISBN 0-07-551143-6

This publication is designed to provide accurate and authoritative information on the subject matter covered. It is sold with the understanding that neither the authors nor the publisher is engaged in rendering legal, accounting, or other professional advice.

∞ This book was printed and bound in Canada using acid-free paper.

1 2 3 4 5 6 7 8 9 10   THB   9 8 7 6 5 4 3 2 1 0

TABLE OF CONTENTS

LIST OF FIGURES...**xii**
LIST OF TABLES ....**xiii**
PREFACE..**xv**
ACKNOWLEDGEMENTS...**xvii**

1.0 THE CHANGING NATURE OF ENVIRONMENTAL MANAGEMENT.......**1**

2.0 AIR QUALITY AND ATMOSPHERIC EMISSIONS................................**9**
   2.1   OVERVIEW 9
   2.2   PROVINCIAL REGULATIONS 10
       2.2.1 Environmental Protection Act 10
       2.2.2 Other Provincial Regulations 11
   2.3   FEDERAL REGULATIONS...12
   2.4   OBTAINING APPROVALS FOR EMISSIONS....................13
   2.5   MONITORING...14
       2.5.1 Objectives 14
       2.5.2 Source Testing Technologies and Frequency 15
       2.5.3 Visible Emissions 15
       2.5.4 Ambient Air Sampling 16
       2.5.5 Odours 17
       2.5.6 The Need for Quality Assurance and Quality Control.........18
   2.6   MODELLING 18
       2.6.1 Overview 18
       2.6.2 Gaussian Plume Models 19
       2.6.3 Long-Range Transport Models.............................19
       2.6.4 Puff Models 19
       2.6.5 Regulation 308 Algorithms 19
       2.6.6 U.S. EPA Models..20
   2.7   REPORTING REQUIREMENTS 21
       2.7.1 General Requirements 21
       2.7.2 Incident Reporting 21
   2.8   PROPOSED CLEAN AIR PROGRAM 22
       2.8.1 Philosophy 22
       2.8.2 Establishing Control Requirements......................23
       2.8.3 Air Quality Standards 25
       2.8.4 Source Registration...25
       2.8.5 Approvals 26
       2.8.6 Modelling...27
       2.8.7 Interpretation of Model Results...........................28
       2.8.8 Non-Attainment Areas 29

2.9   SUMMARY...29

3.0 WATER QUALITY AND LIQUID DISCHARGES 41
3.1   OVERVIEW 41
3.2   PROVINCIAL REGULATIONS AND GUIDELINES
(EXCLUDING MISA) 42
    3.2.1 Environmental Protection Act 42
    3.2.2 Ontario Water Resources Act....................................42
    3.2.3 Water Quality Guidelines 43
3.3   MUNICIPAL AND INDUSTRIAL STRATEGY FOR
ABATEMENT (MISA) PROGRAM..45
    3.3.1 Goals and Objectives 45
    3.3.2 Direct Dischargers 45
    3.3.3 Phase I: Monitoring Regulation 46
    3.3.4 Phase II: Effluent Limit Regulation.............................49
    3.3.5 Phase III: Abatement and Enforcement.....................54
    3.3.6 Indirect Dischargesr...55
    3.3.7 Recommendations for Complying with MISA 55
3.4   FEDERAL REGULATIONS..56
    3.4.1 Canadian Environmental Protection Act 56
    3.4.2 Fisheries Act 57
3.5   MUNICIPAL REQUIREMENTS..57
    3.5.1 Discharges to Sanitary and Combined Sewers.............57
    3.5.2 Discharges to Storm Sewers 58
3.6   OBTAINING APPROVALS FOR DISCHARGES 60
3.7   MONITORING..61
    3.7.1 Monitoring Requirements 61
    3.7.2 Chemical Quality Parameters of Interest 61
    3.7.3 Surrogate Parameters 62
    3.7.4 Sample Collection and Preservation Methods 63
    3.7.5 Analytical Methods..64
    3.7.6 Quality Assurance and Quality Control 64
    3.7.7 Flow Measurement/Estimation Methods....................65
3.8   REPORTING REQUIREMENTS 67
    3.8.1 Reporting Monitoring Data 67
    3.8.2 Incident Reporting 67
3.9   SUMMARY...68

4.0 WASTE MANAGEMENT AND TRANSPORTATION 103
4.1   OVERVIEW OF THE REGULATORY FRAMEWORK....................103
    4.1.1 Provincial Regulations 103
    4.1.2 Federal Legislation..103
4.2   ASSIGNMENT OF RESPONSIBILITIES 104

4.2.1 Waste Generators 104
4.2.2 Transfer of Responsibility 104
4.2.3 Director's Orders 105
4.3 REGULATION 309 WASTE CLASSIFICATION
AND REGISTRATION..106
4.3.1 Overview 106
4.3.2 Hazardous Waste 106
4.3.3 Liquid Industrial Waste 110
4.3.4 Registerable Solid Waste 110
4.3.5 Exempt Wastes 111
4.3.6 Waste Registration..111
4.4 MANIFEST SYSTEM FOR REGISTERABLE WASTE.....................112
4.4.1 Manifests 112
4.4.2 Licensed Carriers 113
4.4.3 Licensed Transfer Stations and Disposal Sites 113
4.5 TRANSPORTATION...114
4.5.1 Documentation 114
4.5.2 Marking and Packaging...115
4.5.3 Safety Standards...115
4.5.4 Emergency Response Plans 115
4.5.5 Training...115
4.5.6 Notification..116
4.5.7 Inspections...116
4.5.8 Responsibilities 116
4.5.9 Classification 117
4.5.10 Exempt Materials 118
4.6 APPROVALS AND PERMITS..118
4.6.1 Waste Management Systems 118
4.6.2 Carriers 119
4.6.3 Transfer Stations...120
4.6.4 The Role of Public Hearings 120
4.6.5 Environmental Assessment...120
4.7 REDUCING, REUSING, AND RECYCLING WASTES...................121
4.8 SUMMARY...122

5.0 DECOMMISSIONING AND DISPOSITION OF
CONTAMINATED LAND..143
5.1 OVERVIEW 143
5.2 PROVINCIAL REGULATIONS AND LEGISLATION 144
5.3 DECOMMISSIONING 145
5.3.1 Current Practice and Guidelines 145
5.3.2 The Role of Ambient (Background) Concentrations............147
5.3.3 Communication and Public Participation 148

5.4   CLEAN-UP GUIDELINES...148
    5.4.1 The Three Options...148
    5.4.2 Relevant MOE Policies and Guidelines...............149
    5.4.3 Soil Guidelines Developed in Other Jurisdictions 149
    5.4.4 Developing Site-Specific Guidelines...................152
    5.4.5 Using Risk Assessment/Management Techniques
           to Develop Guidelines.......................................152
5.5   CLEAN-UP METHODS AND STRATEGIES 153
    5.5.1 Overview 153
    5.5.2 Specific Clean-up Technologies 154
5.6   LEGAL ASPECTS OF BUYING OR SELLING
     CONTAMINATED PROPERTY.......................................155
    5.6.1 The Role of Common Law 155
    5.6.2 The Role of Contract Law 156
5.7   AVOIDING CONTAMINATED PROPERTY 158
    5.7.1 Overview 158
    5.7.2 Review Historical Information 159
    5.7.3 MOE Files...160
    5.7.4 Company Files and Records 160
    5.7.5 Interviews...161
    5.7.6 Site Visits or Inspections 161
    5.7.7 On-Site Conditions to Note 162
    5.7.8 Preliminary Sampling 163
5.8   SUMMARY..164

6.0 NOISE AND VIBRATION 179
6.1   OVERVIEW 179
6.2   PROVINCIAL REGULATIONS 180
    6.2.1 Environmental Protection Act 180
    6.2.2 Municipal Noise By-Laws and Guidelines 181
    6.2.3 Vibration Guidelines..182
6.3   OBTAINING APPROVALS...182
6.4   MONITORING...183
    6.4.1 Estimating Noise Levels 183
    6.4.2 Noise Measurement...185
    6.4.3 Vibration Measurement 185
6.5   SUMMARY...185

7.0 SPECIAL MATERIALS 191
7.1   POLYCHLORINATED BIPHENYLS (PCBs)....................191
    7.1.1 Overview 191
    7.1.2 Definitions and Classifications.............................192
    7.1.3 Environmental Guidelines and Allowable Release Rates.....193

7.1.4 Manufacture, Importation, and Use 194
7.1.5 Decommissioning PCB Equipment 196
7.1.6 Decontamination of PCB Equipment 197
7.1.7 Storage of PCB Waste 198
7.1.8 Transportation...199
7.1.9 Destruction...201
7.1.10 Disposal 201
7.1.11 Summary 203
7.2 ASBESTOS...203
7.2.1 Overview 203
7.2.2 Removal Versus Management..204
7.2.3 Management of Asbestos Waste......................................205
7.2.4 Acceptable Concentrations in Air 206
7.2.5 Summary 206

8.0 ENFORCEMENT 221
8.1 BACKGROUND..221
8.2 INSPECTIONS 222
8.2.1 Authority and Responsibilities of Provincial Officers...........222
8.2.2 Timing of Inspections..222
8.2.3 Obligations of Those Being Inspected 223
8.2.4 Information Gathering 224
8.2.5 Confidentiality 224
8.3 INTERVIEWS 224
8.4 RESPONSES TO VIOLATIONS..226
8.4.1 MOE Responses...226
8.4.2 Federal Responses 228
8.4.3 Municipal Responses 230
8.5 PENALTIES AND LIABILITIES 230
8.5.1 Ontario Environmental Protection Act 230
8.5.2 Ontario Water Resources Act..231
8.5.3 Canadian Environmental Protection Act 232
8.5.4 Transport of Dangerous Goods Act 232
8.5.5 Fisheries Act 232
8.5.6 Municipal Act..233
8.6 DEFENSES AND MITIGATIVE FACTORS 233
8.6.1 Criminal Offences 233
8.6.2 Quasi-Criminal Offences 234
8.7 THE ROLE OF COMMON LAW...235
8.8 SUMMARY...236

9.0 ENVIRONMENTAL FATE 251
9.1 WHY BE CONCERNED ABOUT ENVIRONMENTAL FATE?.........251

9.2 KEY CHEMICAL PROPERTIES..252
9.3 KEY ENVIRONMENTAL PARAMETERS.........................253
9.4 PARTITION COEFFICIENTS...253
9.5 REACTION RATES AND HALF-LIVES...........................257
    9.5.1 Reaction Rates 257
    9.5.2 Overall Rate Constants 258
    9.5.3 Half-Lives 258
9.6 USING ENVIRONMENTAL FATE TO EVALUATE RELEASES.........258
    9.6.1 Overview 258
    9.6.2 Stack and Fugitive Emissions to the Atmosphere 259
    9.6.3 Spills onto Water 259
    9.6.4 Leaks from Underground Storage Tanks 260
9.7 ENVIRONMENTAL FATE MODELS..............................261

10.0 ENVIRONMENTAL AUDITS......................................271
10.1 WHAT IS AN ENVIRONMENTAL AUDIT?.....................271
10.2 PERTINENT REGULATIONS.....................................272
10.3 TYPES OF AUDITS...272
10.4 PREREQUISITES FOR CONDUCTING AUDITS..............274
10.5 STEPS OF AN AUDIT...274
    10.5.1 Selecting the Audit Team 274
    10.5.2 Pre-Audit Preparation 275
    10.5.3 Using Working Papers or Documents 276
    10.5.4 Deciding What to Audit..................................277
    10.5.5 Preparing the Audit Report 279
    10.5.6 Post-Audit Procedures 279
10.6 CONFIDENTIALITY..280
10.7 REACTING TO AN EXTERNAL AUDIT.........................281
10.8 SUMMARY..281

11.0 RISK ASSESSMENT AND MANAGEMENT 293
11.1 OVERVIEW 293
11.2 RISK ASSESSMENT 294
    11.2.1 Purpose and Elements....................................294
    11.2.2 Hazard Identification......................................295
    11.2.3 Exposure Assessment 295
    11.2.4 Dose-Response Assessment 298
    11.2.5 Risk Characterization......................................299
11.3 RISK MANAGEMENT 301
    11.3.1 The Need for Risk Management.........................301
    11.3.2 Factors That Often Need to Be Considered 302
    11.3.3 Possible Applications for Risk Management.........303
11.4 RISK COMMUNICATION 303

11.4.1 Overview 303
11.4.2 The Media 304
11.4.3 Members of the Public.................................. 304
11.5 SUMMARY.. 306

12.0 EMERGENCY PLANNING AND SPILLS 313
12.1 BACKGROUND 313
12.2 LEGAL REQUIREMENTS FOR NOTIFICATION 313
12.2.1 Environmental Protection Act 313
12.2.2 Ontario Water Resources Act........................ 314
12.2.3 Gasoline Handling Act 315
12.2.4 Transportation of Dangerous Goods Act 315
12.2.5 Canadian Environmental Protection Act 315
12.2.6 Ontario Spills Action Centre 316
12.2.7 Aspects of Uncertainty................................ 317
12.3 LEGAL REQUIREMENTS FOR RESTORATION............. 318
12.3.1 Environmental Protection Act 318
12.3.2 Gasoline Handling Act 318
12.3.3 Environmental Compensation Corporation 319
12.4 SPILL PREVENTION 319
12.5 TYPES OF EMERGENCY PROCEDURES AND PLANS 321
12.5.1 Emergency Response Plans........................... 321
12.5.2 Incident Reporting and Clean-up Procedures... 322
12.6 BEST MANAGEMENT PRACTICE PLANS 323
12.7 SHARING EMERGENCY RESPONSE INFORMATION 325
12.7.1 Response Organizations and Associations 325
12.7.2 The Role of the Community........................... 326
12.8 SUMMARY... 327

13.0 THE ROLE OF AQUATIC TOXICITY IN ENVIRONMENTAL
MANAGEMENT.. 331
13.1 BACKGROUND... 331
13.2 TYPES OF TOXICITY TESTS..................................... 332
13.2.1 Acute Lethality Tests 332
13.2.2 Acute Sublethal Tests 334
13.2.3 Sublethal Toxicity Tests 334
13.3 ONTARIO REQUIREMENTS..................................... 336
13.4 FEDERAL REQUIREMENTS 337
13.5 DETERMINING THE CAUSES OF EFFLUENT TOXICITY 337
13.5.1 Conventional Approach................................ 337
13.5.2 U.S. EPA Approach to Toxicant Identification ... 338
13.6 SUMMARY... 341

LIST OF FIGURES

FIGURE   **DESCRIPTION**

3.1   Proposed Process for Determining Effluent Limits 100
3.2   Methods of Calculating Effluent Limits..101
4.1   Waste Identification Flowchart 137
4.2   Environmental Protection Act Generator Registration Report 138
4.3   Regulation 309 Manifest..140
4.4   TDGA Marking for Class 2—Gases...141
4.5   Responsibilities During Transportation Under TDGA.....................142
7.1   PCB Label for Large Equipment 214
7.2   PCB Label for Small Equipment 215
7.3   PCB General Warning Label...216
7.4   PCB Warning Label for Contaminated Equipment..........................217
7.5   TDGA PCB Label 218
7.6   TDGA Class 9 Label 219
7.7   TDGA Class 9 Placard...220
8.1   MOE Organizational Chart...250
9.1   Atmospheric Transport and Transformation Processes 268
9.2   Transport and Transformation of Chemicals in Water 269
9.3   Leakage from an Underground Storage Tank 270
10.1   Typical Block Diagram of Emissions, Discharges and
       Waste Streams 291
10.2   Audit Information Gathered at Three Types of Release Points 292
11.1   Risk Assessment and Risk Management Processes..........................311
11.2   Schematic Plot of Response as a Function of Exposure 312
13.1   Conventional Approach to Identifying Effluent Toxicants 344
13.2   Flowchart for Toxicity Reduction Evaluations 345
13.3   Toxicity Investigation Evaluations—Phase I Tests 346

LIST OF TABLES

TABLE   **DESCRIPTION**

1.1   Summary of Major Ontario and Federal Environmental Acts 6
1.2   Environmental Principles for Corporations...7
2.1   Point-of-Impingement Concentrations 31
2.2   Partial List of Sampling Protocols...37
2.3   Odour Recognition Thresholds..38
2.4   Proposed Interim List of Level 1 Contaminants 39
2.5   CAP Control Technology Classifications and Requirements 40
3.1   Water Quality Guidelines..70
3.2   Drinking Water Quality Objectives 73
3.3   Schedule 1—Analytical Test Group Numbers and Parameters 75
3.4   Limits on Discharges to Sanitary and Combined Sewers 82
3.5   Limits on Discharges to Storm Sewers...83
3.6   Sample Preservatives 84
3.7   Schedule 3, Part A—Analytical Principles and Analytcal Method
       Detection Limits 85
4.1   MOE Waste Classes..124
4.2   Schedule 4 Leachate Quality Criteria 130
4.3   TDGA Classifications of Dangerous Goods 132
4.4   Approaches to Waste Reduction..135
4.5   Waste Exchanges 136
5.1   Examples of Regulations That Can Be Applied to Decommissioning
       and Site Clean-up 168
5.2   Upper Limit of Normal (ULN) Values for Soils 170
5.3   MOE Soil Clean-up Guidelines...171
5.4   MOE Interim Soil Quality Guidelines 172
5.5   Soil and Ground Water Guidelines Recommended by MENVIQ ...173
5.6   Other Sources of Clean-up Guidelines..177
5.7   Preliminary Guide to Assessing Environmental Liabilities 178
6.1   Representative Sound Sources and Levels.......................................187
6.2   Publications Within the MOE Model Municipal Noise Control
       By-Law...188
6.3   Index of Noise Guidelines 189
6.4   Selected References Concerning Sound Measurement....................190
7.1   Summary of PCB Regulations 208
7.2   Physical Parameter Values of Selected PCBs 209
7.3   Allowable Concentrations of PCBs 210
7.4   PCB Storage Facility Requirements 211
7.5   Requirements for Managing Asbestos Wastes 213

8.1   Powers of Provincial Officers Under EPA 238
8.2   Examples of Municipal Enforcement Strategy Using the Model
        Sewer Use By-Law 239
8.3   Penalties Under the Ontario EPA 240
8.4   Examples of Ticketable Offences Under EPA 242
8.5   Penalties Under the OWRA 244
8.6   Penalties Under the CEPA 245
8.7   Penalties Under the TDGA 247
8.8   Penalties Under the Fisheries Act 248
8.9   Penalties Under the Model Sewer Use By-Law (Section 321 of the
        Municipal Act) 249
9.1   Key Environmental Parameters 265
9.2   Selected Environmental Fate Models 266
10.1   Regulations Relevant to Environmental Audits 284
10.2   Checklist for Preparing for an Environmental Audit 287
10.3   What Gets Audited 288
11.1   EPA Rules and Guidelines for Effective Risk Communication 309
12.1   Quantities or Levels for Immediate Reporting Under TDGA 329
12.2   Potential Equipment for Spill Containment and Clean-up 330
13.1   Acute Lethality Test Protocols 343

Preface

The past few years have witnessed a rapid increase in the number of books being published about environmental issues, awareness, philosophy, and management. Some are global in scope and address issues such as deforestation, the greenhouse effect, and the environmental implications of sustainable development. Many are directed toward individuals and ask the readers to re-evaluate their personal attitudes and contributions to recycling, conservation, and the efficient use of energy. Yet others are like textbooks or references: compilations of acts, regulations, standards, by-laws, policies, and guidelines that collectively represent the regulatory framework that now exists for achieving various environmental goals and objectives.

This book is not one of those. It is not global in scope, nor is it intended to help the average person to become more environmentally friendly. It is primarily directed at those people who are responsible for ensuring that various types of businesses and industrial activities in Ontario comply with environmental regulations and requirements—individuals who, whether they look after a small shop or direct the environmental affairs of a large corporation, have a personal stake in environmental management.

The Ontario Environmental Protection Act clearly states that every director or officer of a company has *a duty to take all reasonable care* to prevent the company from contravening the Act. Furthermore, it is an offence for anyone to fail to carry out that duty. It is possible for an individual to be prosecuted even if the company has not been prosecuted or convicted for an offence.

Until now, an environmental manager in Ontario likely would need to have copies of several acts, regulations, municipal by-laws, policy statements, and guidelines close at hand. Over the past few years, matters have become more complex, with the emergence of programs such as MISA and CAP, and new terms such as "environmental audits", "lowest achievable emission rate", "decommissioning", and "toxicity reduction evaluations".

To compound the situation, there now appears to be a genuine and substantial shifting of societal expectations, so that corporations will need to assume a much greater degree of environmental responsibility and accountability.

In such a period of transition, the environmental manager is hard pressed to find enough time to keep informed. While there are some publications that compile environmental regulations, seldom do those publications cut to the heart of the regulation or offer guidance on how to achieve compliance.

It is with this environmental manager in mind that the *Handbook of Environmental Compliance in Ontario* has been prepared. Specifically, the *Handbook* tries to provide information succinctly and directly that addresses the following questions:

- What are the applicable environmental regulations and requirements for a specific situation?
- What should be monitored or tested to evaluate compliance?
- What methods are there for achieving compliance?
- What are the penalties for not complying?
- Are things likely to change in the near future? If so, how?

The *Handbook* addresses a broad range of topics, including air quality and atmospheric emissions, water quality and liquid effluents, waste management and transportation, site decommissioning, noise and vibration, special materials (PCBs and asbestos), enforcement, environmental fate, auditing, risk assessment and management, emergency planning and spills, and the role of aquatic toxicity in environmental management.

The material in this book is based on the experience and opinions of the authors, and on written information available at the time the book was being prepared. Every effort has been made to ensure that the information is current and reflects some of the latest developments in environmental management. The authors welcome suggestions for ways to improve the *Handbook* and information on any errors or misinterpretations that may have been included.

Acknowledgments

This *Handbook* represents the efforts of more than the two authors. During its preparation, and even before, many others shared information, experience, and opinions.

To ensure that the material contained in the *Handbook* has been presented properly and is current, draft versions of each chapter were reviewed by individuals active in that particular area of environmental management. All of the following people freely gave of their time and ideas, and the authors are indebted to each of them for this assistance:

Mr. A. Adler: Coordinator, Waste and Audits, Stelco Inc.

Mr. R. Cameron: Superintendent of Protective Measures, Nanticoke Refinery, Esso Petroleum Canada

Mr. G. Craig: Director, Toxicology, Beak Consultants

Mr. D. Edwardson: Manager, Regulatory Affairs, Laidlaw Environmental Services Limited

Dr. H. Goodfellow: President, Goodfellow Consultants

Ms. H. Hattemer-Frey: Senior Risk Assessment Specialist, Advanced Sciences Inc. (formerly at Oak Ridge National Laboratories)

Mr. D. Hopper: Principal, Angus Environmental Limited

Mr. J. Langan: Sales Supervisor, Laidlaw Environmental Services Limited

Dr. D. Mackay: Professor of Chemical Engineering, University of Toronto

Mr. B. Powers: Senior Environmental Scientist, Angus Environmental Limited

Mr. R. Redhead: Director, Government Relations, Laidlaw Inc.

Mr. M. Richardson: Science Advisor, Environmental Health Directorate, Health Protection Branch, Health and Welfare Canada

Ms. C. Sefton: Counsel, Willms & Shier

Mr. E. Villeneuve: Manager, Environmental Auditing, Noranda Inc.

Mr. G. Zikovitz: Head, Spills Action Centre, Ontario Ministry of the
    Environment

1.0

The Changing Nature of Environmental Management

DURING THE PAST FEW DECADES, there have been several occasions when there were indications that major changes were about to occur in our attitudes and actions toward the environment. The 1960s brought calls for environmental management and by the early 1970s, several major pieces of environmental legislation were being enacted and environmental agencies were being established. But this movement seemed to lose some of its momentum in the mid-70s and early-80s, perhaps because many individuals and companies did not yet perceive an immediate stake in proper managing of the environment. And now, as if riding a pendulum, environmental issues have come back into prominence. This latest surge, however, promises to be distinctly different from earlier efforts. For several reasons, including those outlined below, it will become increasingly difficult to dismiss, ignore, or circumvent the latest tide of change that is occurring to the nature of environmental management.

Environmental regulations are becoming more comprehensive in virtually all aspects of sampling, analysis, and interpretation. More and more regulations outline how samples are to be gathered, the numbers of samples to be collected, which parameters should be measured, how they should be analyzed, and the frequency with which the results must be reported.

Environmental regulations are becoming more stringent. Not only do regulations address more parameters than ever before but the acceptable concentrations of many parameters continue to become more protective of the environment. This is partially the result of continuing advances in analytical techniques which allow smaller and smaller quantities of substances to be measured. It also is influenced by the public resistance that any effort to reduce stringency would face even if less stringent objectives are warranted or supported by scientific information.

Environmental regulations are becoming more complex as they address more aspects of environmental management (such as those noted

1

above) but also due to the participation of more agencies. Laws to protect the environment can be passed by all three levels of government in Canada.

Federal responsibilities for environmental legislation include environmental management at federal facilities (such as airports and international harbours), interprovincial transportation (by road), discharges that may be deleterious to fish, the import and export of goods and wastes, and issues deemed to be in the national interest such as the proper management of special materials (such as polychlorinated biphenyls). The recently issued Canadian Environmental Protection Act (CEPA) covers the registration of new chemicals and will be used to develop regulations to control chemicals on the Priority Substance List.

Provincial jurisdiction includes emissions to air, discharges to water, waste management, and road transportation within a province. Federal regulations can be used by provincial agencies if province-specific regulations have not been passed, but Ontario has issued regulations for many environmental situations. The environmental legislation that has been enacted and proposed over the last few years in Ontario has put it at the forefront of environmental regulation. Keeping pace with the changes has become a major challenge. Table 1.1 lists many of the major pieces of environmental legislation in Ontario and the corresponding federal acts.

Municipal governments can impose environmental requirements on activities within their jurisdictions or that use their facilities. Many municipalities have established requirements for discharges to municipal waste water treatment systems. An increasing number of municipalities in Ontario are becoming involved with the siting and operating of solid waste management facilities. Some have established environmental protection offices or departments which investigate situations of concern. Municipal agencies often act in a cooperative and/or support role to provincial agencies.

Environmental agencies are becoming more resolute in identifying and prosecuting offenders. New provincial legislation such as the Environmental Statute Amendment Act of 1988 provides provincial representatives with greater powers of search and seizure of information and records and greater authority to prosecute those who do not comply. The creation of the Investigations and Enforcement Branch of the Ontario Ministry of the Environment (MOE) illustrates the intent of that agency to pursue offenders.

The liabilities and penalties for non-compliance have greatly increased. New legislation squarely places responsibility not only on corporations and organizations but also on their officers and managers. Both federal and provincial legislation makes the officers of a company who participate, authorize, or acquiesce to an offence guilty of the offence and liable for punishment. Stiff fines and jail terms can be imposed.

Public attitudes and expectations are changing. While the regulatory framework is undergoing massive change, those changes may become secondary to the sweeping changes in attitude among individuals that are now beginning to influence the marketplace and reach into corporate boardrooms. More Canadians than ever before believe that government must get tougher with polluters, even if it means closing facilities and the loss of jobs in their community. Changes in broadly-held attitudes and expectations will have the greatest impact on how environmental management strategies and policies evolve.

Corporate attitudes and expectations are changing. It is not important to determine which came first: the recent awakening of environmental awareness or the new vigour of environmental policy making. What is important is that they support one another. In response to growing concern about the environment, the increased costs of compliance, and the increased liabilities, several companies are taking the lead in environmental protection. The "greening" of the boardroom is underway and spreading quickly. Many companies are beginning to realize that pollution is bad for business and that sound environmental management can protect and enhance the value of physical assets as well as corporate reputations.

Companies that do not have acceptable environmental records will have to struggle for credibility with the public. Each company will have to wrestle with what is the most appropriate way for it to respond to the changes that are occurring. One component of corporate response could be to adopt principles such as those listed in Table 1.2 which are based on the "Valdez Principles", a set of environmental objectives drafted by concerned investors after the tanker accident that spilled oil at Valdez, Alaska in 1989. Such principles can form a code of ethics that would require a company to curb pollution, reduce waste, offer compensation for environmental damage, and report every year about their operations with respect to the environment.

Given all of these changes, how can this *Handbook* help? The *Handbook* is intended to serve as a guide that plant managers, environmental engineers, advisors, and students can consult to understand regulatory requirements, the way(s) to achieve compliance, and the liabilities posed by various types of operations and activities. Each of the following twelve chapters addresses a distinct facet of environmental management in terms of current and proposed legislation, obtaining approvals and permits, methods used to assess compliance, sampling and modelling techniques, penalties and liabilities, and reporting requirements.

Chapter 2 - Air Quality and Atmospheric Emissions presents current regulatory requirements as defined by the Environmental Protection Act (EPA) and Regulation 308 and those being proposed under the Clean

Air Program (CAP). CAP will drastically change the regulatory framework from the current system of point-of-impingement values to one based on bottom-of-the-stack controls and total airshed assessment. The stated objective of CAP is the virtual elimination of toxic emissions.

Chapter 3 - Water Quality and Liquid Discharges focuses on the Municipal, Industrial Strategy for Abatement (MISA) program currently being implemented in Ontario. MISA is "technology driven" and requires that dischargers install the best available technology that is economically achievable (BATEA). Eventually it will be applied to all direct and indirect liquid dischargers including those to storm and sanitary sewers. The stated objective of MISA is the virtual elimination of persistent toxic substances from Ontario discharges.

Chapter 4 - Waste Management and Transportation are the focus of EPA Regulation 309. The regulation requires a comprehensive system for monitoring hazardous and liquid industrial wastes from point of generation to ultimate disposal. The chapter also provides information on the provincial and federal Transportation of Dangerous Goods Acts, both of which describe the requirements in terms of packing, labelling, etc. of dangerous goods, including wastes, during transportation.

Chapter 5 - Decommissioning and Disposition of Contaminated Land are pressing environmental issues whenever contaminated properties are being considered for sale or redevelopment. Like most jurisdictions, Ontario is faced with the difficult task of insuring that contaminated properties are adequately cleaned up prior to rezoning, reuse, or transfer. Recent guidelines on the decommissioning/clean-up of contaminated sites are discussed along with steps to conduct a pre-purchase site audit or inspection. In addition to the guidelines, other pertinent statutes and restrictions under common law and contract law are presented.

Chapter 6 - Noise and Vibration are defined as a contaminants under the EPA. The regulation of noise for the most part, however, is through municipal by-laws which in turn are influenced by the MOE Model Municipal Noise Control By-Law. A brief overview of the noise guidelines in Ontario is presented.

Chapter 7 - Special Materials such as polychlorinated biphenyls (PCBs) are probably one of the most regulated groups of chemicals in Canada. There exist both provincial and federal regulations governing the use, storage, handling, transportation and disposal of PCBs. This chapter also presents the regulatory requirements for asbestos along with information on inspection and storage.

Chapter 8 - Enforcement is a key part of environmental regulation. In Ontario, the Investigation and Enforcement Branch of the MOE investigates and makes recommendations regarding appropriate legal remedies against pollution and polluters as well as supplies information in support of prosecutions. The chapter discusses the various levels of government response to violations and describes both corporate and individual responses to site visits and interviews. Liabilities and penalties under various acts and regulations are summarized.

Chapter 9 - Environmental Fate is a primer to understanding the behaviour of chemicals in the environment which can be a valuable aid to managing the production, storage, handling, transportation, and disposal of chemicals. Information is presented on key environmental parameters, partition coefficients, reaction rates, transport and transformation processes.

Chapter 10 - Environmental Audits increasingly are being incorporated into environmental management programs. Recent changes in regulatory requirements further emphasize the need for well-planned audits. This chapter discusses the objectives and potential applications for various types of audits and addresses the issue of confidentiality.

Chapter 11 - Risk Assessment and Management have become essential to identifying potential sources of risk. Different approaches to risk assessment and the situations where risk assessment can be applied are presented.

Chapter 12 - Emergency Planning and Spills describes the types of procedures that need to be in place to respond to unscheduled releases of materials. In Ontario, Part IX of the EPA (also known as the "Spills Bill") outlines the responsibilities and requirements for the notification and restoration following a spill. The chapter discusses the legal requirements following a spill and spill prevention. In addition, the implications of the proposed use of Best Management Practice (BMP) plans are discussed.

Chapter 13 - The Role of Aquatic Toxicity in Environmental Management describes how toxicity testing is being incorporated into the regulation of liquid effluents. The different types of toxicity tests (acute and chronic) are described as is the potential role of Toxicity Reduction Evaluations.

Table 1.1
SUMMARY OF MAJOR ONTARIO AND FEDERAL ENVIRONMENTAL ACTS

Ontario Acts
- Conservation Authorities Act
- Dangerous Goods Transportation Act
- Environmental Assessment Act
- Environmental Protection Act
- Environmental Protection Statute Law Amendment Act
- Environmental Statute Amendment Act
- Gasoline Handling Act
- Municipal Act
- Ontario Water Resources Act
- Penalties Adjustment Act
- Pesticides Act
- Planning Act

Federal Acts
- Arctic Water Pollution Prevention Act
- Canadian Environmental Protection Act
- Canadian Water Act
- Fisheries Act
- International River Improvement Act
- Northern Inland Waters Act
- Transportation of Dangerous Goods Act

Table 1.2
ENVIRONMENTAL PRINCIPLES FOR CORPORATIONS

---

1. Protection of the Biosphere
Minimize and strive to eliminate the release of substances that may damage the environment or its inhabitants. Safeguard wildlife habitat and open spaces, while preserving biodiversity. Minimize contributions to global concerns such as the greenhouse effect, depletion of the ozone layer, and acid rain.

2. Sustainable Use of Natural Resources
Use natural resources such as water, soils, and forests in ways that are sustainable. Conserve nonrenewable natural resources through efficient use and careful planning.

3. Reduction and Disposal of Waste
Minimize the creation of waste, especially hazardous waste. Wherever possible recycle materials. Dispose wastes safely and responsibly.

4. Efficient Use of Energy
Invest in improved energy efficiency and conservation. Maximize the energy efficiency of products and services.

5. Risk Reduction
Minimize the environmental, health, and safety risks to employees and local communities by employing safe technologies and operating procedures and by being constantly prepared for emergencies.

6. Market Safe Products and Services
Offer products or services that minimize adverse environmental impacts. Inform consumers of the environmental benefits and/or impacts of products or services.

7. Damage Compensation
Take responsibility for harm caused to the environment. Be prepared to restore the environment and compensate persons who are adversely affected.

8. Disclosure
Disclose incidents that cause environmental harm or pose undue hazards to employees and to the public. Disclose potential environmental, health or safety hazards posed by operations. Do not take action against employees

who report any condition that creates a danger to the environment or poses health and safety hazards.

9. Environmental Directors and Managers

Appoint at least one senior officer who is qualified to represent environmental interests. Have them report directly to the chief executive officer. Commit resources to implement these principles and report on a regular basis as to their implementation.

10. Assessment and Annual Audit

Publicly report on progress in implementing these principles and in complying with all applicable laws and regulations.

11. Incorporate the Importance of Environmental Management into Corporate Attitudes

Recognize that environmental management is not something to be avoided or dismissed. Realize that proper environmental management can protect and enhance physical assets and corporate reputations.

2.0

Air Quality and Atmospheric Emissions

2.1 OVERVIEW

Maintaining and/or improving the quality of the air are fundamental components of environmental management. Like most aspects of environmental science and technology, the abilities to measure substances in the air and emission sources, control emissions from various types of sources, identify changes in air quality, and understand the fate and transportation of substances emitted into the atmosphere have improved greatly and continue to improve. At the same time, man's activities have lead to increasing amounts of substances being emitted to the atmosphere.

As recently as the 1970s, air quality concerns tended to be local in nature and often were limited to parameters such as carbon monoxide, sulfur dioxide, or nitrogen oxides, dust, and a few metals. Today's concerns are just as likely to concern regional "airsheds", transboundary migration of substances, or global issues such as acidic precipitation and ozone depletion. Frequently, the substances being studied are those emitted in trace amounts.

In Canada, the control of air pollution sources is largely a provincial responsibility and Ontario has a relatively comprehensive package of regulation, policies, standards, and guidelines in place. Sections 2.2 and 2.3 describe the current provincial and federal regulations, respectively. Section 2.4 outlines the current process followed by the MOE for issuing approvals to emission sources. Section 2.5 describes various techniques that can be used to monitor concentrations of substances in emissions and ambient air. Mathematical models that can be used to estimate air quality are presented in Section 2.6. The current requirements to provide information about sources to the MOE are outlined in Section 2.7.

Many of the aspects of air quality management in Ontario described in Sections 2.4 through 2.7 are entering a transitional phase as current practices become updated, augmented, or replaced in response to the proposed

Clean Air Program, which is outlined in Section 2.8. With the ultimate goal of virtually eliminating toxic emissions from stationary sources, the Clean Air Program will promote lower emission rates and more stringent control technologies, require more information before emission sources are approved, advocate the use of more sophisticated mathematical models for predicting concentrations of substances in air, require emissions to be monitored more often and for more substances, and make information more accessible to the public. In doing so, the Clean Air Program has the potential to alter air quality management efforts and responsibilities of the owners and/or operators of all but the smallest stationary sources of emissions in Ontario.

2.2 PROVINCIAL REGULATIONS

2.2.1 Environmental Protection Act

The Environmental Protection Act (EPA) of 1971 is a broadly worded piece of legislation directed toward the protection and conservation of the natural environment. While much of the original text does not specifically address air quality or atmospheric emissions, those aspects of environmental management are included in the broad intent and general language of the EPA. For example, Part II, Section 13(1) requires that no person shall discharge a contaminant or cause or permit the discharge of a contaminant into the natural environment that causes or is likely to cause an adverse effect. Section 1(1) defines "adverse effect" as:

- impairment of the natural environment for any use that can be made of it,
- injury or damage to property or plant or animal life,
- harm or material discomfort to any person,
- an adverse effect on the health of any person,
- impairment of the safety of any person,
- rendering any property or plant or animal life unfit for use by man,
- loss of enjoyment of normal use of property, and
- interference with the normal conduct of business.

Obviously, several of these types of adverse effects can be caused by emissions to the atmosphere or the way(s) that emissions effect air quality. For example, the loss of enjoyment of normal use of property can include nuisances such as odour and dust.

Air quality and atmospheric emissions are addressed specifically within the EPA by **Regulation 308** which consists of a General Section, Schedule 1 which lists various prescribed air quality concentrations, and an Appendix that describes various air pollution dispersion algorithms.

The **General Section of Regulation 308** addresses the control of air contaminants and use of the Air Pollution Index (API). There is an allowance for curtailing operations of sources of air emissions when the

API reaches certain levels.

Section 5 of the General Section forbids a person from causing or permitting the concentration of a contaminant to exceed the values set out in Schedule 1 at prescribed locations called points of impingement.

Section 6 requires that no person shall cause or permit to be caused the emission of any air contaminant to the extent or degree as may:

- cause discomfort to persons,
- cause loss of enjoyment of normal use of property,
- interfere with normal conduct of business, or
- cause damage to property.

There is some redundancy and inconsistency between the requirements of Section 6 of Regulation 308 and those of Part II, Section 13 of the EPA.

Sections 8(1) and 8(2) of the General Section allow for the control of visible emissions (those that obstruct the passage of light). Requirements for visible emissions are described in Section 2.5.3.

The **Appendix of Regulation 308** presents algorithms (equations) for calculating half-hour, point-of-impingement (POI) concentrations. Different algorithms are identified for various configurations of emission sources, receptor locations, and wake effects of adjacent buildings. The algorithms and input parameters are described in Section 2.6.

Schedule 1 of Regulation 308 contains the half-hour, POI standards for approximately 100 substances which are summarized in Table 2.1. In addition to the standards, the MOE also publishes POI guidelines. Both types of values are regularly updated by the MOE and published in the "List of Ambient Air Quality Criteria, Standards and Guidelines".

The MOE has identified several deficiencies in the current version of Regulation 308 (MOE, 1987a). For example, the overall approach is one that allows dilution to be a means of managing emissions while not encouraging the control of emissions at source. There is no opportunity for direct public participation in setting standards or the process of issuing Certificates of Approval (C of A). There is no provision for a C of A to be reviewed or to expire.

The science of air dispersion modelling has advanced considerably since Regulation 308 was first issued. Some of the specific deficiencies in the modelling approach described in Regulation 308 include the inability to address multiple sources, long-range transport and deposition, very short-term effects, very long-term effects, and synergistic effects of pollutants.

2.2.2 Other Provincial Regulations

Several regulations have been passed to control air emissions from specific industries or industrial sectors in Ontario. These include:

- Regulation 151/81: Lambton Industry Meteorological Alert
- Regulation 281/87: Ontario Hydro
- Regulation 295: Air Contaminants from Ferrous Foundries
- Regulation 297: Asphalt Paving Plants
- Regulation 660/85: Inco Sudbury Smelter Complex - 1994
- Regulation 661/85: Falconbridge Smelter Complex - 1994
- Regulation 663/85: Algoma Sinter Operations - 1986/94

Provincial regulations also have been passed to control the emissions from motor vehicles (Regulation 311), the sulfur content of fuels (Regulation 312), emissions from mobile PCB destruction facilities (Regulation 14/86), emissions from boilers (Regulation 16/86), and emissions of pesticides (Regulation 751).

2.3 FEDERAL REGULATIONS

Prior to 1988, the Clean Air Act was the only piece of federal legislation that covered air pollution. In 1988, the Clean Air Act, the Environmental Contaminants Act, and the Ocean Dumping Control Act were consolidated into the Canadian Environmental Protection Act (CEPA). The key elements of CEPA that are relevant to air quality and atmospheric emissions include:

- provisions to control all aspects of the life cycle of toxic substances including development, manufacturing, storage, transportation, use, and disposal
- the regulation of fuels and components of fuels
- the regulation of emissions from federal departments, boards, agencies, and Crown corporations
- provisions to create guidelines and environmentally safe codes of practice
- provisions to control sources of air pollution in Canada where a violation of international agreement would otherwise result

Section 34 provides for regulating substances specified in Schedule 1, List of Toxic Substances. Schedule 1 also states that the control of atmospheric releases is the most appropriate approach to regulating asbestos (mines and mills), lead (secondary lead smelters), mercury (chloro-alkali mercury plants), and vinyl chloride (vinyl chloride and polyvinyl chloride plants).

While the main responsibility to control air pollution sources is a provincial jurisdiction, the federal government can establish ambient air quality objectives and encourage provinces to adopt them as binding standards.

The Canadian Council of Ministers of the Environment (CCME) directed the federal-provincial steering committee for Long Range Transport of Air Pollution (LRTAP) to develop a comprehensive **Management Plan for Nitrogen Oxides (NO$_x$) and Volatile Organic Compounds**

(VOCs). The Management Plan was designed to identify domestic environmental protection requirements and to ensure that Canada fulfilled its international obligations.

The objective of the Plan is to reduce the one-hour ambient air concentration of ozone to below 82 ppb (160 ug/m^3) across Canada. Both NO_x and VOCs are precursors to ozone formation. The plan will be implemented over a 15-year period and will employ approximately 60 initiatives. The initiatives include (Delbridge Association, 1990):

- vehicle emission standards
- energy conservation measures
- gasoline vapour recovery for service stations
- industrial source control
- power generation source control
- urban transportation management plans
- product modifications

The Management Plan has been designed to be flexible enough so that provinces can replace parts of the plan with equivalent packages. It is anticipated that the Plan will have little impact on Ontario industry as the Clean Air Program (CAP) includes the control of NO_x and VOCs.

2.4 OBTAINING APPROVALS FOR EMISSIONS

Section 8(1) of the EPA requires that a Certificate of Approval (C of A) must be obtained by any person who intends to:

- construct, alter, extend or replace any plant, structure, equipment, apparatus, mechanism or thing that may discharge or from which may be discharged a contaminant into any part of the natural environment other than water; or
- alter the process or rate of production with the result that a contaminant may be discharged into any part of the natural environment other than water or the rate or manner of discharge of a contaminant into any part of the natural environment other than water may be altered.

Section 8(3) identifies several exemptions from the requirement to obtain a C of A:

a) routine maintenance carried out on any plant, structure, equipment, apparatus, mechanism or thing;

b) equipment for the combustion of fuel, other than waste incinerators, in buildings or structures designed for the housing of not more than three families;

c) any equipment, apparatus, mechanism or thing in or used in connection with a building or structure designed for the housing of not more than three families where the only contaminant produced by such equipment, apparatus, mechanism or thing is sound or vibration;

d) any plant, structure, equipment, apparatus, mechanism or thing that may be a source of contaminant of a class exempted from by the regulation;

e) any plant, structure, equipment, apparatus, mechanism or thing used in agriculture;

f) any motor or motor vehicle that is subject to the provisions of EPA, Part III

The process used by the MOE for evaluating atmospheric emission applications has started to include components of the Clean Air Program (see Section 2.8). For example, it is becoming common practice to require emitters of more than 800 g annually of benzene to perform a Level 1 assessment.

To obtain a C of A, any or all of the following types of information may need to be provided:

• a complete description of the process
• a site plan
• zoning maps for the general area
• estimates of the maximum probable emission rates based on the testing of similar sources, mass balances, fuel consumption and composition information, or other valid engineering data
• dispersion calculations using algorithms presented in the Appendix of Regulation 308 (see Section 2.6)
• comparison of POI concentrations to guidelines/standards
• assurances that pollution control equipment will be maintained and the records kept for two years

2.5 MONITORING

2.5.1 Objectives

Monitoring may be needed or advisable for various reasons. Routine monitoring may be a requirement of a control order, C of A, or other directive. An emitter may monitor as part of an internal environmental management program. Special or one-time efforts may be undertaken to investigate specific conditions. Whatever the reason, it is vital that the individuals who collect samples, whether for regulatory purposes or as part of an internal sampling program, be properly trained, follow acceptable protocols, and have samples analyzed using techniques with appropriate detection limits. The cost of air sampling programs and potential impact on evaluations of compliance or decisions to change control technology do not allow for a haphazard approach.

2.5.2 Source Testing Technologies and Frequency

The protocols for source testing are lengthy and comprehensive. Table 2.2 presents a partial list of references for pertinent air sampling protocols. The MOE Source Testing Code (Version 2) describes the currently preferred methodologies. These include:

Method 1:   location of sampling site and sampling points

Method 2:   determination of stack gas velocity and volumetric flow rate

Method 3:   determination of molecular weight of dry stack gas

Method 4:   determination of moisture content of stack gases

Method 5:   determination of particulate matter emissions from stationary sources

There are several basic types of techniques that can be used to sample emissions points such as stacks and exhausts. Gaseous emissions can be sampled and analyzed using continuous, direct-reading instruments. Particulate matter is sampled using isokinetic sample trains. Many organic compounds are sampled using non-isokinetic sample trains that include appropriate absorption solutions or adsorbents. Metals may be present in several forms simultaneously (adsorbed to particles, as vapours, as fumes) and therefore should be sampled using a combination of isokinetic and adsorbents. Dioxins, furans, and trace organic compounds usually are sampled using a modified, particulate matter sampling train.

Isokinetic sampling involves matching the sampling velocity with the gas velocity through alterations in the volumetric flow rate of the sample and the probe nozzle diameter (Sparks, 1984).

Once the proposed Clean Air Program is enacted, the frequency of stack sampling will be dictated by the type of contaminant being emitted (see Section 2.8). Stack sampling for hazardous chemicals may be required once every twelve months. Other types of material may be monitored less frequently.

Emissions from many combustion processes are now believed to be sources of dioxins and furans. Because of concerns about the potential human health effects and environmental distribution of these compounds, considerable attention is being directed at quantifying and reducing combustion emissions. If the MOE suspects that dioxins and furans may be formed during an industrial process, especially one involving high temperatures, a dioxin and furan sampling program may be required.

2.5.3 Visible Emissions

Many emissions are visible due to the presence of liquid sprays or mists, solid particles, or coloured gases. Sections 8(1) and 8(2) of Regulation 308 describe how the acceptability of a visible emission is determined based on its opacity (the degree to which it obstructs the passage of light):

(1)　Subject to subsection (2), no person shall cause or permit to be caused a visible emission that obstructs the passage of light to a degree greater than 20% at the point of emission.

(2)　A visible emission from a source of combustion employing solid fuel may obstruct the passage of light to a degree greater than 20% but no greater than 40% at the point of emission for a period of not more than four minutes in the aggregate in any 30-minute period.

Opacity is the most commonly used parameter for evaluating emissions from stationary sources. There are two ways to determine the opacity of visible emissions: observations of certified observers and Light Detection and Ranging (LIDAR).

The MOE regularly offers courses for training people to become certified as visible emissions observers. The classroom instruction component of the training addresses types of sources, legislation, and the roles of factors such as sun angle, plume angle, and point of observation. Individuals are familiarized with plumes of various colours and opacities. A certificate that is valid for six months is awarded if a sufficient number of randomly selected emissions are properly evaluated during a test at the end of the course. The MOE document entitled "Visible Emissions Identification" is used as the manual for certifying observers (MOE, 1982).

While non-MOE staff can be certified as visible emissions observers, the current version of Regulation 308 only recognizes observations made by trained Provincial Officers during the course of enforcement procedures if the results are being used to assess compliance in a legal context. Such observations must be made in accordance with Section 7(3) of Regulation 308.

In recent years, the number of sources being cited for violations of visible emissions has increased steadily. It is frequently the offence described on "tickets" issued by Provincial Officers (see Section 8.5). Three key parameters used to assess visible emissions are duration of emission, opacity, and the type of fuel involved (if relevant). At facilities where opacity is a concern, on-line opacity meters can be installed which continuously record the opacity of the emission stream as it passes through a stack.

2.5.4 Ambient Air Sampling

Ambient air monitoring may be undertaken by regulatory agencies to evaluate general conditions, establish the concentrations typically present at a location, identify trends in air quality, and identify regional differences or similarities. The MOE maintains a network of stations at locations across the province for monitoring concentrations of various parameters including gases such as sulfur dioxide, suspended particulate matter and its constituents such as lead, and dustfall. Environment Canada maintains the National Air Pollution Surveillance (NAPS) network.

Ambient air quality surveys also can be undertaken prior to a source becoming operational and the data subsequently used to evaluate the effects that the source has on local air quality.

At industrial facilities, ambient air monitoring may be undertaken to assess the potential off-site migration that could occur in the event of a spill or unscheduled release. Such information could be valuable during an emergency response situation.

In most instances, ambient air concentrations are relatively low compared to concentrations in emission sources. The preferred sampling method is to draw air through a loop, cell, or reaction chamber where the concentration(s) is measured and the result is available within a few moments of taking the sample. If such "real-time" analysis is impractical, there are several other approaches that can be employed:

- whole air samples can be pumped into bags or containers often made of special plastics that are later transported to a laboratory
- air can be passed through a filter which traps particles; the filter can be weighed to determine the mass of material collected or the filter can be dissolved and the residue analyzed
- air can be passed through a trap that is maintained at relatively low temperature; the condensed material that collects in the trap can be analyzed
- air can be bubbled through a liquid medium or passed through a packed bed of charcoal granules, synthetic material, or a polyurethane plug to absorb gaseous compounds

2.5.5 Odours

Approximately 50% of citizens' complaints to the MOE are associated with odour. Two approaches can be taken to assess odour. One is to monitor individual substances being emitted and compare their concentrations to odour thresholds. The other is to consider the odour potential of an entire emission. The latter is determined by an odour panel, a group of trained people who smell samples to determine if an odour is discernable. Typically, a series of dilutions are created by mixing samples of the emission with odour-free air. A positive response is produced when 50% or more of the members of the panel can detect an odour in a sample. The findings of an odour panel can be used to describe the total number of odour units associated with an emission.

While the term "odour threshold" implies that detection occurs at a specific concentration, in fact, detectability is highly variable between people and an individual's sensitivity can be influenced by many factors. As a result, odour thresholds may be reported as specific values or ranges, or as geometric averages and standard deviations. Table 2.3 presents a list of odour thresholds for a few selected chemicals. The odour thresholds for some compounds such as hydrogen sulfide are extremely low.

2.5.6 The Need for Quality Assurance and Quality Control

A rigorous Quality Assurance/Quality Control (QA/QC) program is an essential part of air quality and emission testing efforts. The following aspects of sample collection, handling, and analysis should be addressed in a QA/QC program:

- sampling procedures (including the cleaning of equipment between sampling efforts)
- calibration of field equipment
- chain-of-custody forms for samples
- standard reference methods should be employed for laboratory standard solutions
- method blank samples and method blank samples spiked with a standard solution should be included during the course of an analytical run
- assessments of precision, accuracy and completeness

2.6 MODELLING

2.6.1 Overview

Mathematical models can be used to predict how emissions behave in the atmosphere and the concentrations that result at specific times and/or locations. Over the last two decades, the sophistication of such models has grown rapidly. Many of the latest models attempt to address various factors that influence atmospheric dispersion such as atmospheric stability, irregular or complex terrain, multiple emission sources, local building wake effects, and short-term events.

Regulation 308 identifies several relatively simple models for estimating point-of-impingement (POI) concentrations. The results of such calculations can be a key element in decisions for issuing or denying a C of A.

All but the simplest models take into account atmospheric stability, which represents the turbulence of the transporting wind and its ability to disperse emitted materials (Bowne, 1984). Stability categories are semi-quantitatively specified in terms of wind speed, incoming solar radiation during the day and cloud cover during the night (Pasquill and Smith, 1983):

Surface Wind Speed (m/s)	DAY Incoming Solar Radiation Strong	Moderate	Slight	NIGHT Thinly Overcast or $\geq$4/8 low cloud	$\leq$3/8 cloud
<2	A	A-B	B	—	—
2-3	A-B	B	C	E	F
3-5	B	B-C	C	D	E
5-6	C	C-D	D	D	D
>6	C	D	D	D	D

Stability is least for Class A and highest for Class F. The neutral class (D) is assumed to occur for overcast conditions during day or night.

2.6.2 Gaussian Plume Models

Gaussian plume models are used to estimate airborne concentrations of pollutants in the vicinity of a source. Downwind concentrations are calculated based on the height of release, the emission rate, exit velocity and temperature from the source, wind speed, and general atmospheric conditions. This type of model assumes that the plume will spread both laterally and vertically. The concentrations of a substance in such a plume are described in mathematical terms as having a "normal" or Gaussian distribution. Gaussian plume models are generally considered to be capable of predicting annual average concentrations at a point of exposure within a factor of two to four for pollutants released continuously over flat terrain (Cohrssen and Covello, 1989). More complex conditions contribute to greater uncertainty in predictions.

2.6.3 Long-Range Transport Models

Long-range atmospheric transport models attempt to predict pollutant concentrations over geographical regions as large as entire continents. Trajectories that released pollutants might follow are computed based on historical wind data from weather stations within the region. Generally, these models are thought to predict annual average POI concentrations within a factor of three to five (Cohrssen and Covello, 1989).

2.6.4 Puff Models

Puff models are based on the same principles as Gaussian models but they are used to simulate the transport of emissions after episodic or short-duration releases, such as explosions or accidental releases (Cohrssen and Covello, 1989).

2.6.5 Regulation 308 Algorithms

The algorithms identified in Regulation 308 are based on Gaussian dispersion models. The configuration of the building on which the emission point is located and the adjacent buildings determine which of the algorithms is most appropriate for specific situations. To assist in the selection of the appropriate algorithm, figures are provided in Regulation 308 that illustrate various configurations of stack and building heights and location of adjacent buildings. Four different scenarios are described:

Scenario 1   Receptor is located within 5 m of the source and the emission is caught in either the wake of the building or an adjacent building (i.e. less than 100 m).

Scenario 2   Receptor is located greater than 5 m from the source and the emission is caught in either the wake of the building or that of an adjacent building (i.e. less than 100 m).

Scenario 3   Receptor is located greater than 5 m from the source and the emission is not being caught by the wake of the building or an adjacent building (i.e. less than 100 m).

Scenario 4   Multiple sources: worst-case concentrations from aforementioned sections for a receptor are to be added together.

Scenarios 2 and 3 implicitly use atmospheric stability classes C and D in the modelling.

Various parameters may be needed to use the algorithms. These can include stack height, emission exit velocity and temperature, emission rate of the pollutant, and the distance and height of closest receptor.

2.6.6 U.S. EPA Models

The U.S. EPA has recommended atmospheric dispersion models in its "Guidelines on Air Quality Models" (U.S. EPA, 1980). Some of these models may be better suited to evaluating some conditions than the algorithms recommended in Regulation 308.

RAM Gaussian Plume Multiple-Source Air Quality Model—A steady-state model for estimating concentrations of stable pollutants for average times of an hour to a day from point and area sources.

Industrial Source Complex Models (ISC)—Both a short-term and a long-term version of this Gaussian plume dispersion model are available. The models take into account settling, dry deposition of particles, and downwash. In addition, the models can handle area, line or volume sources. Limited adjustments can be made for terrain.

Multiple-Point Gaussian Dispersion Algorithm with Terrain Adjustment (MPTER)—A multiple-point source algorithm with terrain adjustment. It is useful for estimating air concentrations of nonreactive pollutants.

Single-Source Model (CRSTER)—A steady-state Gaussian plume model that is applicable to rural or urban areas and uneven terrain. The model is able to determine the maximum concentration for certain averaging times and can also determine the meteorological conditions that caused the maximum concentration. This is the basic model used by the U.S. EPA for evaluating single-point sources.

Valley Model—The model is a special-purpose model and considers the worst-case impact in complex terrain. It comprises a modified Gaussian plume model which assumes that the horizontal crosswind distribution has a uniform rather than a normal distribution and has special algorithms for situations where a plume impacts elevated terrain.

2.7 REPORTING REQUIREMENTS

2.7.1 General Requirements

Section 12 of the EPA requires that every person who discharges into the natural environment or who is responsible for a source that discharges to the environment any contaminant in an amount, concentration, or level in excess of that prescribed by the regulations shall forthwith notify the Ministry. Accordingly, anyone who emits a substance into the atmosphere in concentrations that exceed the conditions of an order or C of A must notify the MOE.

Reporting requirements will become more frequent and entail more detail under the proposed Clean Air Program (see Section 2.8).

Whether reporting for internal monitoring or to fulfill C of A requirements, it is important that data below the detection limits (DL) be appropriately labelled. If a conservative approach is to be used, i.e. data below the DL are assigned values of the DL, "less than" signs (<) should accompany all values generated from this data.

2.7.2 Incident Reporting

An "incident" is defined in the EPA as the discharge of a contaminant into the environment out of the normal course of events that is likely to cause an adverse effect. There are several sections of the EPA that impose requirements to notify various parties when an incident occurs. Some sections are somewhat generic in nature. For example, Section 14(1) of the EPA requires that every person who discharges a contaminant or causes or permits the discharge of a contaminant into the natural environment out of the normal course of events that causes or is likely to cause an adverse effect shall forthwith notify the Ministry.

Similarly, Section 80(1) of Part IX (also known as the "Spills Bill") requires every person having control of a pollutant that is spilled and every person who spills or causes or permits a spill of a pollutant that causes or is likely to cause an adverse effect shall forthwith notify the following persons of the spill, of the circumstances thereof, and of the action that the person has taken or intends to take with respect to the MOE: the municipality or the regional municipality where the spill occurred, and the owner of the pollutant. Additional information on incident reporting requirements is provided in Section 12.2.

More specific to air quality concerns is Section 9 of Regulation 308 which requires notification where a failure to operate in the normal manner or a change in operating conditions occur, or a shutdown of the source or part thereof is made for some purpose, results in the emission of air contaminants that may result in quantities which exceed the POI concentrations specified in Schedule 1 or exceed any of the criteria specified in Sections 6 or 8 of Regulation 308 (see Section 2.2.1). Under such circumstances, the owner or operator of the source of air pollution shall immediately notify a Provincial Officer and provide details of such failures, change or shutdown. A written account shall be provided as soon as practicable.

A Provincial Officer may authorize, in writing, the continuance of such operation for a reasonable period of time given the circumstances and may impose upon the owner or operator such terms and conditions for continued operation as the Officer considers necessary.

2.8   PROPOSED CLEAN AIR PROGRAM

2.8.1   Philosophy

In August 1990, the MOE released a draft regulation for the proposed Clean Air Program (CAP). A 1991 filing date for the regulation is anticipated. Three philosophical points form the basis of CAP (MOE, 1990) :
- the primary means of controlling emissions should be at the source rather than allowing their dilution in the air;
- emissions of toxic pollutants should be virtually eliminated;
- the atmosphere should not be used as a disposal facility for pollutants.

By requiring that emissions be controlled at source, CAP will eliminate the use of dispersion as a way of dealing with air pollution. It will also remove the option of using tall stacks as a means of complying with air quality criteria.

Under CAP, the level of control will be a function of the "environmental hazard" posed by the substance being emitted. This twinning of the level of control to the level of concern is illustrated in the following CAP terms:

Level 1   Contaminants in this level present a high degree of environmental hazard (i.e. they are persistent or tend to bioaccumulate in the environment). Known and probable human carcinogens likely will be included in Level 1. Control is aimed at virtually eliminating emissions of Level 1 substances. The strictest controls required anywhere in the world are to be used. Economic factors may be considered in the timing of implementation, but not in establishing the emission limit. Table 2.4 presents the proposed interim list of Level 1 contaminants.

Level 2   Contaminants in this level are of significant concern in the environment. They may have an effect on genetic material (possible carcinogencity, teratogenicity), affect distant receptors via long-range transport and/or transformation in the atmosphere. Control is aimed at minimizing emissions to the extent feasible. The best controls demonstrated in use anywhere in the world are to be used, taking into consideration economic factors.

Level 3 Contaminants in this level are of moderate concern but because of significant nuisance effects, controls are required to levels well below those at which health effects could occur. Control is aimed at providing reasonable abatement to avoid nuisances. Economic factors are considered in establishing the emission limit.

The MOE has developed a ranking system for assessing the relative environmental hazard of chemical contaminants. Currently, the scoring system deals only with individual contaminants on the basis of health effects on human beings and animals, and damage to vegetation. It is anticipated that other factors will be included in the system. The factors may include indirect effects on health and the environment.

Other components of the CAP program will include:

- establishing methodologies that can be used to determine appropriate control requirements
- setting Air Quality Standards (AQS)
- source registration (to create a comprehensive inventory of emissions)
- a two-phased approval process (certificates to construct and to operate)
- adopting an airshed approach and new mathematical models

It is anticipated that the first parts of the program will be in place by early 1991 and that the entire program will be phased in over a ten-year period. Priority in the phasing-in will be given to chemicals which are in Level 1, of broad environmental concern, and are being emitted in Ontario in significant quantities.

2.8.2 Establishing Control Requirements

Rather than setting emission limits for types of emission sources, the proposed approach under CAP is for the MOE to outline a methodology for evaluating control technologies. The methodology focuses on the types of data that need to be gathered and the way(s) that the data should be used to determine control requirements. A proponent (the owner and/or operator of a source) will then follow the methodology to identify the appropriate control requirement for a specific source. A draft working document entitled "Guidelines for Determining Level 1 Controls" was issued in 1989 (Smith, 1990). It is anticipated that as experience is gained with its first application, the methodology will be improved and expanded to include the other two levels.

Sources of Level 1 substances will be required to undertake a Level 1 Control Limit Evaluation. The methodology is described by the MOE as a "top-down analysis" in that the most stringent control requirements must be considered first. The methodology consists of four steps:

Step 1   Identification of Control Alternatives
Step 2   Effectiveness Ranking of Control Alternatives
Step 3   Evaluation of Control Alternatives
Step 4   Impact Analysis of Control Alternatives

Step 1 requires the review of technically feasible alternatives to identify the control technology that will provide the **Lowest Achievable Emission Rate** (LAER). The alternatives explored should go beyond simply reviewing existing controls for the source category in question. The types of controls to be assessed should include existing control technology; technically feasible alternatives; innovative control technology; use of production processes, fuels and other raw materials which are inherently less polluting; and specific design or operational parameters.

Once the appropriate control options have been compiled, **Step 2** involves ranking them in order of control effectiveness. Accompanying each option should be a description of control efficiencies, expected emissions, and environmental impacts or benefits.

Step 3 involves assessing the technical feasibility and potential for significant adverse impacts on environmental media other than air, or significant adverse secondary impacts on air quality associated with a particular technology. The cost of achieving the control technology will *not* be included in the assessment.

In **Step 4**, the potential environmental impact associated with each control alternative is assessed. Both beneficial and adverse impacts should be discussed and quantified wherever possible. As the goal of the program is the virtual elimination of toxic emissions, the MOE has stated that the argument for accepting a less stringent control technology of an insignificant air quality impact will not be accepted.

It is anticipated that this approach, which excludes cost and implicitly imposes an acceptable level of risk through the Small Source Designation Limit (described below), will be questioned and possibly challenged by emitters.

In some instances there may be compelling reasons for not instituting LAER control requirements. For such situations and for sources of Level 2 or 3 substances, two other levels of control requirement are available:

Best Available Control Technology (BACT) will be the emission rate achieved by the best control technology generally available, taking into account economic and other factors. A proponent's evaluation should examine options that are more stringent and less stringent and determine the incremental financial aspects of each option and possibly other aspects (such as energy consumption). The methodology for undertaking the evaluations are based on the general principles used for assessing Best Available Technology Economically Achievable for the MISA program (refer to Chapter 3.0).

Reasonably Available Control Technology (RACT) will be the emission rate associated with the minimum level of control demonstrated as acceptable at similar sources. Regional and industrial economic factors may also be included in the evaluation.

The three levels of control requirements are summarized in Table 2.5.

For certain levels of emissions, it may be impractical to require stringent control. Hence, guidelines are being developed for assessing a *de minimis* level of emission below which control is not required. The **Small Source Designation Limit** (SSDL) will be expressed in units of kilograms per year. Examples of SSDL levels for common contaminants are 0.8 kg/yr benzene, 18 kg/yr ammonia and 3 kg/yr chlorine.

SSDL sources will still have to be registered. The MOE may also require these sources to meet ambient air standards in areas where land use and/or similar sources are thought to be causing, or likely to cause, non-compliance of air quality standards or to produce unacceptable risk levels.

Visible Emissions—The procedures specified by the U.S. Environmental Protection Agency (EPA) for determining the opacity of visible emissions will be adopted. The procedure allows for the assessment of visible emissions using trained observers and accepted instrumental methods.

2.8.3 Air Quality Standards

Under CAP, it is intended that Air Quality Standards (AQS) will be established. AQS values will represent the ultimate impact or change in air quality that is acceptable. If a source threatens to violate the AQS in an airshed, it may need to implement more stringent controls or be located elsewhere. Interim AQS values were issued in the draft CAP regulation (MOE, 1990).

2.8.4 Source Registration

The MOE is considering a source registration system for **designated air contaminants** analogous to the U.S. EPA Superfund Reauthorization and Recovery Act (SARA) Title III. The purpose of the program would be to identify and quantify on an annual basis, stationary sources of releases of designated air contaminants into the environment. Registration will be based on the type of contaminant, the facility's Standard Industrial Code, and the number of full-time employees. The following eight contaminants

have been designated for the first phase of implementation:
- acrylonitrile
- benzene
- carbon tetrachloride
- formaldehyde
- vinyl chloride
- lead
- manganese
- dioxins and furans

Contaminants for the next phase of implementation will be selected from a second list of Level 1 contaminants (see Table 2.4). Subsequent phases will incorporate the remainder of Level 1 contaminants, Level 2 contaminants (subject to the availability of well documented rationales and concern level), and finally, Level 3 contaminants.

The data would be reported on an annual basis and include releases to all three environmental media: air, land and water.

The data that registration efforts provide will assist the MOE in the following areas:
- identify stationary source which release specified substances into the environment
- quantify significant sources
- establish a comprehensive emissions inventory
- assess the effectiveness of CAP
- provide information for airshed modelling (see Section 2.8.6).
- inform the public
- aid in the development of Remedial Action Plans (see Section 2.8.8)

2.8.5 Approvals

It is proposed to divide the current approvals process into two parts. The first part will concern approvals for construction and the second will set emission limits and operating conditions for a facility. Permission to construct will require work on the facility to be initiated within 12 months and completed within 24 months of the issuance of the certificate unless cause can be established for the extension.

Certificates to operate will be renewed every ten years. MOE Directors may request more frequent reviews under special circumstances. Approvals may specify stack sampling and ambient air monitoring requirements (see Table 2.5). The emphasis of CAP will be on self-monitoring with the MOE auditing the results.

Generic certificates of approval to construct and operate will be granted to groups of similar industries which have similar emissions. Each member of a class will be required to adhere to general requirements and to specific conditions developed for that class.

2.8.6 Modelling

As part of the "airshed" management approach, the MOE has proposed new dispersion models. All contributing sources within a specified area will be modelled to assess their contribution on the overall airshed.

The models will be used to screen approval applications. It is intended that a proponent must demonstrate compliance of the entire airshed (including the proposed source, after accounting for mandated control equipment) with the air quality standards.

As described in Section 2.6, the algorithms described in Regulation 308 are relatively simple, Gaussian plume models. They were developed to compare sources but not to predict concentrations of contaminants downwind. The proposed models for use in CAP include a worst-case meteorology source assessment program, multiple-source gas dispersion program, and special air dispersion models. It is anticipated that the algorithms used in the worst-case and multiple-source models and one of the special air dispersion models (shoreline fumigation model) will be specified in CAP.

A proponent may use other mathematical dispersion models or physical packages if they can satisfy the MOE that the modelling package has been properly evaluated.

The source characteristics required for the MOE models include the emission rates, release height, stack radius, efflux temperature and efflux velocity to calculate plume buoyancy and momentum, dimensions of nearby buildings or obstructions and dimensions of area or line sources.

The **worst-case meteorology program** is a screening model designed for the quick computation of the meteorological conditions that produce the highest ground level concentration for a given source. The model generates its own possible meteorological conditions and hence input is limited to information on the stack such as its diameter and the emission rate. The model seeks the maximum concentration(s) for each atmospheric stability class considered and the source type. The stability classes cover convective, neutral, stable, and transition conditions. The model is only for single-source emissions.

The **multiple-source gas dispersion model**, also called the "gas model", allows the calculation of the downwind concentration from several sources of emissions at a given set of locations for a given set of meteorological parameters. Hourly meteorological data are required to run this model.

The advection of cooler, stable air from a large water body over relatively warmer, unstable air over land may result in the formation of a Thermal Inversion Boundary Layer (TIBL). Exhaust plumes which are released into the stable air near the shoreline and transported inland by the lake breeze may become entrained in the unstable TIBL. The rapid mixing of the plume once it intersects the TIBL is referred to as continuous fumigation. Such a situation may persist for up to several hours during which receptors may experience high pollutant concentrations. To account for fumigation, a **shoreline fumigation model** (Misra, 1980) is being proposed by the MOE.

Sources located in **complex terrain** or near significant topographic features require individual treatment. Three options are available for evaluating sources in complex terrain: physical modelling, ambient air monitoring, or modifying the worst-case model. Physical modelling may involve wind tunnels or water tanks using a scaled-down version of the source and terrain features. Ambient air monitoring would involve a comprehensive field study at the proposed site. Such a field study would include measurements of the meteorological and pollutant dispersion characteristics at several locations around the source.

Pollutant dispersion from sources located on or near a building(s) may be influenced by the changes in air flow caused by the building(s). The degree to which dispersion is affected depends on meteorological conditions and the relative proximity of the source to the building(s). **Building wake algorithms** are presented in Regulation 308 (MOE, 1990).

2.8.7 Interpretation of Model Results

Under CAP, the results of modelling will be used to divide emissions sources into two groups (MOE, 1990). **Type A sources** or groups of sources are those which are predicted to have little effect on ambient air concentrations of a contaminant, even under worst-case modelling conditions. If the worst-case model result shows the potential to exceed the air quality standard for any appropriate averaging time, then the proponent should undertake detailed modelling to assess model concentrations for multisource situations and for single-source cases with averaging times greater than 1 hour.

Type B sources or source complexes are those sources which require detailed modelling. If a source is located in a region where a relatively uniform background concentration for the contaminant exists (i.e. no other source within the proponent's radius of influence produces a concentration $\geq$ 5% of the AQS), the proponent would perform detailed modelling for their own source and would add the background concentrations for comparison with the AQS.

If the source is located in a region with other sources (i.e. within 25 km) which could produce a concentration $\geq$ 5% of the AQS, then they must be included in the multiple-source modelling. Background concentrations due to uniformly distributed sources (i.e. area sources such as cars or space heating) or long-range transport of the contaminants would be added to the concentrations produced by the multi-source modelling.

If the results of modelling lead to the conclusion that there will be non-attainment of the air quality standards, the source emissions will have to be reduced to appropriate levels or the source may need to be relocated.

2.8.8 Non-Attainment Areas

In areas where modelling or monitoring indicate that local air quality fails to meet the standards, further abatement action on the source(s) emitting the contaminant of concern will be instituted through the Control Order mechanism. The process of establishing Non-Attainment Remedial Strategies (NARS) for a particular area will involve extensive public consultation with all affected stakeholders.

The aim of the NARS will be establishment of a plan outlining what steps will be taken to achieve compliance with the air quality standards over time, including measures to address existing sources and deal with proposals for new sources.

2.9 SUMMARY

Current legislation concerning air quality and atmospheric emissions is being revised. It is anticipated that a revised regulation (Clean Air Program—CAP) will be released by 1991. Several deficiencies have been identified by the MOE with the current version of Regulation 308. These include no requirement for control at source, an outdated approach to modelling contaminant dispersion, and no provision for Certificates of Approval (C of A) to expire. Portions of CAP are already being included in approvals for air emissions.

The ultimate goal of CAP is the virtual elimination of toxic emissions from stationary sources. The mechanisms to be used to accomplish this goal include source categorization, chemical classification, appropriate control technology, C of A for construction and operation, and community Air Quality Standards (AQS). Even if the appropriate emission controls have been implemented by the various sources in an area, further action may be required if the AQS are exceeded. The airshed management approach will be supported by state-of-the-art air pollution models.

REFERENCES

Bowne, N.E., 1984. "Atmospheric Dispersion". *In* Handbook of Air Pollution Technology, (Eds.) Calvert, S., and Englund, H.M., John Wiley and Sons, Toronto.

Clayton, G., and Clayton, F., 1981. "Patty's Industrial Hygiene and Toxicology". John Wiley and Sons, Toronto, p. 3387.

Cohrssen, J.J., and Covello, V.T., 1989. "Risk Analysis: A Guide to Principles and Methods for Analyzing Health and Environmental Risks". Office of the President of the United States, ISBN 0-934213-20-8.

Delbridge Associates, 1990. "Consultation on the NO_x VOCs Management Plan: Report on Phase 2". Prepared for Canadian Council of Ministers of the Environment (CCME), May.

Fazzalari, F., 1978. "Compilation of Odor and Taste Threshold Values Data". American Society for Testing and Materials, DS 48A.

Leonardos, G., 1984. "Odour Sampling and Analysis". *In* Handbook of Air Pollution Technology, (Eds.) Calvert, S., and Englund, H.M., John Wiley and Sons, Toronto.

Misra, P.K., 1980. "Dispersion From Tall Stacks Into a Shore Line Environment". Atmos. Env., 14, pp. 396-400.

Ontario Ministry of the Environment (MOE), 1982. "Visible Emission Identification". Second edition. May.

Ontario Ministry of the Environment (MOE), 1987a. "Stopping Air Pollution at its Source: CAP, Clean Air Program—Discussion Paper". November.

Ontario Ministry of the Environment (MOE), 1987b. "Air Pollution Regulation 308: Appendix H". November.

Ontario Ministry of the Environment (MOE), 1990. "Stopping Air Pollution at Its Source: CAP, Clean Air Program—Draft Regulation, Overview". August.

Pasquill, F., and Smith, F.B., 1983. "Atmospheric Diffusion". Third edition, Ellis Horwood Limited, Chichesten, ISBN 0-85312-587-2.

Smith, K.E., 1990. "Determining State of the Art Emission Controls for Regulatory Purposes". Presented at the Annual Spring Conference of the Air and Waste Management Association—Ontario Section. 22 to 24 April, Toronto.

Sparks, L.E., 1984. "Particulate Sampling and Analysis". *In* Handbook of Air Pollution Technology, (Eds.) Calvert, S., and Englund, H.M., John Wiley and Sons, Toronto.

Stahl, W.H., 1973. "Compilation of Odor and Taste Threshold Values Data". American Society for Testing and Materials, ASTM, Data Series DS48, Philadelphia.

U.S. Environmental Protection Agency, 1980. "Guideline on Air Quality Models". OAQPS Guideline Series, Research Triangle Park, NC.

Table 2.1
POINT-OF-IMPINGEMENT CONCENTRATIONS

Schedule 1

ITEM	COLUMN 1 Name of Contaminant	COLUMN 2 Unit of Concentration	COLUMN 3 Concentration at Point of Impingement—Half Hour Average
1.	Acetic Acid	Micrograms of acetic acid per cubic metre of air	2,500
2.	Acetylene	Micrograms of acetylene per cubic metre of air	56,000
3.	Acetone	Micrograms of acetone per cubic metre of air	48,000
4.	Acrylamide	Micrograms of acrylamide per cubic metre of air	45
5.	Acrylonitrile	Micrograms of acrylonitrile per cubic metre of air	2,200
6.	Ammonia	Micrograms of ammonia per cubic metre of air	3,600
7.	Antimony	Total micrograms of antimony in free and combined form per cubic metre of air	75
8.	Arsenic	Total micrograms of arsenic in free and combined form per cubic metre of air	75
9.	Arsine	Micrograms of arsine per cubic metre of air	10
10.	Benzene	Micrograms of benzene per cubic metre of air	10,000
11.	Beryllium	Total micrograms of beryllium in free and combined form per cubic metre of air	0.03
12.	Boron Tribromide	Micrograms of boron tribromide per cubic metre of air	100
13.	Boron Trichloride	Micrograms of boron trichloride per cubic metre of air	100
14.	Boron Trifluoride	Micrograms of boron trifluoride per cubic metre of air	5.0
15.	Boron	Total micrograms of boron in free and combined form per cubic metre of air	100
16.	Bromine	Micrograms of bromine per cubic metre of air	70
17.	Cadmium	Total micrograms of cadmium in free and combined form per cubic metre of air	5.0

ITEM	COLUMN 1	COLUMN 2	COLUMN 3
	Name of Contaminant	Unit of Concentration	Concentration at Point of Impingement—Half Hour Average
18.	Calcium Hydroxide	Micrograms of calcium hydroxide per cubic metre of air	27
19.	Calcium Oxide	Micrograms of calcium oxide per cubic metre of air	20
20.	Carbon Black	Micrograms of carbon black per cubic metre of air	25
21.	Carbon Disulphide	Micrograms of carbon disulphide per cubic metre of air	330
22.	Carbon Monoxide	Micrograms of carbon monoxide per cubic metre of air	6,000
23.	Carbon Tetrachloride	Micrograms of carbon tetrachloride per cubic metre of air	20,000
24.	Chlorine	Micrograms of chlorine per cubic metre of air	300
25.	Chlorine Dioxide	Micrograms of chlorine dioxide per cubic metre of air	85
26.	Chromium	Total micrograms of chromium in free and combined form per cubic metre of air	30
27.	Copper	Total micrograms of copper in free and combined form per cubic metre of air	100
28.	Cresols	Micrograms of cresols per cubic metre of air	230
29.	Decaborane	Micrograms of decaborane per cubic metre of air	50
30.	Detergent Enzyme (Subtilisin)	Micrograms of subtilisin per cubic metre of air	1.0
31.	Diborane	Micrograms of diborane per cubic metre of air	20
32.	Dicapryl Phthalate	Micrograms of dicapryl phthalate per cubic metre of air	100
33.	Dimethyl Disulphide	Micrograms of dimethyl disulphide per cubic metre of air	40
34.	Dimethyl Sulphide	Micrograms of dimethyl sulphide per cubic metre of air	30
35.	Dioctyl Phthalate	Micrograms of dioctyl phthalate per cubic metre of air	100
36.	Dustfall	Micrograms per square metre	8,000

Item	Column 1	Column 2	Column 3
	Name of Contaminant	Unit of Concentration	Concentration at Point of Impingement—Half Hour Average
37.	Ethyl Acetate	Micrograms of ethyl acetate per cubic metre of air	19,000
38.	Ethyl Acrylate	Micrograms of ethyl acrylate per cubic metre of air	4.5
39.	Ethyl Benzene	Micrograms of ethyl benzene per cubic metre of air	4,000
40.	Ethylene Oxide	Micrograms of ethylene oxide per cubic metre of air	28,500
41.	Ferric Oxide	Micrograms of ferric oxide per cubic metre of air	75
42.	Fluorides, (Gaseous) (April 15 to October 15)	Micrograms of gaseous, inorganic fluoride per cubic metre of air expressed as hydrogen fluoride	4.3
43.	Fluorides, (Total) (April 15 to October 15)	Total micrograms of inorganic fluoride per cubic metre of air expressed as hydrogen fluoride	8.6
44.	Fluorides, (Total) (October 16 to April 14)	Total micrograms of inorganic fluoride per cubic metre of air expressed as hydrogen fluoride	17.2
45.	Formaldehyde	Micrograms of formaldehyde per cubic metre of air	65
46.	Formic Acid	Micrograms of formic acid per cubic metre of air	1,500
47.	Furfural	Micrograms of furfural per cubic metre of air	1,000
48.	Furfuryl Alcohol	Micrograms of furfuryl alcohol per cubic metre of air	3,000
49.	Hydrogen Chloride	Micrograms of hydrogen chloride per cubic metre	100
50.	Hydrogen Cyanide	Micrograms of hydrogen cyanide per cubic metre of air	1,150
51.	Hydrogen Sulphide	Micrograms of hydrogen sulphide per cubic metre of air	30
52.	Iron (metallic)	Micrograms of metallic iron per cubic metre of air	10
53.	Lead	Total micrograms of lead in free and combined form per cubic metre of air	10
54.	Lithium Hydrides	Total micrograms of lithium hydrides per cubic metre of air	7.5

Item	Column 1 Name of Contaminant	Column 2 Unit of Concentration	Column 3 Concentration at Point of Impingement — Half Hour Average
55.	Lithium	Total micrograms of lithium in other than hydride compounds per cubic metre of air	60
56.	Magnesium Oxide	Total micrograms of magnesium oxide per cubic metre of air	100
57.	Manganese	Total micrograms of manganese in free and combined form per cubic metre of air	100
58.	Mercaptans	Total micrograms of mercaptans per cubic metre of air expressed as methyl mercaptans	20
59.	Mercury (alkyl)	Total micrograms of alkyl mercury compounds per cubic metre of air	1.5
60.	Mercury	Total micrograms of mercury in free and combined form per cubic metre of air	5.0
61.	Methyl Acrylate	Micrograms of methyl acrylate per cubic metre of air	4.0
62.	Methyl Alcohol	Micrograms of methyl alcohol per cubic metre of air	84,000
63.	Methyl Bromide	Micrograms of methyl bromide per cubic metre of air	12,000
64.	Methylene Chloride	Micrograms of methylene chloride per cubic metre of air	100,000
65.	Methyl Chloroform (1-1-1 Trichloroethane)	Micrograms of methyl chloroform per cubic metre of air	350,000
66.	Methyl Ethyl Ketone (2-Butanone)	Micrograms of methyl ethyl ketone per cubic metre of air	31,000
67.	Methyl Methacrylate	Micrograms of methyl methacrylate per cubic metre of air	860
68.	Milk Powder	Micrograms of milk powder per cubic metre of air	20
69.	Monomethyl Amine	Micrograms of monomethyl amine per cubic metre of air	25
70.	Nickel	Total micrograms of nickel in free and combined form per cubic metre of air	5
71.	Nickel Carbonyl	Micrograms of nickel carbonyl per cubic metre of air	1.5
72.	Nitric Acid	Micrograms of nitric acid per cubic metre of air	100

Item	Column 1	Column 2	Column 3
	Name of Contaminant	Unit of Concentration	Concentration at Point of Impingement—Half Hour Average
73.	Nitrilotriacetic Acid	Micrograms of Nitrilotriacetic Acid per cubic metre of air	100
74.	Nitrogen Oxides	Micrograms of nitrogen oxides per cubic metre of air expressed as NO_2	500
75.	Ozone	Micrograms of ozone per cubic metre of air	200
76.	Pentaborane	Micrograms of pentaborane per cubic metre of air	3.0
77.	Pentachlorophenol	Micrograms of pentachlorophenol per cubic metre of air	90
78.	Phenol	Micrograms of phenol per cubic metre of air	100
79.	Phosgene	Micrograms of phosgene per cubic metre of air	130
80.	Phosphoric Acids	Micrograms of phosphoric acids per cubic metre of air expressed as P_2O_5	100
81.	Phthalic Anhydride	Micrograms of phthalic anhydride per cubic metre of air	100
82.	Propylene Dichloride	Micrograms of propylene dichloride per cubic metre of air	2,400
83.	Propylene Oxide	Micrograms of propylene oxide per cubic metre of air	78,000
84.	Silver	Total micrograms of silver in free and combined form per cubic metre of air	3
85.	Styrene	Micrograms of styrene per cubic metre of air	400
86.	Sulphur Dioxide	Micrograms of sulphur dioxide per cubic metre of air	830
87.	Sulphuric Acid	Micrograms of sulphuric acid per cubic metre of air	100
88.	Suspended Particulate Matter (particulate less than 44 microns in size)	Total micrograms of suspended particulate matter per cubic metre of air	100
89.	Tellurium (except hydrogen telluride)	Micrograms of tellurium in free and combined form per cubic metre of air	30
90	Tetrahydrofuran	Micrograms of tetrahydrofuran per cubic metre of air	93,000
91.	Tin	Total micrograms of tin in free and combined form per cubic metre of air	30

ITEM	COLUMN 1	COLUMN 2	COLUMN 3
	Name of Contaminant	Unit of Concentration	Concentration at Point of Impingement—Half Hour Average
92.	Titanium	Total micrograms of titanium in free and combined form per cubic metre of air	100
93.	Toluene	Micrograms of toluene per cubic metre of air	2,000
94.	Toluene Di-isocyanate	Micrograms of toluene di-isocyanate per cubic metre of air	1.0
95.	Trichloroethylene	Micrograms of trichloroethylene per cubic metre of air	85,000
96.	Trifluorotrichloro Ethane	Micrograms of trifluoro trichloroethane per cubic metre of air	2.4 million
97.	Vanadium	Total micrograms of vanadium in free and combined form per cubic metre of air	5.0
98.	Vinylidene chloride (1, 1 Dichloro Ethene)	Micrograms of vinylidene chloride per cubic metre of air	26,000
99.	Xylenes	Micrograms of xylenes per cubic metre of air	2,300
100.	Zinc	Total micrograms of zinc in free and combined form per cubic metre of air	100

R.R.O. 1980, Reg. 308, Sched. 1.

Table 2.2
PARTIAL LIST OF SAMPLING PROTOCOLS

1) Ontario Ministry of the Environment, 1980. "Source Testing Code (Version 2)". Report No. ARB-66-80, November.
2) Canadian Standards Association, 1986. "Method for the Continuous Measurement of Oxygen, Carbon Dioxide, Carbon Monoxide, Sulfur Dioxide and Oxides of Nitrogen in Enclosed Combustion Flue Gas Streams". CSA Report No. CAN/CSA-A223.2 M86, September.
3) U.S. Code of Federal Regulations (CFR), 1989. "U.S. Federal Reference Test Methods". Title 40, Part 60, July 1.*
4) U.S. Environmental Protection Agency, 1977. "Measurement of Polycyclic Organic Materials and Other Hazardous Organic Compounds in Stack Gases - State of the Art". EPA Report 600/2-77-202, October.
5) American Society of Mechanical Engineers, 1984." ASME Draft Protocol for the Determination of Chlorinated Organic Compounds in Stack Emissions". Draft Report No. 4, October.
6) U.S. Environmental Protection Agency, 1984. "Protocol for the Collection and Analysis of Volatile POHCs using VOST". EPA Report 600/8-84-007, March.

* Includes test methods for particulates, SO_2, NO_x, CO_2, opacity, H_2S, fluoride, mercury, volatile organics, benzene, vinyl chloride and dioxins.

Table 2.3
ODOUR RECOGNITION THRESHOLDS

Chemical	Recognition Odour Threshold (ppm)	Reference
acetone	100.0	(1)
acrolein	0.21	(1)
ammonia	47.0	(1)
benzene	4.7	(1)
cellosolve	0.550	(2)
cellosolve acetate	0.14	(2)
cyclohexanone	0.120	(2)
hydrogen sulfide	0.00047	(1)
methyl isobutyl ketone (MIBK)	0.28	(2)
nitrobenzene	0.0047	(1)
n-butanol	1.0	(2)
phenol	0.047	(3)
toluene	5.0	(2)
trichloroethylene	21.4	(1)
V.M. and P. naphtha	0.86	(4)

References:
1 - Leonardos, 1989
2 - Fazzalari, 1978
3 - Stahl, 1973
4 - Clayton and Clayton, 1981

Table 2.4
PROPOSED INTERIM LIST OF LEVEL 1 CONTAMINANTS

acrylonitrile	formaldehyde
4-aminobiphenyl	hexachlorobenzene
arsenic	lead
asbestos	N-methyl-N-nitrosourea
benzene	4,4'-methylenebis (2-chloroaniline)
benzidine	2-naphthylamine
beryllium	nickel
bis(chloromethyl) ether	nickel carbonyl
cadmium	N-nitrosodimethylamine
carbon tetrachloride	perchloroethylene
chloroform	polychlorinated biphenyls
chloromethyl methyl ether	polychlorinated dibenzo
chromium	dioxins/furans
diethylsulfate	polycyclic aromatic hydrocarbons
dimethyl sulfate	propylene oxide
dimethylcarbomoyl chloride	silica (respirable)
epichlorohydrin	styrene oxide
ethylene dibromide	vinyl bromide
ethylene oxide	vinyl chloride

Reference: MOE, 1990

Table 2.5
CAP CONTROL TECHNOLOGY CLASSIFICATIONS AND REQUIREMENTS

Lowest Achievable Emission Rate (LAER)
- for Level I substances (e.g. benzene and lead)
- best emission control system available or its equivalent
- requires continuous monitoring systems which reflect process operating conditions and/or maintenance of the emissions control
- stack testing required within 6 months of start-up and subsequently at intervals of not more than 12 months

Best Available Control Technology (BACT)
- for Level II substances (e.g. pentachlorophenol)
- best control technology generally available
- takes into account several factors including economics
- requires installation of continuous monitoring systems which reflect the state of operation and/or maintenance of the emissions controls
- stack testing required within six months of start-up and subsequently at Director's discretion at intervals of 12 months or more

Reasonably Available Control Limits (RACT)
- for Level III substances (e.g. hexane and toluene)
- minimum level of control demonstrated as acceptable at similar sources
- confirmation of emission rates by an approved technique (certified by a registered engineer)

3.0

Water Quality and Liquid Discharges

3.1 OVERVIEW

As a recent inquiry on federal water policy noted, "Water commands a unique place among our natural resources" (Pearse *et al.*, 1985). It supports other resources such as fisheries, provides an important medium of transportation and energy production, influences settlement patterns, is a major recreational resource, inspires artistic and cultural expression, and, of course, is essential for life.

There are several broad similarities between the present status of water management and that of air management in Ontario. Like air management, the last few decades have witnessed quantum improvements in the abilities to measure substances in water and liquid discharges, the development of new and improved control technologies, and an understanding of the fate of substances in aquatic environments. At the same time, our demands for water of suitable quality and quantity have grown steadily. While concerns formerly focused on minimizing the presence of disease-causing organisms and the mechanics of distribution, today's concerns include the presence of organic compounds in trace amounts (some even caused by treatment techniques), protection of ground water supplies, water use reduction and conservation, and the restoration of rivers and lakes.

All three levels of government are involved in water quality management and the regulation of liquid discharges. Like air management, there is a relatively comprehensive package of regulations, policies, guidelines, and by-laws in place in Ontario. Sections 3.2 and 3.3 describe the current provincial regulations and guidelines. Sections 3.4 and 3.5 outline federal and municipal requirements, respectively. The process for receiving provincial approvals to discharge liquid effluents is described in Section 3.6. Monitoring and reporting requirements are outlined in Sections 3.7 and 3.8.

One final way in which water quality management is like that of air

41

management is that it too is in a state of transition, although in the case of water management, the Municipal and Industrial Strategy for Abatement (MISA) program is currently being implemented. MISA will first affect specific industrial sectors but eventually will also apply to municipal dischargers including wastewater treatment facilities. The ultimate goal of the program is the virtual elimination of persistent, toxic contaminants from all discharges into Ontario waterways. Like the Clean Air Program, MISA will require more stringent control on releases and monitoring for more parameters more frequently, and impose greater reporting requirements on dischargers. The MISA program will have a significant effect on most if not all municipal and industrial facilities.

3.2 PROVINCIAL REGULATIONS AND GUIDELINES (EXCLUDING MISA)

3.2.1 Environmental Protection Act

As noted in Section 2.2.1, the Environmental Protection Act (EPA) of 1971 is broadly directed toward the protection and conservation of the natural environment. As such, much of the original text does not specifically mention water quality or liquid discharges but the broad scope of this legislation encompasses water quality and aquatic environments.

Subsection 13(1) states that no person shall discharge a contaminant or cause or permit the discharge of a contaminant into the natural environment that causes or is likely to cause an adverse effect. While the EPA definition of "adverse effect" includes many components (see Section 2.2.1) some that are most appropriate in the context of water management include:

- impairment of the quality of the natural environment for any use that can be made of it,
- injury or damage to property or to plant or animal life,
- an adverse effect on the health of a person,
- loss of enjoyment of normal use of property, and
- interference with the normal conduct of business.

Other sections of the EPA address water quality indirectly. For example, Part IV deals with the discharge of waste upon or over ice.

Despite its initial orientation toward the total environment, the EPA has become a cornerstone in the control of liquid discharges because it holds all of legislation for the Municipal Industrial Strategy for Abatement (MISA) program. Due to its importance and complexity, the MISA program is addressed separately in Section 3.3.

3.2.2 Ontario Water Resources Act

The Ontario Water Resources Act (OWRA) contains a general prohibition against the discharge of any material into water. Section 16(1) requires that "every person that discharges or causes or permits the discharge of any material of any kind into or in any water or on any shore or bank thereof or into or in any place that may impair the quality of the water of any waters is guilty of an offence."

Section 14 of the OWRA indicates that the quality of water shall be deemed to be impaired if any material (or any derivative of such material) is discharged or deposited and causes or may cause injury to any person, animal, bird or other living thing as a result of the use or consumption of any plant, fish or other living matter or thing in the water or in the soil in contact with the water.

Under Section 19(2)(a), it is an offence to place, discharge, or allow to remain within an area defined as a source of public water supply, any material that may impair the quality of the water.

3.2.3 Water Quality Guidelines

Several MOE publications describe water quality guidelines and objectives for various types of water and aquatic environments. Such guidelines and objectives are recommendations and are not legally enforceable but are often used to evaluate water quality in Ontario. Provisions for the protection and enhancement of ambient water quality are outlined in the document entitled "Water Management, Goals, Policies, Objectives and Implementation Procedures of the Ministry of the Environment" (MOE, 1984a). Also referred to as the "Blue Book", it contains several MOE policy statements concerning water quality management and the **Provincial Water Quality Objectives** (or PWQOs).

The PWQOs include narrative and numerical criteria designed for the protection of aquatic life and recreation in and on the water. The PWQOs represent a desirable level of water quality that the MOE strives to maintain in surface waters of the province. They cover conventional parameters, radioactive material, metals, turbidity, pesticides, and some industrial organic compounds (see Table 3.1).

The PWQO values are based on the scientific rationale described in a companion document to the Blue Book entitled "Rationale for the Establishment of Ontario's Provincial Water Quality Objectives". The information base used to set PWQO values is constantly changing and therefore modifications can be made from time to time.

In addition to the PWQOs, the Blue Book assigns the terms **zero tolerance limit** and **undefined tolerance limit** to selected substances (also listed in Table 3.1). Substances with zero tolerance are those that can bioaccumulate or concentrate in the aquatic environment to levels which are harmful or lethal to organisms. It is the intent of the MOE to prohibit any new discharges of these substances and to reduce all existing releases to the lowest practicable levels.

Substances listed as having undefined tolerance limits may pose an adverse effect to health or the environment. The scientific data for such substances is insufficient to establish water quality objectives. Releases of these substances are evaluated on a case-by-case basis, and special measures may be needed to protect the environment.

The Blue Book also addresses the concept of **mixing zones** noting that it is not practical to treat all effluents to the extent that they comply with the PWQO values at the point of release or discharge. Therefore, some volume of water must be provided for dilution or modification of the effluent before the Objectives can be met. While it is permissible to exceed PWQO values within a mixing zone, the effluent cannot be immediately lethal to swimming organisms that are not able to evade the zone. It is possible for an effluent to be toxic but be avoidable. For example, fish can detect and avoid zones of very low pH if given the opportunity to do so.

The mixing zone mainly represents a loss of habitat, but it must not be allowed to become an area where aquatic life is killed or seriously damaged. The MOE has indicated that the use of mixing zones will be severely limited as it represents a loss of habitat.

The MOE has prepared a draft document entitled "Ontario's Water Quality Objectives Development Process" (MOE, 1989). The document outlines the rationale used to develop and revise PWQO values. The rationale considers data for acute and chronic toxicity, bioaccumulation and mutagenicity, and persistence. Also considered is information concerning fate, physical/chemical properties, taste, odour, tainting of fish, impacts on wildlife, recreation (bathing and aesthetics), sediment quality, and the standards of other agencies. Provincial water quality guidelines (PWQGs) may be set for substances for which information is inadequate for setting a PWQO.

It is anticipated that interim PWQO or PWQG values will be available for all chemicals on the MISA Effluent Monitoring Priority Pollutant List (EMPPL) by early 1991. The PWQO and PWQG values may be used in the MISA program to help define the level at which toxic contaminants have been "virtually eliminated" from discharges (see Section 3.3).

A second key MOE publication that identifies water quality objectives is the document entitled "Ontario Drinking Water Objectives" (MOE, 1984b). As the title indicates, this document addresses drinking water quality as compared to the Blue Book which addresses ambient water quality. The MOE currently uses three types of objectives to describe drinking water quality.

The term **Maximum Acceptable Concentration** (MAC) describes limits applied to substances above which there are known or suspected adverse health effects. Drinking water supplies should not exceed MAC limits continuously.

The term **Interim Maximum Acceptable Concentration** (IMAC) describes limits for substances of current concern with known chronic effects in mammals and for which MAC values have not been established. A substance detected at a concentration above its IMAC signals the need for more sampling and investigation. The requirement for corrective action is made on a case-by-case basis.

The term **Maximum Desirable Concentration** (MDC) is used for limits on substances which, when present at concentrations above the limits, are either aesthetically objectionable to an appreciable number of consumers or may interfere with good water quality control practices. The MDC should not be exceeded whenever a more suitable supply or treatment process is or can be made available at a reasonable cost.

Table 3.2 lists numerical values assigned to all three types of drinking water quality objectives.

3.3 MUNICIPAL AND INDUSTRIAL STRATEGY FOR ABATEMENT (MISA) PROGRAM

3.3.1 Goals and Objectives

The MISA program is a major initiative by the MOE to reduce water pollution from industrial and municipal discharges. The overall objective of the program is the **virtual elimination of persistent, toxic contaminants from all discharges** into Ontario waterways. MISA regulations are issued under Section 136 of the EPA.

The program is directed toward several goals:

- identification and measurement of toxic substances in discharges
- increased emphasis on control technology
- augmentation and expansion of the existing water quality impact approach
- strengthened enforcement mechanisms

Other objectives of the MISA program are to involve municipalities, industries, other interest groups, and members of the public in the MISA process.

3.3.2 Direct Dischargers

The MISA program divides all dischargers into two broad categories. One includes industries that discharge effluents directly into surface waters. Such direct dischargers currently are defined as including nine industrial sectors:

Petroleum refining	Industrial minerals
Organic chemicals	Electric power generation
Iron and steel	Metal mining and refining
Pulp and paper	Metal casting manufacturers
Inorganic chemicals	

Regulations that specify effluent monitoring requirements for each sector are being developed in accordance with a process that consists of establishing regulations that describe the monitoring that all facilities in the sector must undertake, establishing regulations that specify the quality of effluents, and an abatement and enforcement phase.

Before sector-specific regulations are developed, several **pre-monitoring activities** are undertaken. This begins with the sampling of selected effluents at representative facilities for each sector. The results are used to assist in drafting a monitoring regulation for the sector that indicates the parameters to be monitored and the frequency of monitoring at facilities in that sector.

Representatives of the MOE, Environment Canada, and the industrial sector participate in the consultative process that precedes the development of a monitoring regulation. The draft regulation is reviewed by both the MISA Advisory Council (MAC), an independent committee of technical and environmental experts, and the public. The MAC provides the Minister with advice and comments on the regulations being developed and other MISA matters.

The last step of pre-monitoring is an economic analysis by the MOE of the cost of implementing the proposed monitoring regulation. The resulting report addresses both the operating and the capital costs of the program, an assessment of the impact on employment levels, and an evaluation of whether any dischargers will suffer "undue financial" burden.

3.3.3 Phase I: Monitoring Regulation

Phase I of MISA is directed toward monitoring the chemicals that are present in effluents. Phase I consists of two regulations. The first is the General Regulation (Regulation 695/88 as amended by Regulation 533/89) which applies to all sectors. It addresses various aspects of monitoring such as analytical procedures, sampling protocols, reporting requirements, and flow measurement.

The second regulatory component consists of the sector-specific effluent regulations. For example, Regulation 321/89 applies to the Iron and Steel Sector. Sector-specific regulations define the discharge streams to be sampled, types of discharge, the parameters to be analyzed, and the frequency of sampling.

Types of Discharges

Eight types of discharge streams can be identified in the sector-specific regulations:

A **process effluent** is discharged water that comes into contact by design with an industrial process. Cooling water is defined as a discharge used to remove heat and that is not intended to come into contact with process material.

The term **combined effluent** appears in sector-specific regulations and the General Regulation. It is defined as an effluent that results from the intentional combination of process effluent with one or more of cooling water, storm water, and waste disposal site effluent.

Storm water means runoff from a storm event or thaw that is discharged from a developed area or a plant. A storm event is defined as a rainfall or series of rainfalls on an operating day that exceeds five millimetres. A thaw is described as the melting of snow or ice sufficient to create an effluent stream at the plant.

Waste disposal site effluent and **storage site effluent** are any liquids and associated materials that are collected from a waste disposal site or storage area for discharge to a surface watercourse.

Any process effluent, waste disposal site effluent, or storage site effluent should be monitored before the place where they are discharged to a surface watercourse, after any final treatment, and upstream of any significant contaminant masking or significant dilution by any other effluent.

Emergency overflow is defined as a diversion of effluent that causes the effluent to bypass a sampling point ordinarily used for that effluent.

Final effluent, as used in the regulation for the iron and steel sector, is a discharge that contains process effluent and one or more of cooling water, storm water and waste disposal site effluent.

Parameters to Be Analyzed

Effluents are to be monitored for five broad groups of parameters during Phase I:

- conventional parameters (such as ammonia, cyanide and pH)
- organic parameters (such as benzene and toluene)
- PCBs and dioxins
- characterization/open characterization
- acute toxicity testing

A detailed list of parameters and the **Analytical Test Groups** (ATGs) to which parameters have been assigned in MISA are presented in Table 3.3.

The monitoring frequency of each parameter is determined by the pre-monitoring sampling, the type of discharge stream, and the upstream processes. Usually conventional parameters like pH and specific conductivity are sampled daily or thrice weekly for a final or combined effluent whereas organic parameters may be sampled only weekly to monthly. PCBs and dioxins are usually monitored semi-annually unless they were detected during the pre-monitoring study and then may be sampled more frequently.

Characterization means the analysis of a sample to identify and quantify all of the parameters in Table 3.3, except those in ATGs 28a, 28b and 29. Additional exceptions may be granted for a particular sector if specific chemicals are not purchased or manufactured by that sector.

Open characterization is an analysis of a sample to identify and quantify ATGs 16, 17, 19, 20 and 23 and to identify and approximately quantify ATGs 28a, 28b and 29.

Acute toxicity tests are conducted using rainbow trout *(Salmo gairdneri)* or the water flea *(Daphnia magna)*. Chapter 13 presents a more detailed discussion of toxicity testing and interpretation of toxicity test results.

Sample Handling and Analysis

The MISA program is relatively explicit it terms of how samples are to be gathered and analyzed and results reported. The MISA regulation specifies sample/laboratory containers, sample type (grab versus composite), material to be used in the sampler, minimum sample volumes, maximum sample storage time, sample preservatives, storage temperature, method detection limits, flow accuracies, quality assurance/quality control procedures, instrument measurement method principles, data storage and reporting procedures, and the retention time of records.

The **method detection limit** (MDL) is the minimum concentration of a parameter in laboratory grade water necessary to infer its presence with a confidence greater than 99%. It is a way to compare laboratories in terms of achieving a level of detection. The MDL should not be confused with the minimum detection limit that a laboratory can achieve. The minimum detection limit can vary from sample to sample depending upon the presence or absence of substances that interfere with analytical techniques (i.e. the "matrix" effect) and/or the ability of the laboratory to prepare a sample for analysis.

Reporting Requirements

At different times during Phase I, various types of monitoring reports must be submitted. The information required for the **initial report** includes plot plans indicating the location of samplers and flow measuring devices, descriptions of operations, descriptions of flow instrumentation and samplers, the accuracy of flow devices, and analytical documentation. It is the responsibility of the discharger to inform the MOE of all changes in the information submitted in the initial report.

Calibration reports, intended sampling date reports, and reports of the **method used to estimate/measure storm water volumes** are all due prior to the commencement of monitoring. The calibration report must show that the devices being used to measure or estimate flow are within the accuracies specified by the regulation (see Section 3.7.7).

Equipment malfunction/problem reports are required when conditions or events interfere with fulfilling the requirements of the regulation (together with a description of remedial action).

Analytical test data reports, which should include analytical results, toxicity information and flow and precipitation data, are to be submitted during the course of the monitoring program at time periods specified by the regulation. The data must be entered into a computer data base provided by the MOE. Both a floppy disk and a hard copy are to be submitted. The data bases used are the MiSA Data Entry System (MIDES) and the Toxicity Data entry system (TOXDATA). User manuals for each data system are provided by the MOE.

Notices of Violations

The stringent and comprehensive reporting requirements of the MISA program is a potential source of violations. While the violations may not lead to prosecutions, they are indicative of the ease with which violations can occur. The MISA reporting requirements also allow more than one violation to arise from a single event (Cotton, 1989).

Violations also can stem from inspections of facilities by the MOE. Samples can be collected for analysis at the MOE laboratory to verify that the samples collected by the discharger are representative of the quality of the effluent. Flow measuring devices can be inspected. It is important that the information provided by the discharger in the initial report be kept current. Facilities should have a master file into which changes to the monitoring program are added before being passed on to the MOE regional MISA office.

The requirements of MISA are backed up by the penalty provisions of the EPA related to non-compliance with regulated requirements and knowingly providing false information. A more detailed description of liability and penalties under the EPA is provided in Chapter 8.5.

3.3.4 Phase II: Effluent Limit Regulation

The objective of Phase II is to establish allowable concentrations of substances in effluents. These effluent limit regulations will be based upon MISA monitoring data, an evaluation of whatever constitutes the best available technology that is economically achievable, and the results of a water quality assessment. The limits will be developed by sector-specific Joint Technical Committees (JTC) that include representatives from the MOE, industry, and Environment Canada.

Figure 3.1 presents the proposed process for the calculation of effluent limits:

- subcategorization of the plant or process,
- selection of parameters for potential treatment,
- evaluation of technology,
- an economic analysis of the best available technology, and
- calculation of effluent limits.

Subcategorization—Prior to initiating the process for parameter selection, each plant/process within a sector will be classified into a homogeneous group to ensure that plant sites or facilities with similar characteristics are treated uniformly in terms of limits.

Selection of Parameters—The approach proposed for parameter selection divides the parameters into two primary categories:

Category A—Persistent toxics

Category B—Non-persistent toxics

Parameters in Category A include bioaccumulative and non-bioaccumulative parameters. A bioaccumulative toxic substance is defined as a toxic substance with a bioconcentration factor (BCF) greater than 1000 or the octanol-water partition coefficient (K_{ow}) greater than 10,000.

Three options are being considered for assessing Category A parameters:

- a persistent, toxic contaminant would not be carried forward if 90% or more of the measured concentrations (95% confidence interval) are less than trigger value (i.e. PWQO or PWQG);
- same as above but the trigger value is replaced by the Regulatory Method Detection Limits (RMDL); or
- a persistent, bioaccumulative contaminant would not be carried forward if 90% or more of the measured concentrations (95% confidence interval) are less than the RMDL; all persistent, non-bioaccumulative contaminants would be deleted using the same statistical range and a trigger of the PWQO or PWQG.

Category B includes conventional and non-conventional parameters. Whether parameters in Category B are carried forward will depend upon the frequency at which a parameter is found above the appropriate PWQO or PWQG value. A parameter will not be carried forward if 90% or more of the measured concentrations (at a 95% confidence interval) were less than the PWQO or PWQG value.

Selection of Best Available Technology—It has been proposed that each JTC will consider at least four Best Achievable Technology (BAT) options for economic analysis. The BAT options must include the demonstrated and combined technologies which best advance the sector or subsector toward the realization of the goals, policies and objectives of the MISA activity. Selection of BAT options should consider the following factors:

- at least one BAT option should be the best technology used in North America, Europe, or Japan
- the BAT option identified by the U.S. EPA; if there is no BAT option, the Best Practicable Technology (BPT) identified by the U.S. EPA for the sector or subsector in question
- the BAT option that utilizes the best technology currently in use in Ontario in the sector or subsector in question
- at least one BAT option that consists of any technologies or combinations of technologies which advance the sector or subsector toward the goals, policies and objectives prescribed by MISA

The fourth factor includes the technology which may provide optimal water conservation, maximum reduction in priority and/or conventional pollutants, minimum impact on other media (atmosphere and land), and maximum use of the 3 Rs (see Section 4.7). In most cases there will exist overlaps with each of the proposed BAT categories, i.e. the BAT which achieves a non-lethal discharge may also be that proposed by the U.S. EPA.

The MOE has prescribed the following criteria for ranking demonstrated BATs:

- non-lethal to fish
- smallest toxic equivalent loading (TEL) of bioaccumulative and bioaccumulative persistent toxic substances
- non-lethal to *Daphnia-magna*
- smallest TEL of persistent and non-persistent toxic substances (non bioaccumulative)
- water conservation
- maximum use of the 3 Rs
- smallest TEL of conventional and non-conventional substances
- smallest transfer to other media
- most cost-effective (e.g. greatest contaminant reduction per dollar)

In the above criteria, "persistent" refers to a substance with a half-life in water of greater than 56 days.

A toxic equivalent loading (TEL) is calculated using the equation:

$$TEL = ETC * Q \tag{3.1}$$

where   ETC = equivalent toxic concentration (ug/L)

   Q   = flow (m^3/day)

The equivalent toxic concentration is determined using the equation:

$$ETC = C * TWF \tag{3.2}$$

where   C   = water concentration (ug/L)

   TWF= toxic equivalent factor

The TWF is derived from water quality criteria by a simple computation. A weighting factor for a substance is calculated by dividing each relevant criterion, expressed as a concentration in micrograms per litre into the criterion for a selected standard substance, copper, and summing the results of each division. Two relevant water quality criteria are used to make up the toxic weighting factor: human health ingestion criterion and aquatic chronic criterion. The criterion for the standard (copper) is 5.6 ug/L.

This method is illustrated in the following TWF calculation for nickel:

water quality criterion for
aquatic chronic toxicity (nickel)   = 96 ug/L

criterion for human health
ingestion (nickel)   = 100 ug/L

aquatic water quality criterion
(copper)   = 5.6 ug/L
TWF = $(5.6 \div 96) + (5.6 \div 100)$
= 0.114

Economic Analysis—A technical cost evaluation of each BAT identified in the previous step would be performed. The costs of at least four BAT options would then be evaluated in terms of affordability by the sector. Affordability would be assessed on a sector or subsector basis using economic and financial indicators and tests. Financial indicators may include total debt/total assets for solvency; return on assets for profitability; and current ratio for liquidity. The particular method to be used is selected by each sector's JTC. How effects are perceived from various perspectives such as competitiveness, profitability, employment, and price impacts would also be considered.

The economic analysis provides decision-makers with the potential economic and financial consequences of different BAT options, including the distribution of these effects on sectors and groups in Ontario. The final outcome of the assessment would be the selection of Best Available Technology Economically Achievable (BATEA).

BATEA does not mean that a specific technology must be employed but rather that the quality of the discharge must equal that which BATEA can achieve. Several approaches may be capable of achieving the effluent associated with BATEA. These include changes in manufacturing processes, substitution of chemicals used in processes, the recycling of waste by-products, and end-of-pipe treatment.

Previous environmental protection costs would be considered to the extent possible, but not added explicitly to relevant MISA costs. The costs of present environmental regulatory initiatives and mandated requirements other than MISA may also be considered in the assessment.

Calculation of Limits—The list of parameters that are treatable by BATEA may be divided into two groups:

1 A short list of parameters that will have a daily maximum limit and monthly average limit based on 30-day measurements and four weekly measurements. These parameters will be indicative of the efficiency of the treatment system.

2 The remaining parameters may only have a daily maximum limit which will be monitored on a quarterly basis.

The statistical approach to setting a limit for each parameter involves the following basic steps:

- calculation of the Long Term Average (LTA) from BATEA plant(s)
- determination of the Variability Factor (VF) from BATEA plant(s)
- calculation of performance value as a product of LTA and VF

The Long Term Average (LTA) is the arithmetic mean of all sample values. All data below the Regulatory Analytical Detection Limits (RMDL) divided by ten would be replaced by a value equal to RMDL/10. For data equal to or greater than RMDL/10, either the reported value or the Laboratory Method Detection Limit (LMDL) would be used.

The daily Variability Factors (VF) would be determined from:

$$VF(1) = P_{99} \div E(x) \tag{3.3}$$

where   VF(1) = daily maximum variability factor

$\quad$ P_{99} $\quad$ = 99th percentile

$\quad$ E(x) $\quad$ = expected mean

For monthly limits, the 95th percentile 30-day mean variability factor would be calculated using the equation:

$$VF(30) = P_{95} \div E(X_{30}) \tag{3.4}$$

The use of P_{99} and P_{95} may result in 30 to 50 violations per year for a large facility employing BATEA. Companies therefore must do better than BATEA to be in compliance continuously. The MOE may propose a daily limit based on the 99.8th percentile, a statistical level which allows one non-compliance event per parameter in a 20-month period.

Three methods of calculating effluent limits have been proposed (Figure 3.2):

1 Linear Method (production-based): The VF and LTA will be calculated from the concentration data of BATEA plant(s). The product of VF, LTA, and the flow per unit production determined from BATEA plant(s) will be expressed as mass per unit of production (e.g. kg contaminant/kg product).

2 Average Loading Method—The product of VF and LTA will be expressed as mass per unit time which is derived from the LTA of loading and the variability factor of loading for BATEA plant(s).

3 The product of VF and LTA will be based on the absolute concentration value which is derived from LTA concentration data and the VF of BATEA plant(s).

Aquatic Toxicity—An acute lethality limit of 50% survival after exposure to 100% effluent for fish and *Daphnia magna* may be employed in the regulations. If a discharger is in non-compliance with the acute toxicity limit a Toxicity Identification Evaluation/Toxicity Reduction Evaluation (TIE/TRE) may be required (see Chapter 13 for additional information about aquatic toxicity). In addition, sublethal tests are being proposed for dischargers that are consistently non-lethal to both fish and *Daphnia magna* that could consider reproduction, inhibition, and survivability.

Best Management Practice (BMP)—Effluent limit regulations may also require that industries have procedures to: (1) manage site runoff and drainage from outdoor process and non-process areas resulting from storm water or thaw events; (2) minimize bypasses from the effluent treatment system; (3) manage sludge and waste disposal from effluent treatment systems; (4) manage once-through cooling water; and (5) minimize the impact of spills that are associated with, or ancillary to, the plant and effluent treatment systems and which may contribute contaminant substances to the receiving waters. The term Best Management Practice (BMP) may be applied to plans for such areas. BMP plans are discussed further in Section 12.6.

In some sectors, discharges will be required to conduct a Stormwater Control Study. The purpose of the study will be to develop a stormwater control plan for the entire plant site.

Water Quality Assessment—An assessment of the impact of an effluent on receiving waters may be performed by the MOE. The assessment may take into account water quality, effluent quality, sediments, aquatic life, and characteristics of the receiving water such as flow rate or currents.

Through this process, the effluent limits required for protecting the quality of receiving waters will be determined. If implementing BATEA will not provide sufficient protection for some sensitive receiving water bodies, a full-scale, detailed assessment of the impacts on the water quality will need to be conducted. Such an assessment may lead to more stringent effluent criteria.

3.3.5 Phase III: Abatement and Enforcement

A model format for compliance regulations is currently being drafted by the MOE. The format will be concise and employ non-legal language. The regulation may refer to guidelines for sampling, analytical protocols, flow measurement, *Daphnia magna* toxicity tests, rainbow trout toxicity tests, and stormwater control studies. Unlike regulations, strict complaince is not required when guidelines are being followed.

Once an effluent limit regulation is in place, there are several mechanisms that will alert the MOE to violations:

1 Dischargers are required to notify the MOE of violations.
2 The MOE will screen submitted monitoring data.
3 The MOE will evaluate data collected during inspections.

MOE responses to a violation may include the issuing a Notification of Violation to the discharger. A notice can request an explanation of reason(s) for the violation and a remedy for the problem. If the MOE makes a written abatement request for action to reduce, prevent or eliminate pollution, a reasonable time to comply will be specified. Additional information on MOE responses is provided in Chapter 8.

Another MOE response option is to issue Control Orders (under either the EPA or the OWRA). Control Orders can require specified abatement actions to be accomplished within a given schedule.

3.3.6 Indirect Dischargers

The second broad category of dischargers in the MISA program is "indirect dischargers". This aspect of MISA will place restrictions on the amounts and concentrations of persistent or toxic contaminants discharged from municipal sewage treatment plants (STPs). The MISA sewer use control program will require municipalities to limit the toxic waste put into sewer systems by industries (the "indirect dischargers").

The following order of activities is being considered:

1 MOE Model Sewer Use By-Laws
2 Submission of waste survey reports by industries
3 Industrial plant inspections by municipal officers
4 Monitoring of waste water treatment plants by municipalities or the MOE
5 Monitoring of significant industrial dischargers by municipalities
6 Development of local limits for selected parameters
7 Development of industrial sector pretreatment limits
8 Joint development (municipal representatives and discharger) of a site-specific permit

Items 1 and 2 are discussed in more detail in Section 3.5.1. The MOE is proposing that the municipalities monitor significant industrial dischargers by collecting one 24-hour composite sample. The sample will be analyzed for most of the parameters on the MISA Effluent Monitoring Priority Pollutant List (EMPPL).

The development of a site-specific permit may involve three separate limit documents: Sewer Use By-Laws, local limits for selected parameters, and limits based upon industrial sector pretreatment standards. The latter limits are being developed by the MOE for the 22 industrial categories. The limits may also reflect the capacity and degree of treatment available at the treatment plant that receives the discharge.

The MOE has indicated that overstrength agreements (refer to Section 3.5.2) should be phased out. This would leave sewage treatment plants to treat primarily domestic waste water.

3.3.7 Recommendations for Complying with MISA

Eventually all liquid effluents from all facilities will be regulated by the MISA program. The program is operationally complex and hence there is a large risk of minor violations occurring (Shaver, 1989). The following are some suggestions for successfully implementing a MISA monitoring program:

- start early to organize a MISA team and ensure that members are properly trained
- at larger facilities, consider dedicating a person to MISA operations and coordination

- consider automatic sampling equipment
- establish a 24-hour on-call maintenance crew for the samplers or obtain a service contract with a reputable company
- provide backup for all activities including sampler personnel, flow measurement equipment, automatic samplers, and the laboratory
- carefully review the abilities of both internal and external laboratories to meet the stringent requirements
- integrate MISA monitoring into routine sampling operations
- maintain an up-to-date version of the initial report
- perform in-house audits of the monitoring program to ensure that proper protocols are being followed for sampling, analysis, data recording, and reporting

3.4 FEDERAL REGULATIONS

3.4.1   Canadian Environmental Protection Act

Section 34(1) of the Canadian Environmental Protection Act (CEPA) allows for the regulation of releases of toxic substances (as defined in Schedule 1) in terms of:

- quantity or concentration
- places or areas where the substance may be released
- the commercial or processing activity which gives rise to the release of the substance
- the manner and conditions in which the substance may be released into the environment, either alone or in combination with any other substance
- the circumstances or conditions under which the minister may, for the proper administration of this Act, modify any requirement for sampling, analysis, testing, measurement or monitoring, or the methods and procedures for conducting any required sampling, analysis, tests, measurements or monitoring

The CEPA also covers the concentration of nutrients in products. Subsection 50(2) prohibits the manufacture for use or sale in Canada or import of any cleaning agent or water conditioners that have nutrient concentrations above those specified by regulations made under the Act. Part VI of the Act addresses ocean dumping, conditions and terms of dumping permits, dumping to avert danger, and the granting of permits to dump.

Under CEPA, National Effluent Regulations for various industrial sectors will be developed. It is anticipated that the first such regulations will be promulgated for the pulp and paper sector in early 1991 and be similar in content to those being developed under the MISA monitoring program. The Federal/Ontario Environmental Accord obliges the Province to enforce, and be accountable for, compliance and reporting on federal requirements.

3.4.2 Fisheries Act

Section 14 of the Fisheries Act forbids the depositing (or permitting the deposit) of a deleterious substance in any type of waters frequented by fish or in any other place under circumstances where the substance could enter the water. A deleterious substance is defined by the Act as:

- any substance that, if added to water, would degrade or alter the quality of that water so that it is rendered harmful to fish, and
- any water that contains a substance in such a quantity or concentration that it would, if added to water, degrade the quality of the water and, therefore, cause harm to fish.

Chapter 13 presents additional information on federal requirements concerning aquatic toxicity testing.

3.5 MUNICIPAL REQUIREMENTS

3.5.1   Discharges to Sanitary and Combined Sewers

In 1988, the MOE developed a Model Sewer Use By-law to provide a uniform basis to regulating sanitary, combined, and storm sewers across Ontario. This by-law is a temporary measure. It is anticipated that within a few years, such discharges will be included within the indirect discharges component of the MISA program.

Table 3.4 presents the allowable concentrations for discharges to sanitary and combined sewers. The by-law expressly prohibits dilution to achieve those limits.

In 1989, the Municipality of Metropolitan Toronto issued its own sewer use by-law (By-law 153-89). It contains some small differences from the MOE model by-law as illustrated in Table 3.4. As part of a program to gather information about waste quantities and quality, waste surveys were distributed to more than 5000 local industries.

Potential sewer discharges that do not originate from a municipality can be discharged if a "permit to take water" has been issued by the MOE for more than 50,000 L/d. For volumes less than 50,000 L/d from a single source, the owner or operator of the premises must provide the municipality with information on the amount of water and its source.

Several materials are not allowed in any amount into sanitary/combined sewers. These include:

- fuels
- PCBs
- pesticides
- severely toxic material
- waste radioactive material

Exemptions include PCB material if the owner/operator has a Certificate of Approval (C of A) which expressly allows the discharge, or the owner/operator has approval from the municipality, or the concentration is less than 5 ug/L of PCBs. The discharge of radioactive materials is allowed if it is in accordance with a licence from the Atomic Energy Control Board.

The by-law also uses the term "wastes" to identify materials prohibited from being discharged to sewers. These wastes are defined according to the same definitions used in Regulation 309 under the EPA (see Section 4.3) and include:

- acute hazardous waste chemicals
- hazardous industrial wastes
- hazardous waste chemicals
- ignitable wastes
- pathological wastes
- PCB wastes
- reactive waste

Exemptions are allowed for the discharge of pathological waste if it has been decontaminated prior to discharge and the owner/operator has a C of A from the MOE or permission from the municipality.

3.5.2 Discharges to Storm Sewers

Table 3.5 presents the allowable limits for discharges to storm sewers as declared in the MOE Model Sewer Use By-Law and the Metropolitan Toronto sewer by-law. In addition, water containing dyes or colouring material which discolour the water or produce a visible sheen are not allowed. The limits only apply to storm water runoff from industrial process areas.

There are several exemptions to the MOE limits. Cooling water is allowed if the owner/operator has a C of A from the MOE, or written approval from the director, or approval from the municipality.

Exemptions can be obtained for total suspended solids (TSS), dyes and colouring, oil and grease, visible sheens, and metal concentrations if the discharger has a C of A issued under the EPA or the OWRA, or has a Best Management Practice (BMP) plan which has been approved by the municipality.

BMP plans should address ancillary sources of water from material storage areas, loading and unloading areas, plant site runoff, in-plant transfer, process and material handling areas, and sludge and hazardous waste disposal areas. A detailed discussion of BMP plans is presented in Section 12.6.

Discharges to storm sewers cannot include:

- automotive or machine oils/greases
- fuels
- paints or organic solvents
- PCBs
- pesticides
- severely toxic material
- waste disposal site leachate
- waste radioactive materials

There are no provisions for exemptions for these wastes.

All companies listed in Schedule B of the Industrial Sectors of the Model Sewer Use By-Law must submit a **waste survey report** to the local municipality if they discharge to a sanitary, combined, or storm sewer.

Such a report should identify all the waste discharges including cooling water to sanitary and storm sewers from significant discharges. The waste survey report should identify sources of water, average flow rates (sanitary, non-contact cooling water, contact cooling water, process water or other), and pollutant information (known and present, suspected to be present, known absent, suspected absent, or expected concentrations).

Completed reports are to be reviewed by the municipality to determine which industries might be major dischargers to the sewer and to assess their impact on the sewage treatment processes. Depending on the quantities and characteristics of discharges, a discharger may enter into any one of several types of agreements with the municipality.

If a discharge to a sewer exceeds by-law limits and the discharger believes that this will continue to be the case, the discharger can enter into an **overstrength agreement** with the municipality whereby the municipality is paid to treat the discharge. Overstrength agreements only apply to the following parameters:

- biochemical oxygen demand (BOD)
- phenolics
- total suspended solids (TSS)
- phosphorus
- total Kjeldahl nitrogen (TKN)
- solvent extractable matter

The payment schedule is based on the excess amount of material being deposited to the sewer. For example, a municipality might impose a surcharge of 28 cents per kilogram of excess BOD in a discharge. Payment typically is made quarterly and based upon the actual flow rate times a concentration specified in the overstrength regulation. Rebates may be possible provided that there is sufficient data to support such a claim. Most overstrength agreements require the installation of a flow measuring device. The accuracy of the flow device must meet that specified by the MISA program (see Section 3.7.7).

For parameters that cannot be covered by an overstrength agreement, a compliance program can be established. A **compliance program** allows for a period of grace while action is being taken to reduce contaminant levels.

A compliance program specifies parameter limits that are not to be exceeded while the program is in effect. If during the compliance program, the average levels of the parameters requiring payment according to an overstrength agreement are exceeded, payment will be required. A compliance program also can specify activities to be undertaken. These can include retaining an engineer, source characterization, treatability studies, start-up of a treatment system, or alteration of a process.

If non-municipal source water is discharged to a sanitary or combined sewer, a discharger must enter into a **water surcharge agreement.**

Credits may be available against the surcharge if municipality source water is treated and discharged directly to a water body.

3.6   OBTAINING APPROVALS FOR DISCHARGES

Prior to the establishment, extension, or change in sewage works, a Certificate of Approval (C of A) as per Section 24 of the OWRA must be obtained. Sections 24(1) and (2) of the OWRA require that:

(1)   No person shall establish, alter, extend or replace new or existing sewage works except under and in accordance with an approval granted by the Director.

(2)   A Director may require an applicant for an approval under Subsection (1) to submit plans, specifications, engineer's report and other information and to carry out and report on tests or experiments relating to the location of the discharge of effluent or work to be undertaken and, subject to Subsection (4), the Director may grant the approval.

The MOE currently takes a very firm stand when the construction of facilities begins before a C of A is issued. There are cases of construction being stopped by the owner so as to not jeopardize a pending C of A, and of the MOE refusing to issue a C of A for completed facilities. The supplying of utility services to a site, such as those covered by a Municipal Building Permit, does not seem to be of concern to the MOE.

The MOE is developing generic provisions that would be put into all approvals for wastewater discharges, an example of which is the "visual observation" provision which requires that a discharge be essentially free of floating and settlable solids and not contain oil or any other substance in amounts sufficient to create a visible film or sheen or foam on the receiving waters.

The MOE is also requesting that the monitoring protocol specified in the MISA general regulations be employed and that detailed wastewater treatment systems operation manuals be prepared.

Submissions typically take four to eight months before a C of A is obtained. It is therefore in a discharger's best interest to make sure that an application is submitted at the earliest possible stage of a project and that the application provides sufficient information for its evaluation.

If, in the opinion of a Director, it is in the public interest to do so, the Director may refuse to grant approval, grant the approval on such terms and conditions as the Director considers necessary, impose new terms and conditions, revoke, or suspend the approval.

As of 1 October 1991, operators of municipal water treatment and wastewater treatment plants will require certification, but only for present employees. It is anticipated that a similar requirement will be in place by 1992 for operators of industrial wastewater treatment plants.

3.7 MONITORING

3.7.1 Monitoring Requirements

As described in previous sections of this chapter, monitoring requirements may be imposed on a facility via various acts and regulations including MISA (as either a direct and/or an indirect discharger), the federal Fisheries Act, National Effluent Regulations, MOE Certificates of Approval (C of As), control orders, clean-up orders, overstrength agreement monitoring with a municipality, or compliance agreement monitoring with a municipality.

In addition to the monitoring that is imposed upon it by regulatory agencies, a facility may perform in-house monitoring for various reasons:

- assess compliance
- operate a wastewater treatment facility
- obtain a rebate for an overstrength agreement
- source assessment of elevated contaminants levels
- Toxicity Reduction Evaluation (see Chapter 13)
- assess the effects of an incident
- determine net loadings
- assess "background" conditions prior to constructing a facility

In some cases, the procedures used for sampling and analysis may be different for the non-regulated monitoring compared to those of regulated monitoring programs. For example, higher method detection limits (MDL) may be suitable for an in-house program to track down the source of a substance in a wastewater stream as compared to measurements in final effluent.

3.7.2 Chemical Quality Parameters of Interest

The chemicals present in an effluent or discharge stream are influenced by various factors that include the use of the water (e.g. non-contact versus contact cooling water), the source of the water (e.g. river water versus blowdown), whether chemical additives such as chlorine or algicides are used, pre- and final treatment, and whether sources include ground water inflow or runoff.

Table 3.3 presents the Analytical Test Groups (ATGs) of the MISA program. In addition to the MISA parameters, the following parameters may need to be analyzed, especially when assessing the operations of a wastewater treatment system or considering the possible reuse of an effluent stream:

- alkalinity and acidity
- biochemical oxygen demand (BOD)
- chemical oxygen demand (COD)
- chlorine and chloride*

- cyanide (free)
- dissolved gases: oxygen, hydrogen sulphide, etc.
- fluoride*
- iron*
- magnesium, calcium, sodium and potassium
- oil and grease: mineral and animal/vegetable
- sulphate
- temperature

The asterisks denote parameters that MISA may require for some industrial sectors. (Iron for the Iron and Steel Sector; chloride and fluoride for the Industrial Minerals Sector.)

Biochemical Oxygen Demand (BOD) is the amount of molecular oxygen required to stabilize the decomposable matter present in a water by aerobic biochemical action. Because the complete stabilization of a given waste may take too long, a standard laboratory BOD test has been developed which incubates the material for a period of 5 days at 20 °C. The results of a BOD_5 test are often used to assess the efficiency of both municipal and industrial biological treatment plants and the appropriateness of the wastewater.

Chemical Oxygen Demand (COD) test measures the non-biodegradable as well as the ultimate biodegradable organic compounds in terms of oxygen consumption to stabilize the decomposition.

The parameter Oil and Grease is used extensively by municipalities to assess the acceptability of wastewaters being discharged to the municipalities' wastewater treatment plant, and more recently, for surcharges according to overstrength agreements. The MOE protocol uses methylene chloride as the extraction solvent. The "Standard Methods for the Examination of Water and Sewage" identifies freon (trichlorotrifluoroethane) as the extraction solvent. Analysis of the same sample using these two technologies can show large differences in the concentration of oil and grease because methylene chloride is a stronger extraction solvent than freon.

3.7.3 Surrogate Parameters

There are many situations in which it is sufficient or appropriate to use surrogate parameters to assess effluent or water quality. Most surrogate parameters provide information that is similar but not exactly the same as the parameters or conditions that are of actual concern. For example, an effluent might be analyzed for total phenols when in fact it is a specific phenolic compound that is of interest.

Most surrogates are used because the sample requirements are simpler, or the samples require less time or expense to analyze than the compound of interest. Some surrogates lack the sensitivity of specific compounds but this may not be a limitation for assessing certain situations.

Surrogates should be used only after a correlation between it and the parameter of concern has been developed. For example, some effluents have shown a strong correlation between absorbed metals and TSS. In such cases, TSS can be used to monitor a discharge stream on a frequent basis and specific metals analyzed only if a pre-defined TSS concentration is exceeded.

Another example is the COD test, which is more reproducible and less time-consuming than a BOD test; however, the COD/BOD correlation is such that it is normally only a qualitative value. A change in the ratio of biodegradable to non-biodegradable organic compounds can affect the correlation (WPCF and ASCE, 1982).

The analysis of organic parameters is relatively expensive when compared to conventional parameters and many of the surrogate parameters deal with organic compounds. For example, total oil and grease, dissolved organic carbon, total organic carbon, total halogens, or total phenols can be monitored on a regular basis with the provision for analyzing specific compounds if a threshold concentration is exceeded.

For some groups of organic compounds, specific members may either be used as indicators of the possible presence of other group members or become recognized as the compounds of greatest potential concern and therefore the prime objective of frequent monitoring. For example, benzene may be the only non-halogenated volatile compound of concern in an effluent. Similarly, benzo(a)pyrene can be used as a surrogate for other polyaromatic hydrocarbons. While large cost savings can be realized, such selections are best based on substantial supporting data.

3.7.4 Sample Collection and Preservation Methods

Prior to the introduction of the MISA monitoring program, the most common form of sampling was **grab sampling**. It is still widely used when only a few samples are required. The MISA monitoring program requires that grab samples be taken for five ATGs: 15—sulphide, 16—halogenated volatiles, 17—non-halogenated volatiles, 18—water-soluble volatiles, and 28a—open characterization for volatiles.

One weakness of grab samples is that the samples may only be indicative of effluent quality at the time that the sample is collected. To improve the representativeness of effluent sampling efforts, automatic samplers or on-line analyzers can be used.

Automatic samplers can operate in one of two modes: collecting and combining equal-volume sub-samples at equal time intervals, or collecting and combining samples which are flow-proportional. The benefits of these types of devices are that the manpower commitment is reduced and the data represents a truer mean of the concentration of the discharge stream as more sub-samples can be collected.

On-line analyzers have been available for many years but only recently have capabilities been extended beyond conventional parameters such as pH and conductivity. On-line analyzers are now available that continuously analyze effluents for organic compounds. For example, on-line effluent analyzers are now available for benzene, toluene and xylene.

A relatively complex monitoring system has been providing continuous analysis of volatile organic compounds in the St. Clair River for over a period of two years. The equipment was installed by a local environmental association of 15 chemical and oil refining companies along the St. Clair River that are part of the industrial complex at Sarnia. The monitoring equipment has detection limits in the low ppb range for eight target compounds. Valid data capture typically averages greater than 90%. The system is being used to alert association members to spills as they occur, thus allowing the company to contain the spill immediately and take remedial action as appropriate.

Depending upon the chemicals to be analyzed in a sample, preservatives should be added to either the sample container or the laboratory container to ensure a concentration which is representative of the discharge quality. The chemicals that are used to preserve samples sometimes are categorized as either pre-preservatives or preservatives. **Pre-preservatives** are added to the sample container before the sample itself. For example, a pre-preservative should be used if an automatic sampler is being used to collect samples which will be analyzed for ATG 2 - cyanide or 14 - phenols. **Preservatives** are added after the sample has been collected in the sample container. Table 3.6 presents a list of the preservatives for all of the MISA monitoring parameters.

3.7.5 Analytical Methods

Table 3.7 presents the analytical protocols and method detection limits for each of the MISA Analytical Test Groups. Additional information of analytical techniques is provided in the MISA General Effluent Monitoring Regulation (Regulation 695/88 as amended by Regulation 533/89).

Various other sources are available that describe analytical protocols. One of long standing is "Standard Methods," which is revised and reissued every few years (APHA, AWWA, WPCF, 1985).

3.7.6 Quality Assurance and Quality Control

It is essential that an effective Quality Assurance/Quality Control (QA/QC) program be implemented with all monitoring programs. It assures the controllability, accountability, and retraceability of the work being performed.

A good QA program involves close supervision and surveillance of all field operations, documentation and review of sampling procedures, and the assurance that appropriate laboratory analysis techniques are employed.

The QC program should ensure that data are generated within known limits of accuracy and precision. This involves the application of method detection limits (MDL) and travelling blank samples, and the collection of replicate samples and duplicates samples.

The MISA program has several requirements concerning QA/QC:

- a MDL must be calculated for each parameter
- "standard reference materials" must be employed to ensure that the laboratory standard solutions be validated
- reasonable control limits must be developed for the analyses of method blank samples
- during the course of an analytical run for specified ATGs a replicate sample, a method blank sample and a method blank sample spiked with a standard solution be included
- travelling blanks and travelling spiked blanks must be used
- replicate and duplicate samples must be provided

A **replicate sample** refers to one of at least two samples removed from a single-sample container in a manner that minimizes the difference between the samples. A **duplicate sample** is one of two samples collected at a sampling point and time.

3.7.7 Flow Measurement/Estimation Methods

Flow systems are assigned to two basic categories: flow in closed channels and flow in open channels. Closed channel flow is defined to be flow in completely filled pressure conduits (pipes). Pressure conduits are usually used for fresh-water lines or for industrial processes, and flow through them is often measured by some type of device inserted into the line. Measuring devices for closed channel flow include the venturi meter, flow nozzle, orifice meter, magnetic flow meter, and pitot tube flow meter (ISCO, 1981).

Open channel flow is defined to be the flow in any channel in which the liquid flows with a free surface. Examples are runoff ditches, canals, flumes, and other uncovered conduits. Certain closed channels, such as sewers and tunnels when flowing partially full, and not under pressure, are classified as open channels. There are numerous methods of determining the rate of flow in an open channel (ISCO, 1981).

Timed Gravimetric—Collection of the entire contents of the flow during a fixed length of time.

Dilution—The flow rate is measured by determining the degree of dilution of an added tracer solution by the flowing water.

Velocity—The flow rate is calculated by determining the mean flow velocity across a cross-section and multiplying this by the width of the channel at this point and the measured liquid level, the latter being measured by a second device. The sophistication and accuracy of this type of system has improved measurably in recent years.

Hydraulic Structure—Some type of hydraulic structure such as a weir is introduced into the flow stream. The function of the hydraulic structure (primary device) is to produce a flow that is characterized by known relationship (usually nonlinear) between a liquid level measurement (head) at some location and the flow rate of the stream.

Slope-Hydraulic Radius Area—Measurements of water surface slope, cross-sectional area, and wetted perimeter over a length of uniform section channel are used to determine the flow rate, utilizing a resistance equation such as the Manning formula. The flow channel itself serves as the primary device.

The MISA monitoring regulations specify the accuracies by which various types of flows must be measured or estimated:

Combined Effluent (and Final Effluent for the Iron and Steel Sector)—An accuracy of ± 20% of the actual flow is required during the monitoring phase of MISA. However, the MOE has proposed that combined effluent streams be continuously monitored with an overall flow device accuracy of ± 7% during the compliance phase.

Best Professional Judgement (BPJ) may be used by the Joint Technical Committee (JTC) to permit the continued use of existing flow measurement devices which do not meet the above requirements, provided that sufficient technical justification is provided.

Cooling Water, Storm Water, or Waste Disposal Site Effluent—An accuracy of ± 20% of the actual flow is required; however, for some industrial sectors, flow measurement is not required for storm water discharges or waste disposal site effluent. Instead the duration and volume of these discharges must be estimated or measured.

Process Subcategory Effluent—Must measure within an accuracy of ± 15% during the monitoring phase if the flow measuring devices was installed prior to the MISA monitoring program. If a new device is to be installed during the monitoring phase or the company is in the compliance phase of MISA an accuracy of ± 5% of the actual flow for the primary flow measuring device and ± 2% of full-scale flow for the design range of the flow measuring system for the secondary flow measuring device is required.

Note that the accuracy of the primary devices may be determined by either calibration or certification reports. A certification report must certify that the primary flow device was installed according to international standards.

Flow measurement is a key element in the determination of the mass loading of a particular chemical. As such, it has become an integral part of the MISA monitoring program and municipal overstrength agreements.

In the next few years, flow measurement may take on an even greater importance as water conservation is promoted by the Ontario Ministry of

Natural Resources and the MOE. Surcharges on the use of water may come to play a larger role in water conservation policy.

3.8 REPORTING REQUIREMENTS

3.8.1 Reporting Monitoring Data

Many of the monitoring programs described in this chapter require the timely reporting of data. The actual reporting requirements are a function of the particular monitoring program.

Reports can vary from a letter containing a few analytical results to computer disks containing information for the MIDES or TOXDATA systems, and associated hard copy of outputs for the MISA monitoring system.

It is in a discharger's interest, regardless of reporting requirements, to begin compiling an environmental parameter data base. The data base should assist in the generation of reports and performing error checks, and allow for easier assessment of past trends in contaminant loadings and overall compliance.

3.8.2 Incident Reporting

As defined by the EPA, an incident is the discharge of a contaminant into the environment out of the normal course of events that is likely to cause an adverse effect. Section 14(1) of the EPA states that every person who discharges a contaminant or causes or permits the discharge of a contaminant into the natural environment out of the normal course of events that causes or is likely to cause an adverse effect shall forthwith notify the Ministry.

Section 80 requires that every person having control of a pollutant that is spilled and every person who spills or causes or permits a spill of a pollutant that causes or is likely to cause an adverse effect shall forthwith notify the following persons of the spill, of the circumstances, and of the action that the person has taken or intends to take with resect to:

- the MOE;
- the municipality or, if the spill occurred within the boundaries of a regional municipality, the regional municipality within the boundaries of which the spill occurred;
- where the person is not the owner of the pollutant and knows or is able to ascertain readily the identity of the owner of the pollutant, the owner of the pollutant;
- where the person is not the person having control of the pollutant and knows or is able to ascertain readily the identity of the person having control of the pollutant, the person having control of the pollutant.

Section 16(2) of the OWRA also deals with incident reporting in that every person that discharges or causes or permits the discharge of any material of any kind, if such discharge is not in the normal course of events, or from whose control material of any kind escapes into or in any waters or on any shore or bank thereof or into any place that may impair the quality of the water of any waters, shall forthwith notify the minister of the discharge or escape.

If a toxic substance (as defined by Schedule 1) is released into the environment in contravention of the CEPA, then Section 36 of the CEPA requires that a person who owns or has charge of a substance immediately before its initial release or its likely initial release into the environment, or who causes or contributes to the initial release or increases the likelihood of the initial release, must report the incident as soon as possible in the circumstances and make a reasonable effort to notify any member of the public who may be adversely affected by the release or likely release.

Additional incident reporting requirements are described in Chapter 12.

3.9 SUMMARY

The two prime pieces of legislation that govern the water quality and liquid discharges in Ontario are the EPA and the OWRA. Numerical guidelines for assessing water quality and narrative policies concerning the management of water resources in Ontario are described in various MOE publications such as the Blue Book.

The legislation concerning liquid discharges is currently in transition as the MISA program becomes operational. Direct dischargers from several industrial sectors are being addressed first but eventually indirect dischargers will also be addressed. MISA clearly places the responsibility for rigorous monitoring, effluent control, and reporting on the owners and/or operators of facilities that discharge effluents. The overall objective of the MISA program is the virtual elimination of persistent, toxic contaminants from all discharges into Ontario waterways. The stringent requirements of the MISA program will affect most if not all municipal and industrial facilities in Ontario.

REFERENCES

American Public Health Association (APHA), American Water Works Association (AWWA), Water Pollution Control Federation (WPCF), 1985. "Standard Methods for the Examination of Water and Wastewater". Sixteenth Edition.

Cotton, R., 1989. "101 New Liabilities Under MISA, Your Rights and Responsibilities". Presented at Effluent Management for the 1990's, June 5-6, Toronto.

Environmental Resources Management Group (ERM), 1990. "Hard Water". Resources, Vol. 12, No. 1.

Municipality of Metropolitan Toronto, 1989. "By-Law 153-89". 8 November 1989.

Ontario Ministry of the Environment (MOE), 1984a. "Water Management Goals, Policies, Objectives and Implementation Procedures of the Ministry of the Environment". Revised May (Blue Book).

Ontario Ministry of the Environment (MOE), 1984b. "Ontario Drinking Water Objectives". Revised 1983.

Ontario Ministry of the Environment (MOE), 1988. "Model Sewer Use By-Law". O-7729-4419-9, August.

Ontario Ministry of the Environment (MOE), 1989. "Ontario's Water Quality Objective Development Process", Draft, Aquatic Criteria Development Committee, May 12.

Pearse, P.H., Bertrand, F., and MacLaren, J.W., 1985. "Currents of Change —Final Report, Inquiry on Federal Water Policy". Prepared for Environment Canada.

Shaver, R.A., 1989. "Refinery Experience with the MISA Monitoring Program". Presented at the Ontario Ministry of the Environment Waste Management Conference, June 13, Toronto.

Water Pollution Control Federation (WPCF) and American Society of Civil Engineers (ASCE), 1982. "Wastewater Treatment Plant Design". WPCF Manual of Practice No. 8 and ASCE Manual on Engineering Practice No. 36.

Table 3.1
WATER QUALITY GUIDELINES

I) Provincial Water Quality Objective (PWQO)

Parameter	Guideline*
Alkalinity	25% decrease
pH	6.5 to 8.5
Ammonia	0.02 mg/L
Chlorine	0.002 mg/L
Cyanide	0.005 mg/L
Phenols	1 ug/L
Total Phosphorus	10 ug/L (for lakes)
	30 ug/L (for rivers/streams)

Gases:

Hydrogen Sulphide	0.002 mg/L
Dissolved Gases	110% of saturation value
Dissolved Oxygen	8 mg/L at 0°C
	7 mg/L at 5°C
	6 mg/L at 10 to 15°C
	5 mg/L at 20 to 25°C

Radionuclides:

Cesium 137	50 Becquerel/L
Iodine 131	10 Bq/L
Radium 226	1 Bq/L
Strontium 90	10 Bq/L
Tritium	40,000 Bq/L

Metals:

Arsenic	100 ug/L
Beryllium	11 ug/L if alkalinity <75 mg/L $CaCO_3$
	1100 ug/L if alkalinity >75 mg/L $CaCO_3$
Cadmium	0.2 ug/L
Copper	5 ug/L
Iron	300 ug/L
Lead	5 mg/L if alkalinity <20 mg/L $CaCO_3$
	10 mg/L if alkalinity 20 to 40 mg/L $CaCO_3$
	20 mg/L if alkalinity 40 to 80 mg/L $CaCO_3$
	25 mg/L if alkalinity >80 mg/L $CaCO_3$

Parameter	Guideline*
Mercury	0.2 ug/L
Nickel	25 ug/L
Selenium	100 ug/L
Silver	0.1 ug/L
Zinc	30 ug/L

Pesticides:

Dicamba	200 ug/L
Diquat	0.5 ug/L
Diuron	1.6 ug/L
Dalapon	110 ug/L
Simazine	10 ug/L
2,4-D(BEE)	4 ug/L
Chlordane	0.06 ug/L
Chlorphyrifos	0.001 ug/L
Diazinon	0.08 ug/L
Endosulphan	0.003 ug/L
Fenthion (Baytex)	0.006 ug/L
Guthion	0.005 ug/L
Malathion	0.1 ug/L
Methoxychlor	0.04 ug/L
Pyrethrum	0.01 ug/L
Aldrin/Dieldrin	0.001 ug/L
DDT & metabolites	0.003** ug/L
Heptachlor and Heptachlor epoxide	0.001 ug/L
Lindane	0.01 ug/L
Toxaphene	0.008 ug/L
Parathion	0.008 ug/L

Industrial Organics:

Dibutylphthalate	4.0 ug/L
Diethylhexylphthalate	0.6 ug/L
Other Phthalates	0.2 ug/L
Dechlorane (Mirex)	0.001** ug/L
Polychlorinated Biphenyl	0.001** ug/L

II) Substances with Zero Tolerance Limits

Mercury
DDT and metabolites
Polychorinated Biphenyl (PCB)
Polybrominated Biphenyl (PBB)
Dechlorane (mirex)

Notes:
* * unfiltered sample
* ** chemicals having a zero tolerance limit

III) Substances with Undefined Tolerance Limits

Metals:

Aluminum	Manganese
Antimony	Molybdenum
Barium	Strontium
Boron	Thallium
Cesium	Tin
Cobalt	Vanadium

Organic Compounds:

Acrylonitrile	Furfural
Alkyl Amines	Haloforms
Aryl Amines	Mercaptans
Aryl Chlorides	Nitrosamines
Aryl Sulfonic Acids	Nitro Aromatics
Azo & Diazo Compounds	Phenols and Derivatives
Benzene & Aliphatic Derivatives	Polycyclic Aromatic Hydrocarbons
Carbon Tetrachloride	Quinoline
Chlorinated Ethylenes	Styrene
Chlorophenols	Sulphonates

Pesticides:

Bayer '73	Alochlor (Lasso)
Benomyl (Benilate)	Amitrole
Dichlorobenil	Atrazine
Disulfoton (Disyston)	Cutrine
Kelthane (Dicofol)	Cyanazine
Methyl Parathion (Metaphos)	Glyphosate
Naled (Dibrom)	Paraquat
Rotenone	Trifluralin (Treflan)
PMA	2,4,5-T
TFM	

Table 3.2
DRINKING WATER QUALITY OBJECTIVES

I) Maximum Acceptable Concentrations (MAC)

Parameter	Guideline*
Arsenic	0.05 mg/L
Barium	1.0 mg/L
Boron	5.0 mg/L
Cadmium	0.005 mg/L
Chromium	0.05 mg/L
Cyanide (free)	0.2 mg/L
Fluoride	2.4 mg/L
Lead	0.05 mg/L
Mercury	0.001 mg/L
Selenium	0.01 mg/L
Silver	0.05 mg/L
Nitrate (as N)*	10.0 mg/L
Nitrite (as N)	1.0 mg/L
Nitrilotriacetic Acid	0.05 mg/L
Trihalomethanes	0.35 mg/L
Turbidity	1 Formazin Turbidity Unit

Pesticides:

Aldrin + Dieldrin	0.0007 mg/L
Carbaryl	0.07 mg/L
Chlordane	0.007 mg/L
DDT**	0.03 mg/L
Diazinon	0.014 mg/L
Endrin	0.0002 mg/L
Heptachlor and Heptachlor Epoxide	0.003 mg/L
Lindane	0.004 mg/L
Methoxychlor	0.1 mg/L
Methyl Parathion**	0.007 mg/L
Parathion	0.035 mg/L
Toxaphene	0.005 mg/L
2,4-D	0.1 mg/L
2,4,5-TP	0.01 mg/L

Notes:

* If both are present, the total of nitrate plus nitrite should not exceed 10 mg/L.
** If more than one of these pesticides is present, the total shall not exceed the sum of the MAC values or 0.1 mg/L, whichever is less.

II) Interim Maximum Acceptable Concentration (IMAC)

Parameter	Guideline*
Polychlorinated Biphenyls	0.003 mg/L
Uranium	0.02 mg/L

Selected Pesticides:**

Alachlor	0.005 ug/L
Aldicarb	0.009 ug/L
Atrazine (and D-ethyl Atrazine)	0.046 ug/L
Cyanazine	0.01 ug/L
Dicamba	0.087 ug/L
Metolachlor	0.105 ug/L
Metribuzin	0.06 ug/L
Prometryn	0.001 ug/L
Simazine (and D-ethyl Simazine)	0.01 ug/L
2,4 Dichlorophenoxybutyric Acid (2,4 DB)	0.018 ug/L

III) Maximum Desirable Concentration (MDC)

Chloride	250 mg/L
Copper	1.0 mg/L
Iron	0.3 mg/L
Manganese	0.05 mg/L
Methane	3 L/m^3
Organic Nitrogen*	0.15 mg/L
Phenols	0.002 mg/L
Sulphate	500 mg/L
Total Dissolved Solids	500 mg/L
Total Organic Carbon	5 mg/L
Zinc	5 mg/L
Sulphide	inoffensive
Odour	inoffensive
Colour	5 True Colour Units
Temperature	15°C

Notes:
* Total Kjeldahl nitrogen minus ammonia nitrogen
** IMAC values for selected pesticides recommended by the MOE in 1986 and 1988.

Table 3.3
SCHEDULE 1—ANALYTICAL TEST GROUP NUMBERS AND PARAMETERS

ANALYTICAL TEST GROUP #	NAME	PARAMETERS
1	Chemical Oxygen Demand	Chemical oxygen demand (COD)
2	Total cyanide	Total cyanide
3	Hydrogen ion (pH)	Hydrogen ion (pH)
4a	Nitrogen	Ammonia plus Ammonium Total Kjeldahl nitrogen
4b	Nitrogen	Nitrate + Nitrite
5a	Organic carbon	Dissolved organic carbon (DOC)
5b	Organic carbon	Total organic carbon (TOC)
6	Total phosphorus	Total phosphorus
7	Specific conductance	Specific conductance
8	Suspended solids	Total suspended solids (TSS) Volatile suspended solids (VSS)
9	Total metals	Aluminum Beryllium Cadmium Chromium Cobalt Copper Lead Molybdenum Nickel Silver Thallium Vanadium Zinc
10	Hydrides	Antimony Arsenic Selenium
11	Chromium (Hexavalent)	Chromium (Hexavalent) (NOTE 1)
12	Mercury	Mercury
13	Total alkyl lead	Tetra-alkyl lead (NOTE 2) Tri-alkyl lead (NOTE 2)

ANALYTICAL TEST GROUP		PARAMETERS
#	NAME	
14	Phenolics (4AAP)	Phenolics (4AAP)
15	Sulphide	Sulphide
16	Volatiles, Halogenated	1,1,2,2-Tetrachloroethane 1,1,2-Trichloroethane 1,1-Dichloroethane 1,1-Dichloroethylene 1,2-Dichlorobenzene 1,2-Dichloroethane (Ethylene dichloride) 1,2-Dichloropropane 1,3-Dichlorobenzene 1,4-Dichlorobenzene Bromoform Bromomethane Carbon tetrachloride Chlorobenzene Chloroform Chloromethane Cis-1,3-Dichloropropylene Dibromochloromethane Ethylene dibromide Methylene chloride Tetrachloroethylene (Perchloroethylene) Trans-1,2-Dichloroethylene Trans-1,3-Dichloropropylene Trichloroethylene Trichlorofluoromethane Vinyl chloride (Chloroethylene)
17	Volatiles, Non-Halogenated	Benzene Ethylbenzene Styrene Toluene o-Xylene m-Xylene and p-Xylene (NOTE 3)
18	Volatiles, Water Soluble	Acrolein Acrylonitrile

ANALYTICAL TEST GROUP		PARAMETERS
#	NAME	
19	Extractables, Base Neutral	Acenaphthene
		5-nitro Acenaphthene
		Acenaphthylene
		Anthracene
		Benz(a)anthracene
		Benzo(a)pyrene
		Benzo(b)fluoranthene
		Benzo(g,h,i)perylene
		Benzo(k)fluoranthene
		Camphene
		1-Chloronaphthalene
		2-Chloronaphthalene
		Chrysene
		Dibenz(a,h)anthracene
		Fluoranthene
		Fluorene
		Indeno(1,2,3-cd)pyrene
		Indole
		1-Methylnaphthalene
		2-Methylnaphthalene
		Naphthalene
		Perylene
		Phenanthrene
		Pyrene
		Benzylbutylphthalate
		Bis(2-ethylhexyl)phthalate
		Di-n-butylphthalate
		4-Bromophenyl phenyl ether
		4-Chlorophenyl phenyl ether
		Bis(2-chloroisopropyl)ether
		Bis(2-chloroethyl)ether
		2,4-Dinitrotoluene
		2,6-Dinitrotoluene
		Bis(2-chloroethoxy)methane
		Diphenylamine (NOTE 4)
		N-Nitrosodiphenylamine (NOTE 4)
		N-Nitrosodi-n-propylamine

| ANALYTICAL TEST GROUP | | PARAMETERS |
#	NAME	
20	Extractables, Acid (Phenolics)	2,3,4,5-Tetrachlorophenol
		2,3,4,6-Tetrachlorophenol
		2,3,5,6-Tetrachlorophenol
		2,3,4-Trichlorophenol
		2,3,5-Trichlorophenol
		2,4,5-Trichlorophenol
		2,4,6-Trichlorophenol
		2,4-Dimethylphenol
		2,4-Dinitrophenol
		2,4-Dichlorophenol
		2,6-Dichlorophenol
		4,6-Dinitro-o-cresol
		2-Chlorophenol
		4-Chloro-3-methylphenol
		4-Nitrophenol
		m-Cresol
		o-Cresol
		p-Cresol
		Pentachlorophenol
		Phenol
21	Extractables, Phenoxy Acid Herbicides	
22	Extractables, Organochlorine Pesticides	
23	Extractables, Neutral -Chlorinated	1,2,3,4-Tetrachlorobenzene
		1,2,3,5-Tetrachlorobenzene
		1,2,4,5-Tetrachlorobenzene
		1,2,3-Trichlorobenzene
		1,2,4-Trichlorobenzene
		2,4,5-Trichlorotoluene
		Hexachlorobenzene
		Hexachlorobutadiene
		Hexachlorocyclopentadiene
		Hexachloroethane
		Octachlorostyrene
		Pentachlorobenzene

ANALYTICAL TEST GROUP		PARAMETERS
	NAME	
24	Chlorinated Dibenzo-p-dioxins and Dibenzofurans	2,3,7,8-Tetrachlorodibenzo-p-dioxin
		Octachlorodibenzo-p-dioxin
		Octachlorodibenzofuran
		Total heptachlorinated dibenzo-p-dioxins
		Total heptachlorinated dibenzofurans
		Total hexachlorinated dibenzo-p-dioxins
		Total hexachlorinated dibenzofurans
		Total pentachlorinated dibenzo-p-dioxins
		Total pentachlorinated dibenzofurans
		Total tetrachlorinated dibenzo-p-dioxins
		Total tetrachlorinated dibenzofurans
25	Solvent Extractables	Oil and grease
26	Fatty and Resin Acids	
27	Polychlorinated Biphenyls (PCBs) (Total)	PCBs (Total)
28a	Open Characterization - Volatiles	
28b	Open Characterization - Extractables	
29	Open Characterization - Elemental	Aluminum
		Antimony
		Arsenic
		Barium
		Beryllium
		Bismuth
		Boron
		Cadmium
		Calcium
		Cerium
		Cesium
		Chromium
		Cobalt
		Copper
		Dysprosium
		Erbium
		Europium
		Gadolinium
		Gallium
		Germanium
		Gold
		Hafnium
		Holmium
		Indium

ANALYTICAL TEST GROUP		PARAMETERS
	NAME	
29	Open Characterization - Elemental (continued)	Iridium
		Iron
		Lanthanum
		Lead
		Lithium
		Lutetium
		Magnesium
		Manganese
		Mercury
		Molybdenum
		Neodymium
		Nickel
		Niobium
		Osmium
		Palladium
		Phosphorus
		Platinum
		Potassium
		Praseodymium
		Rhenium
		Rhodium
		Rubidium
		Ruthenium
		Samarium
		Scandium
		Selenium
		Silicon
		Silver
		Sodium
		Strontium
		Sulfur
		Tantalum
		Tellurium
		Terbium
		Thallium
		Thorium
		Thulium
		Tin
		Titanium
		Tungsten
		Uranium

ANALYTICAL TEST GROUP NAME		PARAMETERS
29	Open Characterization - Elemental (continued)	Vanadium
		Ytterbium
		Yttrium
		Zinc
		Zirconium

NOTE 1: Analyze for hexavalent chromium only if total chromium is greater than 1.0 milligrams per litre.

NOTE 2: Analyze for alkyl leads only if total lead is greater than 1.0 milligrams per litre.

NOTE 3: m-Xylene and p-Xylene often co-elute in the analysis. A single combined result may be reported as m-Xylene.

NOTE 4: Diphenylamine & N-Nitrosodiphenylamine often co-elute in the Gas Chromatography/Mass Spectrometry (GC/MS) analysis. A single combined result may be reported as Diphenylamine.

Table 3.4
LIMITS ON DISCHARGES TO SANITARY AND COMBINED SEWERS

Parameter	Limit
Temperature	< 65°C
pH*	5.5 to 9.5
Total Suspended Solids	350 mg/L
Biological Oxygen Demand	300 mg/L
Phenolic Compounds	1 mg/L
Total Kjeldahl Nitrogen	100 mg/L
Oil and Grease (mineral)	15 mg/L
Oil and Grease (animal/veg.)	150 mg/L
Total Cyanides	2 mg/L
Chlorides	1500 mg/L
Fluorides	10 mg/L
Sulfates	1500 mg/L
Phosphorus	10 mg/L
Aluminum	50 mg/L
Iron	50 mg/L
Antimony	5 mg/L
Arsenic	1 mg/L
Bismuth	5 mg/L
Cadmium	1 mg/L
Chromium	5 mg/L
Cobalt	5 mg/L
Copper	3 mg/L
Lead	5 mg/L
Manganese	5 mg/L
Mercury	0.1 mg/L
Molybdenum	5 mg/L
Nickel	3 mg/L
Selenium	5 mg/L
Silver	5 mg/L
Tin	5 mg/L
Titanium	5 mg/L
Vanadium	5 mg/L
Zinc	3 mg/L

Notes:
* All limits are the same in the MOE and Metro Toronto by-laws except for pH. The Metro Toronto limit for pH is 6.0 to 10.5.

References: MOE, 1988; Metropolitan Toronto, 1989

Table 3.5
LIMITS ON DISCHARGES TO STORM SEWERS

Parameter	MOE Limit	Metro Limit (if different)
Temperature	< 65°C	< 40°C
pH	6.0 to 9.0	
Total Suspended Solids	15 mg/L	
Biological Oxygen Demand	not set	15 mg/L
Oil and Grease (any source)	not set	no sheen
Cadmium	1 ug/L	
Chromium	200 ug/L	
Copper	10 ug/L	
Lead	50 ug/L	
Mercury	1 ug/L	
Nickel	50 ug/L	
Zinc	50 ug/L	
Fecal Coliform	200 per 100 mL	

References: MOE, 1988; Metropolitan Toronto, 1989

Table 3.6
SAMPLE PRESERVATIVES

Parameter ATG	Sample Preservative
1*, 4a, 5a, 5b and 6	Add sulphuric acid after sampling to lower pH to 2 but not < 1.5.
2	Add sodium hydroxide (cyanide-free) to raise pH to 12.
3, 4b, 7, 8, 10** 11, 13, 19, 20, 23, 24, 25, 26, 27, 28a, 28b, chloride, sulphate and fluoride	None.
9, 10**, 29 and iron	Add nitric acid (containing < 1mg/L of all analytes) to lower pH to <2.
12	Add 1 to 2 mL of nitric acid per 250 mL sample followed by at least 0.5 mL of potassium dichromate solution to produce definite yellow colour.
14	Add sulphuric acid solution prior to sampling to lower pH to 2 but not <1.5: diluted acid may be used. Or, prior to sampling, add 1 mL of solution containing 3N phosphoric acid and 0.5 g/L copper sulphate pentahydrate per 250 mL sample.
15	Add 0.5 mL 2N zinc acetate solution per 250 mL sample followed dropwise by 5% sodium carbonate or 5% sodium hydroxide to pH 10.
16, 17 and 18	Only for samples containing residual chlorine. Prior to sampling add 80 mg sodium thiosulphate per 1 L. Store in the dark.

Notes:

   * No preservative may be added but the maximum storage time is reduced from 28 days to four.

  ** Can be either none or same as for metals if to be analyzed from same sample.

Table 3.7
SCHEDULE 3, PART A—ANALYTICAL PRINCIPLES AND ANALYTICAL METHOD DETECTION LIMITS

Column 1 ANALYTICAL TEST GROUP #	Column 2 PARAMETERS CONVENTIONAL AND METAL PARAMETERS	Column 3 SAMPLE PREPARATION METHOD PRINCIPLES	Column 4 INSTRUMENTAL MEASUREMENT METHOD PRINCIPLES	Column 5 ALTERNATE INSTRUMENTAL MEASUREMENT METHOD PRINCIPLES	Column 6 ANALYTICAL METHOD DETECTION LIMITS mg/L
1	Chemical oxygen demand (COD)	Preparation for measurement system as appropriate followed by reflux or oven digestion at 150°C in presence of oxidizing reagents	Back titration or Colourimetric measurement of trivalent chromium (Cr III)	N/A	1 0
2	Total cyanide	Acid distillation	Ion Chromatography or Colourimetry or Specific Ion Electrode or Titration	Polarography via the method of standard addition in the presence of suitable electrolyte	0.005
3	Hydrogen ion (pH)	Preparation for measurement system as appropriate	pH electrode and pH meter	N/A	N/A
4a	Ammonia plus Ammonium	Preparation for measurement system as appropriate eg. distillation	Colourimetry or Specific Ion Electrode or Titration or Ion Chromatography	N/A	0.25 as Nitrogen
	Total Kjeldahl nitrogen	Preparation for measurement system as appropriate followed by Kjeldahl digestion procedure	Colourimetry or Specific Ion Electrode or Titration or Ion Chromatography	N/A	0.5 as Nitrogen
4b	Nitrate + Nitrite	Preparation for measurement system as appropriate	Colourimetry or Ion Chromatography	N/A	0.25 as Nitrogen

Column 1	Column 2	Column 3	Column 4	Column 5	Column 6
ANALYTICAL TEST GROUP #	PARAMETERS CONVENTIONAL AND METAL PARAMETERS	SAMPLE PREPARATION METHOD PRINCIPLES	INSTRUMENTAL MEASUREMENT METHOD PRINCIPLES	ALTERNATE INSTRUMENTAL MEASUREMENT METHOD PRINCIPLES	ANALYTICAL METHOD DETECTION LIMITS mg/L
5a	Dissolved organic carbon (DOC)	Preparation for measurement system as appropriate followed by filtration through glass fibre filter, retention size approximately 2 micrometers	Quantitative conversion of carbon to carbon dioxide (CO_2) by one of: i) Ultra violet persulphate digestion or ii) combustion at >800°C with a catalyst or iii) combustion at >1100°C, catalyst optional followed by infrared or colourimetric detection. DOC may be determined directly using a sample free of inorganic carbon or as the difference between total carbon and inorganic carbon.	N/A	0.5 as Carbon

Column 1 ANALYTICAL TEST GROUP #	Column 2 PARAMETERS CONVENTIONAL AND METAL PARAMETERS	Column 3 SAMPLE PREPARATION METHOD PRINCIPLES	Column 4 INSTRUMENTAL MEASUREMENT METHOD PRINCIPLES	Column 5 ALTERNATE INSTRUMENTAL MEASUREMENT METHOD PRINCIPLES	Column 6 ANALYTICAL METHOD DETECTION LIMITS mg/L
5b	Total organic carbon (TOC)	Preparation for measurement system as appropriate. Particulates must be reduced in size sufficiently to ensure effective processing by the measurement system. Particulates may be separated from the liquid with subsequent exclusive analysis of both phases.	Quantitative conversion of carbon to carbon dioxide (CO_2) by one of: i) Ultra violet persulphate digestion or ii) combustion at >800°C with a catalyst or iii) combustion at >1100°C, catalyst optional followed by infrared or colourimetric detection. TOC may be determined directly using a sample free of inorganic carbon or as the difference between total carbon and inorganic carbon or by appropriate combination of the results from the analysis of the sample phases.	N/A	5 as Carbon
6	Total phosphorus	Preparation for measurement system as appropriate followed by perchloric acid digestion or a mixture of nitric acid to sulphuric acid (HNO_3/H_2SO_4) at a ratio of 5:1 or a Kjeldahl equivalent mixture.	Colourimetry or Inductively Coupled Plasma - Atomic Emission Spectrometry	N/A	0.1 as Phosphorus

Column 1 ANALYTICAL TEST GROUP #	Column 2 PARAMETERS CONVENTIONAL AND METAL PARAMETERS	Column 3 SAMPLE PREPARATION METHOD PRINCIPLES	Column 4 INSTRUMENTAL MEASUREMENT METHOD PRINCIPLES	Column 5 ALTERNATE INSTRUMENTAL MEASUREMENT METHOD PRINCIPLES	Column 6 ANALYTICAL METHOD DETECTION LIMITS mg/L
7	Specific conductance	Preparation for measurement system as appropriate	Conductivity meter and cell	N/A	5 µS/cm
8	Total suspended solids (TSS)	Preparation for measurement system as appropriate	Filtration - particle retention of glass fibre filter < or = 2 micrometres followed by drying of filter and particulates at 103°C ± 3°C and gravimetry	N/A	5
	Volatile Suspended solids (VSS)	Perform TSS analysis	Ignite filter at 550°C for 4 hr. or until filter weight remains constant.	N/A	10
9	Aluminum Beryllium Cadmium Chromium Cobalt Copper Lead Molybdenum Nickel Silver Thallium Vanadium Zinc	Nitric evaporation or aqua regia digestion	Atomic absorption spectrometry and/or Emission Spectrometry - Inductively Coupled Plasma (ICP) or Direct Current Argon Plasma Spectrometry (DCP)	See Analytical Test Group 2	0.03 0.01 0.002 0.02 0.02 0.01 0.03 0.02 0.02 0.03 0.03 0.03 0.01

Column 1 ANALYTICAL TEST GROUP #	Column 2 PARAMETERS CONVENTIONAL AND METAL PARAMETERS	Column 3 SAMPLE PREPARATION METHOD PRINCIPLES	Column 4 INSTRUMENTAL MEASUREMENT METHOD PRINCIPLES	Column 5 ALTERNATE INSTRUMENTAL MEASUREMENT METHOD PRINCIPLES	Column 6 ANALYTICAL METHOD DETECTION LIMITS mg/L
10	Antimony Arsenic Selenium	Acid Digestion	Hydride Generation Atomic Absorption	See Analytical Test Group 2	0.005 0.005 0.005
11	Chromium (Hexavalent) (Analyze for hexavalent chromium only if total chromium >1.0mg/L)	i) None iii) Solvent extraction	i) Colourimetry ii) Atomic absorption	See Analytical Test Group 2	0.01
12	Mercury	Oxidative acid digestion	Cold vapour atomic absorption	N/A	0.0001
13	Tetra-alkyl lead Tri-alkyl lead (-inorganic ligand) (Analyze for alkyl leads only if total lead is >1.0mg/L)	i) Liquid/liquid extraction iii) Derivatization	i) Colourimetry using Dithiozone reagent or Atomic absorption iii) Gas Liquid Chromatography	N/A	0.002 0.002
14	Phenolics (4AAP)	Preparation for measurement system as appropriate followed by distillation from acidified (pH <4) sample	Colourimetry of buffered sample or Colourimetry of chloroform extract	N/A	0.002
15	Sulphide	Filtration and dissolution of precipitate	Methylene blue colourimetry or Specific Ion Electrode or ion chromatography	See Analytical Test Group 2	0.02

Column 1 ANALYTICAL TEST GROUP #	Column 2 PARAMETERS ORGANIC PARAMETERS	Column 3 SAMPLE PREPARATION METHOD PRINCIPLES	Column 4 INSTRUMENTAL MEASUREMENT METHOD PRINCIPLES	Column 5 ALTERNATE INSTRUMENTAL MEASUREMENT METHOD PRINCIPLES	Column 6 ANALYTICAL METHOD DETECTION LIMITS FOR STANDARDS IN REAGENT WATER μg/L
16	1,1,2,2-Tetrachloroethane	Purge and trap	Gas Chromatography/ Mass Spectrometry (GC/MS) Capillary column	Gas Chromatography/ Electron Capture or Hall Single capillary column	1.0*
	1,1,2-Trichloroethane				1.0*
	1,1-Dichloroethane				1.0*
	1,1-Dichloroethylene				1.0*
	1,2-Dichlorobenzene				1.0*
	1,2-Dichloroethane (Ethylene dichloride)				1.0*
	1,2-Dichloropropane				1.0*
	1,3-Dichlorobenzene				1.0*
	1,4-Dichlorobenzene				1.0*
	Bromoform				ND*
	Bromomethane				1.0*
	Carbon tetrachloride				1.0*
	Chlorobenzene				1.0*
	Chloroform				ND*
	Chloromethane				1.0*
	Cis-1,3-Dichloropropylene				1.0*
	Dibromochloromethane				1.0*
	Ethylene dibromide				1.0*
	Methylene chloride				1.0*
	Tetrachloroethylene (Perchloroethylene)				1.0*
	Trans-1,2-Dichloroethylene				1.0*
	Trans-1,3-Dichloropropylene				ND*
	Trichloroethylene				1.0*
	Trichlorofluoromethane				ND*
	Vinyl chloride (Chloroethylene)				ND*

Column 1 ANALYTICAL TEST GROUP #	Column 2 PARAMETERS ORGANIC PARAMETERS	Column 3 SAMPLE PREPARATION METHOD PRINCIPLES	Column 4 INSTRUMENTAL MEASUREMENT METHOD PRINCIPLES	Column 5 ALTERNATE INSTRUMENTAL MEASUREMENT METHOD PRINCIPLES	Column 6 ANALYTICAL METHOD DETECTION LIMITS FOR STANDARDS IN REAGENT WATER µg/L
17	Benzene	Purge and trap	Gas Chromatography/ Mass Spectrometry (GC/MS) Capillary column	Gas Chromatography Flame Ionization or Photo Ionization Single capillary column	1.0*
	Ethylbenzene				1.0*
	Styrene				1.0*
	Toluene				1.0*
	o-Xylene				1.0*
	m-Xylene/p-Xylene (NOTE 1)				1.0*
18	Acrolein	Purge and trap	Gas Chromatography/ Mass Spectrometry (GC/MS) Capillary column	Gas Chromatography Electron Capture/Hall & Flame Ionization/ Photo Ionization Single capillary column	ND*
	Acrylonitrile				ND*

Column 1 ANALYTICAL TEST GROUP #	Column 2 PARAMETERS ORGANIC PARAMETERS	Column 3 SAMPLE PREPARATION METHOD PRINCIPLES	Column 4 INSTRUMENTAL MEASUREMENT METHOD PRINCIPLES	Column 5 ALTERNATE INSTRUMENTAL MEASUREMENT METHOD PRINCIPLES	Column 6 ANALYTICAL METHOD DETECTION LIMITS FOR STANDARDS IN REAGENT WATER μg/L
19	Acenaphthene	Liquid/liquid extraction	Gas Chromatography/ Mass Spectrometry (GC/MS) Capillary column	High Performance Liquid Chromatography Ultra Violet or Fluorescence Detection	10*
	5-nitro Acenaphthene				10*
	Acenaphthylene				10*
	Anthracene				10*
	Benz(a)anthracene				10*
	Benzo(a)pyrene				10*
	Benzo(b)fluoranthene				10*
	Benzo(g,h,i)perylene				10*
	Benzo(k)fluoranthene				10*
	Camphene				10*
	1-Chloronaphthalene				10*
	2-Chloronaphthalene				10*
	Chrysene				10*
	Dibenz(a,h)anthracene				10*
	Fluoranthene				10*
	Fluorene				10*
	Indeno(1,2,3-cd)pyrene				10*
	Indole				ND*
	1-Methyl naphthalene				10*
	2-Methyl naphthalene				10*
	Naphthalene				10*
	Perylene				10*
	Phenanthrene				10*
	Pyrene				10*

Column 1 ANALYTICAL TEST GROUP #	Column 2 PARAMETERS ORGANIC PARAMETERS	Column 3 SAMPLE PREPARATION METHOD PRINCIPLES	Column 4 INSTRUMENTAL MEASUREMENT METHOD PRINCIPLES	Column 5 ALTERNATE INSTRUMENTAL MEASUREMENT METHOD PRINCIPLES	Column 6 ANALYTICAL METHOD DETECTION LIMITS FOR STANDARDS IN REAGENT WATER μg/L
19 cont'd	Benzylbutylphthalate	Liquid/liquid extraction	Gas Chromatography/ Mass Spectrometry (GC/MS) Capillary column	N/A	10*
	Bis(2-ethylhexyl)phthalate				10*
	Di-n-butylphthalate				10**
	4-Bromophenyl phenyl ether				10*
	4-Chlorophenyl phenyl ether				10*
	Bis(2-chloroisopropyl)ether				10*
	Bis(2-chloroethyl)ether				10*
	2,4-Dinitrotoluene				10*
	2,6-Dinitrotoluene				10*
	Bis(2-chloroethoxy)methane				10*
	Diphenylamine (NOTE 2)				10*
	N-Nitrosodiphenylamine (NOTE 2)				10*
	N-Nitrosodi-n-propylamine				10*

Column 1 ANALYTICAL TEST GROUP #	Column 2 PARAMETERS ORGANIC PARAMETERS	Column 3 SAMPLE PREPARATION METHOD PRINCIPLES	Column 4 INSTRUMENTAL MEASUREMENT METHOD PRINCIPLES	Column 5 ALTERNATE INSTRUMENTAL MEASUREMENT METHOD PRINCIPLES	Column 6 ANALYTICAL METHOD DETECTION LIMITS FOR STANDARDS IN REAGENT WATER µg/L
20	2,3,4,5-Tetrachlorophenol	Liquid/liquid extraction pH adjusted to <2 Derivatization, if appropriate Cleanup	Gas Chromatography/ Mass Spectrometry (GC/MS) Capillary column	N/A	1 0 *
	2,3,4,6-Tetrachlorophenol				1 0 *
	2,3,5,6-Tetrachlorophenol				1 0 *
	2,3,4-Trichlorophenol				1 0 *
	2,3,5-Trichlorophenol				1 0 *
	2,4,5-Trichlorophenol				1 0 *
	2,4,6-Trichlorophenol				1 0 *
	2,4-Dimethylphenol				1 0 *
	2,4-Dinitrophenol				1 0 *
	2,4-Dichlorophenol				1 0 *
	2,6-Dichlorophenol				1 0 *
	4,6-Dinitro-o-cresol				1 0 *
	2-Chlorophenol				1 0 *
	4-Chloro-3-methylphenol				1 0 *
	4-Nitrophenol				1 0 *
	m-Cresol				1 0 *
	o-Cresol				1 0 *
	p-Cresol				1 0 *
	Pentachlorophenol				1 0 *
	Phenol				1 0 *
21	Extractables, Phenoxy Acid Herbicides	N/A	N/A	N/A	N/A
22	Extractables, Organochlorine Pesticides	N/A	N/A	N/A	N/A

Column 1 ANALYTICAL TEST GROUP #	Column 2 PARAMETERS ORGANIC PARAMETERS	Column 3 SAMPLE PREPARATION METHOD PRINCIPLES	Column 4 INSTRUMENTAL MEASUREMENT METHOD PRINCIPLES	Column 5 ALTERNATE INSTRUMENTAL MEASUREMENT METHOD PRINCIPLES	Column 6 ANALYTICAL METHOD DETECTION LIMITS FOR STANDARDS IN REAGENT WATER µg/L
23	1,2,3,4-Tetrachlorobenzene	Liquid/liquid extraction Neutral pH Cleanup if necessary	Gas Liquid Chromatography Electron capture Dual capillary or Gas Chromatography/ Mass Spectroscopy (GC/MS) Capillary column	N/A	0.01
	1,2,3,5-Tetrachlorobenzene				0.01
	1,2,4,5-Tetrachlorobenzene				0.01
	1,2,3-Trichlorobenzene				0.01
	1,2,4-Trichlorobenzene				0.01
	2,4,5-Trichlorotoluene				0.01
	Hexachlorobenzene				0.01
	Hexachlorobutadiene				0.01
	Hexachlorocyclopentadiene				0.01
	Hexachloroethane				0.01
	Octachlorostyrene				0.01
	Pentachlorobenzene				0.01
24	2,3,7,8-Tetrachlorodibenzo-p-dioxin	Liquid/liquid extraction and cleanup or if TSS >15mg/L filter sample, extract solids by Soxhlet using toluene, extract filtrate normally, combine both extracts	Gas Chromatography/ Mass Spectroscopy (GC/MS) Capillary column	N/A	0.0003
	Octachlorodibenzo-p-dioxin				0.0003
	Octachlorodibenzofuran				0.0003
	Total heptachlorinated dibenzo-p-dioxins				0.0003
	Total heptachlorinated dibenzofurans				0.0003
	Total hexachlorinated dibenzo-p-dioxins				0.0003
	Total hexachlorinated dibenzofurans				0.0003
	Total pentachlorinated dibenzo-p-dioxins				0.0003
	Total pentachlorinated dibenzofurans				0.0003
	Total tetrachlorinated dibenzo-p-dioxins				0.0003
	Total tetrachlorinated dibenzofurans				0.0003

Column 1 ANALYTICAL TEST GROUP NUMBER	Column 2 PARAMETERS ORGANIC AND INORGANIC PARAMETERS	Column 3 SAMPLE PREPARATION METHOD PRINCIPLES	Column 4 INSTRUMENTAL MEASUREMENT METHOD PRINCIPLES	Column 5 ALTERNATE INSTRUMENTAL MEASUREMENT METHOD PRINCIPLES	Column 6 ANALYTICAL METHOD DETECTION LIMITS FOR STANDARDS IN REAGENT WATER µg/L
25	Oil and Grease	Acidify with a mineral acid to approximately pH 2 Liquid/liquid extraction plus solvent rinsings of sample containers	Gravimetric	N/A	1000
26	Fatty and Resin Acids	N/A	N/A	N/A	N/A
27	Polychlorinated Biphenyls (PCBs) (identify Aroclors present & total concentration)	Liquid/liquid extraction Neutral pH Cleanup if necessary	Gas Liquid Chromatography Electron capture Single capillary column or Gas Chromatography/ Mass Spectroscopy (GC/MS) Capillary column Report as PCB Aroclors	N/A	0.1

NOTE 1: m-Xylene and p-Xylene often co-elute in the analysis. A single combined result may be reported as m-Xylene.

NOTE 2: Diphenylamine & N-Nitrosodiphenylamine often co-elute in the Gas Chromatography/Mass Spectrometry (GC/MS) analysis. A single combined result may be reported as Diphenylamine.

Column 1 ANALYTICAL TEST GROUP NUMBER	Column 2 PARAMETERS ORGANIC AND INORGANIC PARAMETERS	Column 3 SAMPLE PREPARATION METHOD PRINCIPLES	Column 4 INSTRUMENTAL MEASUREMENT METHOD PRINCIPLES	Column 5 ALTERNATE INSTRUMENTAL MEASUREMENT METHOD PRINCIPLES	Column 6 LIMIT OF CHARACTERIZATION µg/L
28a	Open Characterization - Volatiles	Purge and trap	Gas Chromatography/ Mass Spectroscopy (GC/MS)	N/A	10* against 1,3-Dichlorobutane
28b	Open Characterization - Extractables	Liquid/liquid extraction Neutral pH followed by Liquid/liquid extraction pH <2 Derivatization of acidic extract optional Cleanup optional	Gas Chromatography/ Mass Spectroscopy (GC/MS)	N/A	10* against D10 Phenanthrene
29	Aluminum	Nitric evaporation or aqua regia digestion	Atomic absorption spectrometry and/or Emission Spectrometry - Inductively Coupled Plasma (ICP) or Direct Current Argon Plasma Spectrometry (DCP) or Inductively Coupled Plasma/Mass Spectroscopy (ICP/MS)	N/A	50*
	Antimony				50*
	Arsenic				50*
	Barium				50*
	Beryllium				50*
	Bismuth				50*
	Boron				50*
	Cadmium				50*
	Calcium				50*
	Cerium				50*
	Cesium				50*
	Chromium				50*
	Cobalt				50*
	Copper				50*
	Dysprosium				50*
	Erbium				50*
	Europium				50*
	Gadolinium				50*

Column 1 ANALYTICAL TEST GROUP NUMBER	Column 2 PARAMETERS ORGANIC AND INORGANIC PARAMETERS	Column 3 SAMPLE PREPARATION METHOD PRINCIPLES	Column 4 INSTRUMENTAL MEASUREMENT METHOD PRINCIPLES	Column 5 ALTERNATE INSTRUMENTAL MEASUREMENT METHOD PRINCIPLES	Column 6 LIMIT OF CHARACTERIZATION µg/L
29 (continued)	Gallium	Nitric evaporation or aqua regia digestion	Atomic absorption spectrometry and/or Emission Spectrometry - Inductively Coupled Plasma (ICP) or Direct Current Argon Plasma Spectrometry (DCP) or Inductively Coupled Plasma/Mass Spectroscopy (ICP/MS)	N/A	50*
	Germanium				50*
	Gold				50*
	Hafnium				50*
	Holmium				50*
	Indium				50*
	Iridium				50*
	Iron				50*
	Lanthanum				50*
	Lead				50*
	Lithium				50*
	Lutetium				50*
	Magnesium				50*
	Manganese				50*
	Mercury				50*
	Molybdenum				50*
	Neodymium				50*
	Nickel				50*
	Niobium				50*
	Osmium				50*
	Palladium				50*
	Phosphorus				50*
	Platinum				50*
	Potassium				50*
	Praseodymium				50*
	Rhenium				50*
	Rhodium				50*
	Rubidium				50*
	Ruthenium				50*
	Samarium				50*

Column 1 ANALYTICAL TEST GROUP NUMBER	Column 2 PARAMETERS ORGANIC AND INORGANIC PARAMETERS	Column 3 SAMPLE PREPARATION METHOD PRINCIPLES	Column 4 INSTRUMENTAL MEASUREMENT METHOD PRINCIPLES	Column 5 ALTERNATE INSTRUMENTAL MEASUREMENT METHOD PRINCIPLES	Column 6 LIMIT OF CHARACTERIZATION µg/L
29 (continued)	Scandium	Nitric evaporation or aqua regia digestion	Atomic absorption spectrometry and/or Emission Spectrometry Inductively Coupled Plasma (ICP) or Direct Current Argon Plasma Spectrometry (DCP) or Inductively Coupled Plasma/Mass Spectroscopy (ICP/MS)	N/A	5 0 *
	Selenium				5 0 *
	Silicon				5 0 *
	Silver				5 0 *
	Sodium				5 0 *
	Strontium				5 0 *
	Sulfur				5 0 *
	Tantalum				5 0 *
	Tellurium				5 0 *
	Terbium				5 0 *
	Thallium				5 0 *
	Thorium				5 0 *
	Thulium				5 0 *
	Tin				5 0 *
	Titanium				5 0 *
	Tungsten				5 0 *
	Uranium				5 0 *
	Vanadium				5 0 *
	Ytterbium				5 0 *
	Yttrium				5 0 *
	Zinc				5 0 *
	Zirconium				5 0 *

* Value above which all organic compounds or elements must be identified and their approximate concentration determined in open characterization analyses as per the publications cited in subsection 4(4).

Figure 3.1
PROPOSED PROCESS FOR DETERMINING EFFLUENT LIMITS

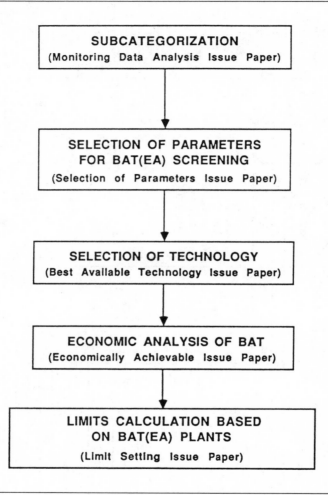

Figure 3.2
METHODS OF CALCULATING EFFLUENT LIMITS

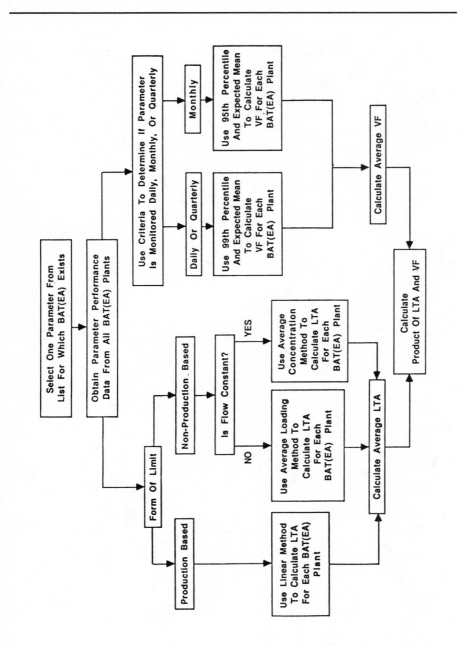

4.0

Waste Management and Transportation

4.1 OVERVIEW OF THE REGULATORY FRAMEWORK

4.1.1 Provincial Regulations

The regulation of waste management in Canada is primarily a provincial jurisdiction. In Ontario, many aspects of waste management are addressed in the Environmental Protection Act (EPA). Part V of the EPA outlines the responsibilities of several parties including waste generators and waste management system operators (including carriers). It also sets out the requirements for obtaining approvals for waste management systems, the role of public hearings in evaluating waste management concerns, and the Director's role in issuing orders regarding wastes (see Section 4.2).

EPA Regulation 309 addresses the classification and registration of wastes and assigns definitions to various types of waste (see Section 4.3). It also provides a comprehensive manifest system for tracking wastes from their point of generation to recycling or disposal (see Section 4.4).

The Ontario Dangerous Goods Transportation Act (DGTA) pertains to the transportation of hazardous materials including waste within the province using roads. Its federal counterpart, the Transport of Dangerous Goods Act (TDGA), pertains to marine, air, rail and interprovincial and international road transportation. The DGTA is patterned strongly after the TDGA.

4.1.2 Federal Legislation

The major piece of federal legislation that influences waste management is the Canadian Environmental Protection Act (CEPA) which includes provisions for the control of all aspects of the life cycle of toxic substances including their importation, transport, distribution, and ultimate disposal as waste. CEPA has the following elements related to waste management:

- authority to regulate waste handling and disposal practices of federal departments, boards, agencies and Crown corporations;

103

- provisions to create guidelines and codes for environmentally sound practices as well as objectives setting desirable levels of environmental quality; and
- provisions to issue permits to control dumping at sea from ships, barges, aircraft and man-made structures (excluding normal discharges from off-shore facilities involved in the exploration for, and exploitation and processing of, seabed mineral resources).

Until specific legislation is developed for toxic chemicals, the effect of the CEPA on waste management and transportation in Ontario is minimal.

The federal Transport of Dangerous Goods Act (TDGA) covers the transportation and management of dangerous goods within provinces via any means except road, between provinces, and international transportation by any means. It also provides emergency clean-up assistance (see Section 4.5). The Act is administered by Transport Canada. Environment Canada provides technical advice and recommendations for regulatory initiatives or matters related to hazardous waste.

When radioactive materials are involved, conditions of the Transport Packaging of Radioactive Materials Regulation also must be met.

4.2 ASSIGNMENT OF RESPONSIBILITIES

4.2.1 Waste Generators

Part V of the Environmental Protection Act (EPA) clearly places responsibility for the proper disposal and identification of waste on the generator of the waste. Section 39 of Part V prohibits any person from depositing waste without a Certificate of Approval (C of A) "upon, in, into or through any land or land covered by water or in any building that is not a waste disposal site" for which a C of A has been issued except if in accordance with the terms and conditions of such a certificate.

Section 40 of Part V limits the equipment and facilities that may be used in conjunction with a waste management system in that "no person shall use any facilities or equipment for the storage, handling, treatment, collection, transportation, processing or disposal of waste that is not part of a waste management system" for which a C of A has been issued and except in accordance with the terms and conditions of such a certificate.

4.2.2 Transfer of Responsibility

Part V of the EPA also allows responsibility for disposal of a waste to be transferred from the generator to a third party (a disposal site operator, the owner of a disposal site, or the owner of a transfer station). This is a major difference between the approach to waste management in Ontario and that used in some other jurisdictions, notably the United States where generators essentially are responsible for their wastes forever

(Shaw, 1989). The MOE is considering changes to the current system in terms of the transfer of responsibility.

Section 40a of Part V outlines several conditions that apply to the transfer of responsibility from a waste generator to a disposal facility operator:

(1) The ownership of waste that is accepted at a waste disposal site by the operator of the site is transferred to the operator upon acceptance.

(2) Where waste is deposited but not accepted at a waste disposal site, the ownership of the waste shall be deemed to be transferred to the operator of the site immediately before the waste is deposited.

(3) Subsections (1) and (2) apply only in respect of a waste disposal site for which a C of A or a provisional C of A is in force.

(4) Subsection (1) applies only in the absence of a contract to the contrary.

(5) Subsections (1) and (4) do not relieve any person from liability except liability as owner of a waste that is delivered to and accepted by the operator of a waste disposal site in accordance with law including an applicable C of A or provisional C of A.

(6) Where the operator of a waste disposal site is not the owner of the land on which the site is located, subsections (1) and (2) do not prevent the ownership of waste that is accepted or deposited at the site from being transferred to the owner of the land.

The generator of a waste is responsible for ensuring that the disposal site receiving the waste has an appropriate C of A. It is becoming common practice for generators to ask for a copy of the C of A or the certificate number prior to entering into an agreement with a disposal site operator (Shaw, 1989).

While a waste is being transported, both the generator of the waste and the carrier of the material are liable should there be an incident involving the material. Generators can make it a contractual condition that ownership of the waste is transferred when the carrier picks up the material. Such a transfer of ownership may not be recognized in court if it is seen as trying to circumvent liability specified under Part IX of the EPA (Shaw, 1989).

4.2.3 Director's Orders

Section 41, Part V of the EPA provides the Director with the statutory authority to order an occupant or the person having charge and control of land or a building to remove wastes and restore the site to a condition satisfactory to the Director if the location has not been approved as a waste disposal site. Section 42 authorizes the Director to require a waste management system or operator to comply with the requirements of the

EPA. Section 43 gives the Director the authority to perform the necessary work to ensure that a waste management system conforms with the requirements of the EPA and to charge the owner with the costs incurred to achieve conformity.

4.3 REGULATION 309 WASTE CLASSIFICATION AND REGISTRATION

4.3.1 Overview

All products and by-products from waste transfer, bulking, treatment or processing facilities are considered to be **waste**. These include oil recovered from oily water treatment facilities as well as blended or bulked waste solvents destined for disposal or recycle. Commercial chemical products or by-products, including those that are off-specification or that have exceeded their expiry date, are also considered to be wastes. Economic value is not a good indicator of whether or not a material is a waste. Waste materials that are sold for heating value or otherwise being reused, recycled, or reclaimed are still considered to be wastes (MOE, 1989a).

Some wastes are **exempt** by definition (see Section 4.3.5). A **recyclable material** is not considered a waste but rather a raw material (MOE, 1989a). By-products or intermediates from a series of traditional refining operations, such as mineral or metal recovery, are not wastes. For example, sludges from an electrolytic recovery process for metals which are subsequently processed to remove precious metals, such as silver or gold, are not considered wastes. Material that is not waste is exempt from the registration requirements outlined in Section 4.3.6. There also are **small quantity exemptions** (SQE) for several of the waste categories.

Waste generators include operators of commercial and manufacturing facilities that produce waste as well as operators of waste transfer, bulking, treatment, or processing facilities that forward materials off-site for subsequent management.

Any material identified as being a waste must be classified. The MOE has developed the system illustrated in Figure 4.1 for classifying wastes and assessing whether a material must be registered. The three basic classes for wastes are "hazardous", "liquid industrial", and "registerable solid". Hazardous and liquid industrial wastes are also referred to as "subject" wastes. Table 4.1 presents the various waste classes. Classification is a one-time process.

4.3.2 Hazardous Waste

Of the three classes of waste, the definition of hazardous waste is the most extensive. The first step in the identification of a hazardous waste is

to review those wastes which are exempted:
- waste from a municipally-owned sewage works
- hauled sewage or domestic wastes
- incinerator ash resulting from the incineration of waste that is neither hazardous waste nor liquid industrial waste
- non-acute-hazard waste produced per month, accumulated or residues from a spill clean-up in an amount less than 5 kg
- acute-hazard waste that is produced per month, accumulated or residues from a spill clean-up in an amount less than 1 kg
- empty containers or liners that contained a non-acute-hazard waste
- empty containers (< 20 L) or liners (< 10 kg) that contained an acute-hazard waste

Regulation 309 previously exempted incinerator ash resulting from the incineration of domestic waste. That exemption was superseded by Regulation 138/90 so that now only ash from the incineration of waste that is neither hazardous waste, liquid industrial waste, nor domestic waste is excluded.

There are ten categories that can be used to assign a waste to the hazardous classification. Regardless of the category, all hazardous waste in a volume greater than the small quantity exemption (SQE) must be registered (see Section 4.3.6). The categories are listed below according to a hierarchy that can be followed sequentially to determine the priority of classification and identify the **primary** classification of the waste. Once the primary classification if found, the letter which represents this classification, e.g. "S" for severely toxic wastes, is added to the three-digit waste class number which is provided in Appendix 2 of Regulation 309 so that an appropriate **waste class** can be determined.

1   A waste that contains any of the substances listed in Schedule 3 of Regulation 309 at a concentration greater than 1 ppm is characterized as being **Severely Toxic (S)**. Examples can include pesticides such as 2,4,5-T and pentachlorophenol. There is no small-quantity exemption for such wastes. Empty containers and inner liners are also considered to be hazardous waste.

2   A waste that contains any part of the human body, including tissues and bodily fluids, but excluding fluids, extracted teeth, hair, nail clippings and the like which are non-infectious; any part of the carcass of an animal infected with a communicable disease or suspected by a licensed veterinarian to be infected; or non-anatomical waste infected with communicable disease—is characterized as **Pathological (P)**. There is no small-quantity exemption for such wastes. Empty containers and liners are also hazardous unless they have been incinerated, autoclaved or otherwise sterilized to make them non-infectious.

3   A waste that is defined to be a PCB waste according to Regulation

11/82 is characterized as a **PCB Waste (D)**. Generally, wastes that contain PCBs at concentrations greater than 50 parts per million (ppm) by weight are PCB Wastes. The only small-quantity exemption is for electrical capacitors that have never contained over one kilogram of PCBs. These types of capacitors do not need to be registered. (See Chapter 7 for additional details.)

4 & 5 Any commercial products or manufacturing intermediates that are off-specification or otherwise unacceptable for use and that contain any of the substances listed in Schedules 2(a) or 2(b) of Regulation 309 are characterized as being either **Acute Hazardous Waste Chemical (A)** or **Hazardous Waste Chemical (B)**. The definition includes materials such as pharmaceutical or pesticide waste products that contain active ingredients from Schedules 2(a) or 2(b). Active ingredients are constituents that have been included in a formulated product for an intended effect.

For waste listed in Schedule 2(a) the small-quantity exemption is 1 kg of waste per month. Containers greater than 20 litres in capacity that contained the Schedule 2(a) material are considered to be hazardous unless triple-rinsed using an appropriate solvent. Inner liners weighing more than 10 kg that contained Schedule 2(a) products are also considered hazardous unless they have been triple-rinsed using an appropriate solvent.

For a waste found in Schedule 2(b) the small-quantity exemption is 5 kg of waste per month. Empty containers and inner liners are not considered hazardous.

6   An industrial waste stream that is generated from a process listed in Schedule 1 of Regulation 309 is characterized as being **Hazardous Industrial Waste (H)**. There is a small-quantity exemption of 5 kg per month. Empty containers and inner liners are not hazardous. The "heel" rule, i.e. less than one inch (2.54 cm) of material, is used to determine if a container is empty.

7   A waste that meets the Regulation 309 definition for ignitability is characterized as being **Ignitable Waste (I)**. There is a small-quantity exemption of 5 kg per month. Empty containers and inner liners are not hazardous.

Wastes are defined as being ignitable according to the following criteria:

- liquid with a flash point less than 61°C (e.g. ethanol or gasoline);
- a solid capable, under standard temperature and pressure, of causing fire due to friction, absorption of moisture, or spontaneous chemical changes and, when ignited, burns so vigorously and persistently that is creates a hazard (e.g. charcoal);
- ignitable compressed gas having a critical temperature less than 50°C

or an absolute vapour pressure greater than 294 kPa at 50°C, or exerts an absolute pressure, in the cylinder, packaging tube or tank in which it is contained, greater than 275 ± 1 kPa at 21.1°C or 717 ± 2 kPa at 54.4°C, and are ignitable at normal atmospheric pressure when in a mixture of 13% or less by volume with air, or have a flammability range of at least 12 (e.g. methane, butane and propane);

- an oxidizing substance which readily yields oxygen to stimulate, or contribute to, the combustion of other materials (e.g. chlorates, permanganate and nitrates).

8   A waste that meets the Regulation 309 definition for corrosivity is characterized as being **Corrosive Waste (C)**. There is a small-quantity exemption of 5 kg per month. Empty containers and inner liners are not hazardous.

A waste is considered to be corrosive waste according to the following definitions:

- it is aqueous and has a pH less than or equal to 2.0 or greater than 12.5
- it is a liquid and corrodes steel (SAE 1020) at a rate greater than 6.35 millimetres per year at a test temperature of 55°C using the National Association of Corrosion Engineers test method TM-01-69.

9   A waste that meets the Regulation 309 definition for reactivity is characterized as being **Reactive Waste (R)**. There is a small-quantity exemption of 5 kg per month. Empty containers and inner liners are not hazardous.

A waste is considered to be reactive according to the following definitions:

- normally unstable and readily undergoes violent change without detonating
- reacts violently with water
- forms potentially explosive mixtures with water
- when mixed with water it generates toxic gases, vapours or fumes in a quantity sufficient to present danger to human health or the environment
- is a cyanide- or sulfide-bearing waste which, when exposed to pH conditions between 2.0 and 12.5, can generate toxic gases, vapours or fumes in a quantity sufficient to present danger to human health or the environment
- capable of detonation or explosive reaction if it is subjected to a strong initiating source or if heated under confinement
- readily capable of detonation or explosive decomposition or reaction at standard temperature and pressure
- is a Class 1 explosive as defined by the TDG Regulation (refer to Schedule II, List I of the TDG regulation)

10   Any waste that produces a leachate which contains any of the substances at concentration greater than 100 times the concentrations listed in Schedule 4 of Regulation 309 (see Table 4.2) is characterized as being **Leachate Toxic (T)**. There is a small-quantity exemption of 5 kg per month. Empty containers and liners are not hazardous.

In addition, waste from plants that produce coal tar should be treated as hazardous waste (Waste Class 222H). For contaminated soils and sediments, the following applies (MOE, 1989b):

- If the concentration of benzo(a)pyrene (BaP) in leachate is above 1 ppb then the material is classified as hazardous (Waste Class 222T).
- If the concentration of BaP in the leachate is 1.0 ppb or less, but greater than 0.1 ppb, then the material is classified as non-hazardous but registerable solid waste, provided it passes the "Slump Test" (Waste Class 222N).
- If the concentration of BaP in the leachate is 0.1 ppb or less, but greater than 0.01 ppb, then the contaminated material is classified as non-hazardous solid waste, provided it passes the "Slump Test".
- If the concentration of BaP in the leachate is 0.01 ppb or less, then the material does not have to be removed from the site.

4.3.3 Liquid Industrial Waste

A waste is a **Liquid Industrial Waste (L)** if it meets none of the criteria for hazardous waste and is a liquid as defined by the slump test described in Regulation 309. This class is broadly defined to include any liquid waste from industrial, commercial, manufacturing, research or experimental activities. Sludges that fail the slump test included in the regulation are also classified as liquid wastes. Exemptions include:

- hauled sewage
- waste from the operation of a water works subject to the Ontario Water Resources Act
- waste that is produced in any month in an amount less than 25 L or otherwise accumulated in an amount less than 25 L
- waste directly discharged from a waste generation facility into a sewage system subject to the Ontario Water Resources Act
- waste from a food packing, processing, and preparation operation including wineries and cheese-making facilities
- drilling fluids and produced waters associated with oil and gas exploration, development and production
- processed organic waste
- asbestos waste

4.3.4 Registerable Solid Waste

A waste is classified as being **Registerable Solid Waste (N)** if it produces a leachate that contains any of the substances at concentrations between 10 and 100 times the concentrations listed in Schedule 4 of Regulation 309 (see Table 4.2). The small-quantity exemption is 25 kg of waste per month. While Registerable Solid Wastes must be registered, they are not assigned a Generator Registration Number by the MOE, nor are they subject to the same handling and disposal requirements as hazardous and liquid industrial waste.

4.3.5 Exempt Wastes

In addition to the exemptions noted for specific types of hazardous wastes, registration is not required in anticipation of wastes that may be generated through spills. Emergency registration procedures are available for spill situations.

Recyclable material as defined below is also exempted:

- wholly utilized in an ongoing agricultural, commercial, manufacturing, or industrial process or operation used principally for functions other than waste management and that does not involve combustion or land application of waste
- where it is promptly packaged for retail sale
- where it is offered for retail sale to meet a realistic market demand, but does not include Hazardous Waste or Liquid Industrial Waste unless transportation from generator to site is direct

Recyclable materials are considered to be raw materials and as such are exempt from the registration and all other provisions of Regulation 309. In most cases the question of whether or not a process is being used for waste management can be determined by reviewing its viability if the waste were not available. Processes or operations that are not viable without the incoming waste are deemed to be in the business of waste management.

4.3.6 Waste Registration

A Generator Registration Report must be completed by every generator of hazardous, liquid industrial, or registerable solid wastes above the small-quantity exemption (SQE). The report must be filed with the MOE and a Generator Registration Number obtained.

Figure 4.2 presents a Generator Registration Report. Part 1 requires information on the Company's name and address and a company official and position. Consultants who act on behalf of the company cannot sign the report.

In Part 2, Waste Identification, descriptions of the waste, generating process and quantity are required. In addition, information on the primary and secondary characteristics of the waste, the laboratory performing the analysis, and waste class may also be required.

Part 3 of the report covers waste management and in particular the principal intended receiver and carriers.

It is an offence to store, process, dispose, or transport waste unless a Generator Registration Number has been obtained. An out-of-province waste generator who transports or disposes of hazardous or liquid industrial wastes in Ontario must also register them with the MOE.

Any changes to processes or the types of wastes that are generated must be reported to the Director of the Waste Management Branch of the MOE in writing.

An additional responsibility imposed on the generator of a waste regulated by Regulation 309 is the requirement to notify the MOE if the wastes are stored on property for longer than three months. This necessitates some type of waste inventory system to track the duration of waste storage. Such systems should be reviewed during environmental audits (see Chapter 10).

4.4   MANIFEST SYSTEM FOR REGISTERABLE WASTE

4.4.1 Manifests

Regulation 309 includes a manifest system that must accompany registered wastes during their transportation, transfer, and disposal.

The manifest described in Regulation 309 is compatible with the one required under TDGA regulation, so that only one form needs to be filled out (see Figure 4.3) for transportation within Canada. Additional paperwork is required for international shipments. If the wastes have been determined to be hazardous or liquid industrial waste, a manifest must be issued for each shipment of the waste. The manifests track shipments by involving the generator, carrier and receiver in the shipping documentation process, each with their own part to play and their own responsibilities specifically laid out in the regulation. The MOE oversees the whole system to make sure every aspect is being properly followed.

The six-copy manifest is broken into three parts:

Section A   Completed by the Consignor (generator)
Section B   Completed by the Carrier
Section C   Completed by the Consignee (receiver)

A generator must fill out Part A of the manifest, including the name of the intended receiver. In addition, the generator must ensure that Part B of the manifest is completed by the carrier. The generator must then remove the **first copy** and forward it to the Director of the Waste Management Branch within three working days of the transfer. The **second copy** is to be removed and retained on file for a period of two years. The four remaining copies of the manifest are to be given back to the carrier.

The **third copy** of the manifest must be sent to the MOE within three working days after the waste transfer. The **fourth copy** of the form must be returned to the carrier, the **fifth copy** must be kept on file by the receiver for two years. The **sixth copy** must be sent to the generator three working days after the waste transfer (Tricil, not dated).

Within two weeks of the transfer of waste, the generator should have received back the **sixth copy** of the manifest from the receiver of the wastes. If this doesn't happen, the generator should contact the receiver to ensure that the waste did in fact reach its intended destination. If unable to trace the waste within four weeks of the waste transfer, the Director of the Waste Management Branch must be notified. These time periods may differ if sending waste outside Ontario (Tricil, not dated).

The public has access to the information provided in the generator registration. This includes the type of waste, the volumes generated, and the generator's name and address.

4.4.2 Licensed Carriers

A licensed carrier must obtain a certificate of approval (C of A) and comply with all of the transportation requirements imposed by Regulation 309 and the TDGA, where applicable (see Section 4.5). The C of A will include conditions regarding types of waste to be hauled, geographical areas where material can be transported, acceptable disposal sites, etc. The carrier must carry the C of A in the vehicle at all times and only transfer those wastes specified in the certificate.

A carrier must complete Section B of the manifest and retain the manifest during the transfer of the waste. The carrier must only transport the wastes to a transfer station or disposal site that is operating under a C of A and transport only those wastes specified in Section C of the manifest. Prior to leaving the site of a waste transfer, the carrier must obtain the **fourth copy** of the completed manifest from the receiver of the waste and retain the document for a period of two years (Tricil, not dated).

Carriers typically have a contract with the waste generator. The carrier will arrange with the generator for samples of the waste stream, fill out necessary forms at the disposal site, arrange for the disposal codes to be put in place, and finally to arrange the scheduling at the receiving site, be it a transfer site or a final disposal site (Shaw, 1989).

If the disposal site refuses to receive a load, the carrier is responsible for either finding an alternative approved receiver or taking the waste back to the generator. The generator is legally required to accept the material back. If the waste is returned to the generator, the generator is then classified as a receiver and must follow the appropriate procedures.

4.4.3 Licensed Transfer Stations and Disposal Sites

There are essentially two types of licensed transfer stations: bulking operations and processing sites. At a bulking operation, wastes of similar characteristics are bulked together prior to being transported to a final processing site. At a processing site the wastes are treated and the resulting material is either recycled, reused or sent for final disposition (Shaw, 1989).

The types of disposal sites include landfilling sites, incineration sites and organic soil conditioning sites.

A receiver can only accept those waste classes for which a C of A has been received. The operation of the site must be in accordance with the conditions which are specified in the certificate. These conditions may restrict the types of waste, the geographical area from which waste can be received, etc.

If the disposal facility is owned by a municipality (usually a landfill site), additional constraints on the wastes to be received may be imposed through by-laws.

The receiver must complete Section C and obtain the four remaining copies of the manifest. The **third copy** of the manifest must be sent to the MOE; the **fourth copy** returned to the carrier; the **fifth copy** retained by the receiver for two years; and the **sixth copy** sent to the generator within three working days after the waste transfer.

If the waste is refused by the receiver, a load refusal report must be prepared outlining the manifest number, generator registration number and reason for the refusal. The report must be sent to the Director of Waste Management Branch within three working days after the refusal (Tricil, not dated).

Under Section 69 of the EPA, a licence must be obtained if the waste to be disposed is from a septic tank or other sewage wastes.

4.5 TRANSPORTATION

4.5.1 Documentation

Part IV of the federal TDGA requires all shipments of dangerous goods to be accompanied by a shipping document providing information on the substance, companies involved in its shipment, etc. The consignor, carrier (excluding a roll-on/roll-off) and consignee must retain a copy of the document for a period of two years.

If the dangerous goods are being transferred by road vehicle, a copy of the document must be kept in the cab within the driver's reach. If the driver is not in the cab, the documentation must be kept either on the driver's seat or in a pocket mounted on the driver's door.

The shipping document for a hazardous waste is termed a manifest and is compatible with most provincial manifests. A manifest must provide:

- detailed information on the types and amounts of hazardous waste being shipped
- a record of various firms or individuals involved in the shipment
- information on the treatment, storage and/or disposal of the hazardous wastes when they reach their final destination

If the waste is hazardous, the consignor (i.e. the shipper), must insert the word "waste" immediately preceding the shipping name.

The Regulation 309 manifest presented in Figure 4.3 is sufficient for TDGA requirements. Section 4.4 presents the specified time periods at which government officials must receive a copy of the various parts of the manifests.

4.5.2 Marking and Packaging

All hazardous waste must be properly packaged and marked with proper safety marks, labels, signs and placards. Part V and Schedule V of the TDGA describes the proper markings required for hazardous goods. Marking involves the use of dangerous good labels and safety marks on small containers, and the use of placards on large transport units. It is the generator's responsibility to ensure that the appropriate placards are in place prior to shipment. The carrier, however, is responsible during the transportation of the dangerous good. Examples of the placards are presented in Figure 4.4 for Class 2—Gases.

Before a container which has contained a hazardous waste can be marked as EMPTY, the container must be emptied and cleaned or purged of all residue so that a hazard does not exist. The general rule is that containers should be rinsed three times with high-quality water.

4.5.3 Safety Standards

In addition to safety labels and markings, the TDGA also specifies safety standards in Schedule III and in Part II. One of the standards addresses the control of temperature for goods listed in Column IV of List II of Schedule II.

4.5.4 Emergency Response Plans

For some of the dangerous substances specified in Schedule XII of the TDGA regulation, the generator or consignor of the waste must file an emergency response plan with the Director General of the TDGA regulation. The documents for each shipment must show the emergency response plan number and the telephone number for activating the plan. These wastes include infectious wastes, explosives, certain gases and radioactive wastes. The plan must outline the assistance that can be provided in the event of an emergency (Tricil, not dated).

Some industrial associations have established regional centres to respond to emergencies. One example is the Canadian Chemical Producers' (CCPA) Transportation Emergency Assistance Program (TEAP). Chapter 12 provides a more detailed discussion on emergency response.

4.5.5 Training

Any person who handles, offers for transport, or transports dangerous goods must be trained or be directly supervised by a trained person. The training must be relevant for the types of duties performed. Following the completion of training, employees must be given a certificate of TDGA training. The certificate is valid for three years and must be issued to each employee. After three years, the employee must be retrained. A trained person may be required to produce the certificate upon request by an inspector. Training sessions can be conducted in-house or by an external third party (Tricil, not dated).

Some facilities appoint a TDGA administrator who is responsible for the proper implementation of the Act, interpretation of the conditions of the Act, and the training of employees. The training of employees must also include the requirements under Regulation 309.

4.5.6 Notification

If a "dangerous occurrence" occurs, notification of certain government agencies by the person in charge at the time must occur immediately. In Ontario, the MOE Spills Action Centre (SAC) can be called (see Section 12.2.6). The analogous federal agency is the National Environmental Emergencies Centre in Hull, Quebec.

For any international shipment of hazardous material, prenotification is required 60 days in advance. Many industrialized nations, including Canada, are establishing requirements which prohibit the shipment of hazardous wastes across international borders without approval. A company or individual wishing to export wastes from Canada should contact the Conservation and Protection Branch of Environment Canada.

Proposed shipments of hazardous waste from the United States to Canada should be preceded by notification to the Waste Management Branch of Environment Canada. If destined for a facility in Ontario, the documents will be forwarded to the MOE Waste Management Branch and then to the MOE district office where the facility is located to verify that all certificates have been issued and other forms of registration have been filed. Objections can be raised and routed back to Environment Canada and the U.S. Environmental Protection Agency.

4.5.7 Inspections

Under the TDGA, designated officials have the power to stop a vehicle for inspection at any time, take samples of the goods and examine and make copies of the shipping documents. Designated officials can be representatives of Transport Canada, the Ontario Ministry of the Environment, provincial police forces, the Royal Canadian Mounted Police, and weigh scale operators.

4.5.8 Responsibilities

The basic responsibilities of the consignor, carrier and consignee are presented in Figure 4.5. The responsibilities include the aforementioned documentation, packaging and information requirements. Responsibilities and information requirements to complete the shipping manifest are provided in Figure 4.3. For intraprovincial and interprovincial shipments of hazardous waste, the manifest must be distributed as follows:

Copy 1   mailed by the consignor to the appropriate authority of the province/territory in which the consignee is located within two days, exclusive of holidays, after the goods have been received by the carrier;

Copy 2   retained by the consignor for a period of two years after the goods have reached their destination;

Copy 3   mailed by the consignee to the appropriate authority in his province/territory within two days, exclusive of holidays, after the goods are received from the carrier;

Copy 4   retained by the carrier for a period of two years after the goods have reached their destination;

Copy 5   retained by the consignee for a period of two years after the goods have reached their destination; and

Copy 6   mailed by the consignee to the consignor.

Some consignors' province/territory may also require to receive copies of the manifest for wastes that are shipped out of the province. The appropriate authorities should be contacted, and if required the consignor should send a photocopy of copy 1 and the consignee a photocopy of copy 3.

4.5.9 Classification

Classification involves assigning dangerous goods and hazardous waste into classes and divisions based on hazard criteria that are described in Part III of the TDGA regulation. The particular classification is performed for both goods and waste either by picking the substance from a comprehensive list given in the regulation, or by comparing the properties of the substance to criteria given in the regulation. The comprehensive list of specific and generic dangerous goods and hazardous wastes is presented in Schedule II, List II of the TDGA.

There are nine different classes of dangerous goods and hazardous wastes:

1 Explosives
2 Gases
3 Flammable and Combustible Liquids
4 Flammable Solids
5 Oxidizing Substances and Organic Peroxides
6 Poisonous (toxic) and Infectious Substances
7 Radioactive Material
8 Corrosives

9 Miscellaneous Dangerous Goods

Each type of good or waste is assigned one of the nine classes as its primary classification. In addition, one or more subsidiary classifications may be assigned. The primary classification describes the main hazardous properties of a particular dangerous good or hazardous waste. A subsidiary classification describes other hazardous properties. These properties are considered to be of secondary concern in transportation when compared with the main hazardous properties of the good or waste. For example, the Class 2 – Gases include Division 2.1 Flammable Gas, Division 2.2 Non-flammable Gas, and Division 2.3 Poisonous Gas among others.

Table 4.3 presents preliminary descriptions of each class of dangerous good. Note that in Class 9.2, an environmentally hazardous substance refers to chemicals which bioaccumulate in the food chain and/or are persistent.

The following definitions of waste and hazardous waste are not part of the TDGA regulations but are widely used as working definitions (Environment Canada, 1986):

Waste is any substance for which a consignor/generator has no further use and which he discards.

Hazardous Waste is potentially hazardous to human health and/or the environment due to its nature and quantity, and which requires special disposal techniques.

4.5.10 Exempt Materials

The following are exceptions to the TDGA:

- gasoline
- retail purchases
- movement of less than one kilometre between plants or properties of the same owner
- service truck exemption for material being used in repair
- limited-quantity exemptions

Recyclable material was previously exempted from the regulation if it was waste transferred by a generator and destined for a site where it would be wholly utilized (other than for combustion or land application), promptly packaged for retail sale or offered for retail sale. However, materials going for recycling must now be manifested as per Schedules 8 and 12 of the TDGA.

4.6 APPROVALS AND PERMITS

4.6.1 Waste Management Systems

Waste management systems, including incinerators, landfills and waste collection, handling and processing facilities require certificate of approvals. Section 27 of the EPA specifies that no person shall use, operate, establish, alter, enlarge or extend a waste management system or a waste disposal site unless a certificate or provisional certificate has been issued by the director and except in accordance with any conditions set out in such certificate. **Operating a waste system without a certificate is an offence.**

Once a site has been classified as a waste management site, certain restrictions are imposed upon it. Section 45 of the EPA states that if a land or land covered by water was used for disposal of waste, a period of 25 years from the year in which the waste disposal ceased is required before the land can be used for another purpose unless approval from the Minister has been obtained.

4.6.2 Carriers

To transport waste regulated under Regulation 309, a carrier must have a Provisional C of A for a Waste Management System issued by the MOE. The carrier must make an application to the MOE and satisfy certain requirements with respect to driver training and insurance prior to obtaining a C of A. Regulation 309 requires that carriers must have automotive insurance coverage in the amount of $1,000,000. For certain wastes (PCBs and pathological waste), carriers must post security with the MOE, above the insurance requirements (Shaw, 1989).

A C of A will identify the vehicles that the carrier can use, the waste classes that the carrier can transport and the disposal sites or transfer stations that the carrier can use. In addition to the conditions of the certificate, the regulation itself imposes certain standards upon the carrier:

- construction of waste collection vehicles and waste carriers to ensure safe transfer of waste without leakage, emission of offensive odours or falling or blowing of waste material from the vehicle;
- a vehicle used for transporting liquid industrial waste or hazardous waste must be clearly marked or placarded in accordance with the TDGA and display the name and number from the certificate of approval;
- driver training must be provided for the operation of the vehicle and waste management equipment, relevant legislation, environmental and safety concerns and emergency management procedures;
- a copy of the certificate of approval that authorizes the transport must be kept in the vehicle when liquid industrial waste or hazardous waste is being transported;
- requirement that the driver, generator or receiver be present whenever liquid industrial waste or hazardous waste is being transferred.

Under the Provincial Dangerous Goods Transportation Act, a permit may be issued by a minister or a person designated by him exempting from the application of the Act the transportation of dangerous goods in a vehicle.

4.6.3 Transfer Stations

The transfer station is an intermediate point between the original generator and the ultimate disposal site of the waste. For a transfer station to receive waste, it must have one of two types of certificates: a C of A for a waste disposal site (bulking) or a C of A for a waste disposal site (processing). A public hearing may be required to obtain the certificates (Shaw, 1989).

4.6.4 The Role of Public Hearings

Section 30(1) of the EPA states that the Director shall require the Environmental Assessment Board to hold a hearing prior to issuing or refusing to issue a C of A in response to an application for the use, operation, establishment, alteration, or enlargement of a waste disposal site for liquid industrial waste or hazardous waste.

If a C of A application is received for a waste management system that does not include a waste disposal site, under Section 32 the Director may require a public hearing before responding to the application.

In an emergency situation (one in which there is a danger to public health or the environment), Section 31 of the EPA empowers the Director to issue a C of A if the situation will be alleviated by the use, operation, establishment, alteration, enlargement or extension of a waste disposal site without requiring the Environmental Assessment Board to hold a hearing.

4.6.5 Environmental Assessment

All waste management facilities for treatment and/or disposal require an Environmental Assessment (EA). A description of the EA process is beyond the scope of this book. The key requirements of an EA document include:

- the purpose for the undertaking
- a statement and description of the reasons behind the project and its alternatives
- a description of how the project and its alternatives will affect the environment
- a description of the environment effects and the actions necessary to prevent, change, mitigate or remedy environmental effects
- evaluation of advantage/disadvantage to the environment of the project and its alternatives

The rationale for the undertaking should not only identify reasons for pursuing the undertaking but also provide an explanation of why the other options were considered less acceptable in terms of environmental effects and fulfilling the intended purpose. The evaluation of options is considered to be the cornerstone of the Environmental Assessment Act (EEA). One must assess a "reasonable range" of possibilities. The same philosophy applies to the rationale for the selection of the technology and site.

4.7 REDUCING, REUSING, AND RECYCLING WASTES

The ever-increasing costs of waste management, transportation, and disposal are constant incentives for all waste generators to seek ways to minimize the amounts of waste they create. Increasing numbers of organizations and agencies are emphasizing the three Rs: reduction, reuse, recycling. Recovery is sometimes included as a fourth R. It has also been suggested that a fifth R is emerging: "re-think".

Reduction can be achieved several ways. The amounts of material needed at a facility often can be reduced by implementing changes to processes or better process control. Internal audits such as those described in Chapter 10 can identify ways to achieve reductions and monitor their effectiveness. Examples of waste reduction approaches and potential waste exchanges are presented in Tables 4.4 and 4.5.

The Ontario Waste Exchange (OWE) is a technical assistance program that provides free assistance to industrial waste generators in Ontario. The co-sponsors of the program are the Ontario Waste Management Corporation (OWMC) and the MOE. The OWE is also seen as the active component of the Canadian Waste Materials Exchange Program (CWME) in Ontario. The CWME is a passive waste exchange which issues bulletins every two months on lists of wastes available and wastes wanted by different industry sectors (Varangu and Laughlin, 1988).

In 1988, approximately 3500 companies participated in the OWE system and approximately 290 million kg of wastes were transferred. Companies are finding that the economic incentive to reduce, as disposal costs for both non-hazardous and hazardous wastes steadily increase, is becoming very attractive.

The OWE provides assistance to the companies in the following form (Varangu and Laughlin, 1988):

- find industrial users for wastes generated in different industrial sectors
- assist in finding sources of wastes as alternative raw materials
- provide recycling industry contacts
- conduct literature reviews for selected waste reduction topics
- conduct research on selected hazardous waste streams
- provide technical assistance in waste reduction
- conduct plant visits to assist in improving waste management practices

The research projects being conducted are directed. toward the technical efficacy of waste reduction and reuse. Both the OWE and the Ontario section of the CWME are operated by the Ontario Research Foundation.

4.8 SUMMARY

The major piece of provincial legislation that addresses waste management in Ontario is EPA Regulation 309. The identification and proper disposal of waste is clearly the responsibility of waste generators. Identification should be done in accordance with the classification system set out in Regulation 309. Every generator must file a Generator Registration Report and be issued a Generator Registration Number. Federal regulations that address waste management issues may eventually be issued under the CEPA.

The transportation of waste is governed by the Ontario DTGA which is patterned after the federal TDGA. Procedures that utilize a six-copy manifest must be followed by the generator, carrier, and receiver. Carriers must be licensed in accordance with provincial and federal requirements. Similarly, owners/operators of waste management systems, disposal sites, and transfer stations must comply with provincial requirements. At present, responsibility for the disposal of waste can be transferred to a third party (usually the owner or operator of a disposal site or transfer station).

The ever-increasing costs of waste management, transportation, and disposal are constant incentives for all waste generators to seek ways to minimize the amounts of waste they create. The Ontario Waste Exchange (OWE) provides assistance to industrial waste generators in Ontario.

REFERENCES

Environment Canada, 1986. "Users' Guide to Hazardous Waste Classification (Transportation of Dangerous Goods Regulation)". First Edition, April.

Ontario Ministry of the Environment (MOE), 1985. "Registration Guidance Manual for Generators of Liquid Industrial and Hazardous Waste". July.

Ontario Ministry of the Environment (MOE), 1989a. "Regulation 309: Revised Regulations of Ontario, 1980 as Amended to O. Reg. 460/88". January.

Ontario Ministry of the Environment (MOE), 1989b. "Interim Position on the Classification and Disposal of Coal Tar and Contaminated Soils, Sediment and Water at Abandoned Sites". Revised June.

Shaw, J., 1989. "An Insider's Perspective of Ontario's Waste Management Industry". Environmental Science and Engineering, October, pp. 12-15.

Tricil, not dated. "The Tricil Guide: Your Guide on What to Know, What to Do, and Where to Find Out About Hazardous Waste Legislation in Ontario".

Varangu, L., and Laughlin, B., 1988. "The Ontario Waste Exchange Program: Helping Industries Reduce Waste". Presented at the 35th Ontario Waste Management Conference, 12 to 15 June, Toronto.

Table 4.1
MOE WASTE CLASSES

INORGANIC WASTES

Acid Solutions	**Examples**
111 Spent pickle liquor	Acid solutions of sulphuric and hydrochloric acids containing ferrous salts from steel pickling.
112 Acid solutions, sludges and residues containing heavy metals	Solutions of sulphuric, hydrochloric and nitric acids containing copper, nickel, chromium, zinc, cadmium, tin, lead, or other heavy metals; chromic acid waste; acidic emission control sludges from secondary lead smelting.
113 Acid solutions, sludges and residues containing other metals and non-metals	Solutions of sulphuric, hydrochloric, hydrofluoric and nitric acids containing sodium, potassium, calcium, magnesium or aluminum; equipment cleaning acids; cation regenerant; reactor acid washes; catalyst acid and acid washes.
114 Other inorganic acid wastes	Off-specification acids; by-product hydrochloric acid; dilute acid solutions; acid test residues.

Alkaline Solutions

121 Alkaline solutions, sludges and residues containing heavy metals	Metal finishing wastes; plating baths; spent solutions containing metals such as copper, zinc, tin, cadmium; case hardening sludges; spent cyanide destruction residues; dewatered solids from metal and cyanide finishing wastes and cyanide destruction.
122 Alkaline solutions, sludges and residues containing other metals and non-metals, not containing cyanides	Alkaline solutions from aluminum surface coating and etching; alkali cleaner wastes; waste lime sludges and slurries; anion regenerants.
123 Alkaline phosphates	Bonderizing wastes; zinc phosphates; ferrous phosphates; phosphate cleaners.

Aqueous Salts

131 Neutralized solutions, sludges and residues containing heavy metals

Metal finishing waste treatment sludges containing copper, nickel, chromium, zinc or cadmium; neutral salt bath sludges and washes; lime sludge from metal finishing waste treatment; dewatered solids from these processes.

132 Neutralized solutions, sludges and residues containing other metals

Aluminum surface coating treatment sludges; alum and gypsum sludges.

133 Brines, chlor-alkali sludges and residues

Waste brines from chlor-alkali plants; neutralized hydrochloric acid; brine treatment sludges; dewatered solids from brine treatment.

134 Wastes containing sulphides

Petroleum aqueous refinery condensates.

135 Wastes containing other reactive anions

Wastes containing chlorates; hypochlorite; bromate or thiosulphate.

Miscellaneous Inorganic Wastes and Mixed Wastes

141 Inorganic wastes from pigment manufacturing

Wastewaters and sludges from the production of chrome yellow, molybdate orange, zinc yellow, chrome green and iron pigments; dewatered solids from these sources.

142 Primary lead, zinc and copper smelting wastes

Slurries, sludges and surface impoundment solids; treatment plant sludges; anode slimes and leachate residues; dewatered solids from these sources.

143 Residues from steel making

Emission control sludges and dusts; precipitator residues from steel plants; dewatered solids from these sources.

144 Liquid tannery waste sludges

Lime waste mixtures; chrome tan liquors; dehairing solutions and sludges.

145 Wastes from the use of paints, pigments and coatings

Paint spray booth sludges and wastes; paper coating wastes; ink sludges; paint sludges.

146 Other specified
inorganic sludges,
slurries or solids

Flue gas scrubber wastes; wet fly ash; dust col-
lector wastes; metal dust and abrasives wastes;
foundry sands; mud sediment and water; tank
bottoms from waste storage tanks that contained
mixed inorganic wastes; heavy sludges from
waste screening/filtration at transfer/processing
sites not otherwise specified in this table.

147 Chemical fertilizer
wastes

Solutions, sludges and residues containing
ammonia, urea, nitrates and phosphates from
nitrogen fertilizer plants.

148 Miscellaneous
waste inorganic
chemicals

Waste inorganic chemicals including laboratory,
surplus or off-specification chemicals, that are
not otherwise specified in this table.

149 Landfill leachate

Surface run-off and leachate collected from
landfill sites.

150 Inert inorganic
wastes

Sand and water from catch basins at car washes;
slurries from the polishing and cutting of marble.

ORGANIC WASTES

Non-halogenated Spent Solvents

211 Aromatic solvents
and residues

Benzene, toluene, xylene solvents and residues.

212 Aliphatic solvents
and residues

Acetone, methylethylketone and residues, alco-
hols, cyclohexane and residues.

213 Petroleum distil-
lates

Varsol, white spirits and petroleum distillates,
thinners.

Fuels

221 Light fuels

Gasoline, kerosene, diesel, tank drainings/wash-
ings/bottoms, spill clean-up residues.

222 Heavy fuels

Bunker, asphalts, tank drainings/washings/bot-
toms, spill clean-up residues.

Resins and Plastics

231 Latex wastes

Waste latexes, latex crumb and residues.

232 Polymeric resins   Polyester, epoxy, urethane, phenolic resins, intermediates and solvent mixtures.

233 Other polymeric wastes   Off-specification materials, discarded materials from reactors.

Halogenated Organic Wastes

241 Halogenated solvents and residues   Spent halogenated solvents and residues such as perchloroethylene, trichloroethylene and carbon tetrachloride (dry cleaning solvents); halogenated still bottoms; residues and catalysts from halogenated hydrocarbon manufacturing or recycling processes.

242 Halogenated pesticides and herbicides   2,4-D, 2,4,5-T wastes, chlordane, mirex, silvex, pesticide solutions and residues.

243 Polycholorinated biphenyls (PCB)   Askarel liquids such as Aroclor, Pydraul, Pyranol, Therminols, Inerteen, and other PCB contaminated materials.

Oily Wastes

251 Waste oils/sludges (petroleum based)   Oil/water separator sludge; dissolved air flotation skimming; heavy oil tank drainage; slop oil and emulsions.

252 Waste crankcase oils and lubricants   Collected service station waste oils; industrial lubricants; bulk waste oils.

253 Emulsified oils   Soluble oils; waste cutting oils; machine oils.

254 Oily water/waste oil from waste transfer/processing sites   Waste oil and oily water limited to classes 251, 252 and 253 that have been bulked/blended/processed at a waste transfer/processing site.

Miscellaneous Organic Wastes and Mixed Wastes

261 Pharmaceuticals   Pharmaceutical and veterinary pharmaceutical wastes other than biologicals and vaccines; solid residues and liquids from veterinary arsenical compounds.

262 Detergents and   Laundry wastes.
     soaps

263 Miscellaneous   Waste organic chemicals including laboratory
     waste organic   surplus or off-specification chemicals that are
     chemicals   not otherwise specified in this table.

264 Photoprocessing   Photochemical solutions, washes and sludges.
     wastes

265 Graphic arts wastes Adhesives; glues; miscellaneous washes; etch
                          solutions.

266 Phenolic waste   Cresylic acid; caustic phenolates; phenolic oils;
     streams   creosote.

267 Organic acids   Carboxylic or fatty acids; formic, acetic, propi-
                          onic acid wastes; sulphamic and other organic
                          acids that may be amenable to incineration.

268 Amines   Waste ethanolamines; urea; tolidene; Flexzone
                          waste; Monex waste.

269 Organic non-halo-   Organophosphorus chemical wastes; arsenicals;
     genated pesticide   wastes from MSMA and cacodylic acid.
     and herbicide
     wastes

270 Other specified   Tank bottoms from mixed organic waste bulking
     organic sludges,   tanks at waste transfer sites; mixed sludges from
     slurries and solids waste screening/filtration at waste transfer/pro-
                          cessing sites not otherwise specified in this
                          table.

**Processed Organic
Wastes from Transfer
Stations**

281 Non-halogenated   Blended/bulked non-halogenated solvents, oils
     rich organics   and other rich organics prepared at transfer/pro-
                          cessing sites for incineration.

282 Non-halogenated   Blended/bulked aqueous wastes prepared at
     lean organics   transfer/processing sites for incineration and
                          contaminated with non-halogenated solvents,
                          non-halogenated oils and other non-halogenat-
                          ed organics.

Plant and Animal Wastes

311 Organic tannery wastes

Fleshings; trimmings; vegetable tan liquors; Bate solutions.

312 Pathological wastes

Human anatomical waste; infected animal carcasses; other non-anatomical waste infected with communicable diseases; biologicals and vaccines.

OTHER WASTES

Explosive Manufacturing Wastes

321 Wastes from the manufacture of explosives and detonation products

Wastewater treatment sludges; spent carbon; red/pink waters from TNT manufacturing; residues from lead base initiating compounds.

Compressed Gases

331 Waste compressed gases, including cylinders

Methane (natural gas); nitrous or nitric oxide; propane; butane.

Table 4.2
SCHEDULE 4 LEACHATE QUALITY CRITERIA

Hazardous Waste Number	Contaminant	Concentration (mg/L)
ON4001	2,4,5-TP/Silvex/ 2-(2,4,5,-Trichlorophenoxy) propionic acid	0.01
ON4002	2,4-D	0.1
ON4003	Aldrin + Dieldrin	0.0007
ON4004	Arsenic	0.05
ON4005	Barium	1.0
ON4006	Boron	5.0
ON4007	Cadmium	0.005
ON4008	Carbaryl/1-Naphthyl- N-methyl carbamate/ Sevin	0.07
ON4009	Chlordane	0.007
ON4010	Chromium	0.05
ON4011	Cyanide (free)	0.2
ON4012	DDT	0.03
ON4013	Diazinon/Phospordithioic acid, 0,0-diethyl 0-(2-iso- propyl-6-methyl- 4-pyrimidinyl) ester	0.0002
ON4014	Endrin	0.0002
ON4015	Fluoride	2.4
ON4016	Heptachlor + Heptachlor epoxide	0.003
ON4017	Lead	0.05
ON4018	Lindane	0.004
ON4019	Mercury	0.001
ON4020	Methoxychlor/ 1,1,1-Trichloro-2, 2-bis (p-methoxyphenyl) ethane	0.1
ON4021	Methyl Parathion	0.007
ON4022	Nitrate + Nitrite	10.0
ON4023	Nitrilotriacetic acid	0.05

ON4024	Nitrite	1.0
ON4025	PCBs	0.003
ON4026	Parathion	0.035
ON4027	Selenium	0.01
ON4028	Silver	0.05
ON4029	Toxaphene	0.005
ON4030	Trihalomethanes	0.35
ON4031	Uranium	0.02

Reference: MOE (1989a)

Table 4.3
TDGA CLASSIFICATIONS OF DANGEROUS GOODS

Canada
Transportation of Dangerous Goods Regulation (TDGR)SOR/85-77
as amended under the Transportation of Dangerous Goods Act.
Discarded dangerous goods and listed industrial process waster types in quantities 5 kg (solid) or 5 L (liquid), listed in TDGR Schedule II, List II, PLUS:

Class I—Explosives (Never a waste by definition)
TDGR 3.9
Use TDGR, Schedule II, List I for listed explosives. Refer to Energy, Mines and Resources Canada for classification of unlisted explosives.
Definition of explosives:
- Capable, by self-sustaining chemical reaction, of producing gas at such temperature, pressure and speed as to damage the environment.
- Manufactured for the purpose of making a practical explosive or pyrotechnic effect.

Class 2—Compressed Gases
TDGR 3.10-3.11
Use TDGR, Schedule II, List II for specified gases. If not specified, use the following criteria and return to Schedule II, List II for best general name:
   a) Critical temperature <50°C or absolute vapour pressure >294 kPa at 50°C.
   b) Absolute pressure >275 kPa ± 1 kPa at 21.1°C.
   c) Absolute vapour pressure >275 kPa at 37.8°C using Reid Vapour Test (ASTM-D323-82).
   d) Refrigerated liquid gases boiling point <-84°C at 101.325 kPa.
   e) Liquid carbon dioxide.
Class 2.1—Ignitable in mixture of 13% or less of air at normal pressure. Flammability range of at least 12.
Class 2.2—When not in any other division of Class 2.
Class 2.3—LC50 <5000 mL/m^3 by reason of toxicity.
Class 2.4—LC50 <5000 mL/m^3 by reason of corrosion on respiratory tract.

Class 3—Flammable Liquids
TDGR 3.12-3.14
Use TDGR, Schedule II, List II for specified flammable liquids. If not specified, use the following criteria and return to Schedule II, List II for best general name:
- Flash point <61°C, using one of the following tests: Tag Closed Tester

(ASTM-D323-82); Pensky-Martens Closed Tester (ASTM-D93-80); Setaflash Closed Tester (ASTM-D3828-81 or ASTM D3278-82) depending on the viscosity of the flammable liquid.

Division/Packing Group	Flash Point	Boiling Point
Class 3.1	<-18°C	
Class 3.2	>-18°C & <23°C	
Class 3.3	>23°C & <61°C	
Pack, Group I		<35°C at 101.325 kPa
Pack, Group II	<23°C	>35°C at 101.325 kPa
Pack, Group III	>23°C & <37.8°C	>35°C at 101.325 kPa

Class 4—Flammable Solids, Spontaneously Combustible, Flammable Gas When Wet
TDGR 3.15-3.16

Class 4.1—Solids which are ignitable and burn vigorously and persistently. They cause fire through friction or from related heat from manufacturing.

Class 4.2—Spontaneously combustible substances.

Class 4.3—Substances that on contact with water emit flammable gases or become spontaneously combustible.

Class 5—Oxidizing Substances & Organic Peroxides
TDGR 3.17-3.18

Use TDGR, Schedule II, List II for specified oxidizers and organic peroxides. If not specified, use the following criteria and return to Schedule II, List II for the best general name:

Class 5.1—Oxidizing substances which cause the combustion of other material by yielding oxygen, whether or not the substance is combustible.

Class 5.2—Organic compounds which contain the "-0-0-" bivalent structure.

Class 6—Poisonous (Toxic) & Infectious Substances
TDGR 3.19-3.23

Use TDGR, Schedule II, List II for specified poisonous or toxic substances. If not specified, use the following criteria and return to Schedule II, List II for best general name:

Class 6.1—

Substance Form	LD50	LC50
• Solid (oral toxicity)	<50 mg/kg	
ʺ Liquid (oral toxicity)	<50 mg/kg	
• Substance (dermal toxicity)	<200 mg/kg	
• Dusts/mists (inhalation toxicity)		<2000 mg/m^3
• Substances with saturated vapour concentration LC50 (mL/m^3)		<3000 mL/m^3

Use the LD50 and LC50 formulae in TDGR 3.23, for various mixtures.

Class 6.2—Organisms and their toxins which are reasonably believed to be infectious to humans or animals. Use the list in TDG Regulations, Schedule VII for infectious organisms and their toxins.

Class 7—Radioactive Materials (Never a Waste by Definition)
TDGR 3.24
Use TDGR, Schedule II, List II for listed radioactive materials. If unlisted, refer to Atomic Energy Control Board for classification.
Radioactive materials are defined as products or substances with activity >74 kBq/kg.

Class 8—Corrosives
TDGR 3.25
Use TDGR, Schedule II, List II for specified corrosives. If not specified, use the following criteria and return to Schedule II, List II for best general name:
a)   Corrodes SAE 1020 steel or 7075-T6 non-clad aluminum at a rate >6.25 mm/year at 55°C using Metal Corrosion Test (NACE TM-01-76).
b)   Has a pH factor <2.0 or >12.5

Class 9—Miscellaneous Dangerous Goods
TDGR 3.27
Use TDGR, Schedule II, List II for listed miscellaneous dangerous goods. If unlisted, they are not regulated. Class 9 substances are classified and listed by Transport Canada and Environment agencies only.
Class 9.1—Possess a hazard not already described in a previous class.
Class 9.2—Substance which is hazardous to the environment.
Class 9.3—Dangerous wastes that possess a hazard not described in a previous class.

Class 9—Basis for Listing
Class 9.2 and 9.3 are classified by Environment Canada and Provincial Environment Ministries. These agencies use a list of criteria not stated in the Regulations, and in addition to those used for Classes 1 to 8. The additional criteria enable them to determine all the characteristics of a substance or waste which may be hazardous to human health or the environment. The additional criteria include:
- chronic toxicity (carcinogenic, teratogenic, genotoxic);
- aquatic toxicity;
- bioaccumulation;
- persistence in the environment.

Substances or wastes that satisfy these additional criteria are assigned to Class 9.2 & 9.3.

Table 4.4
APPROACHES TO WASTE REDUCTION

Waste Abatement

Substitution of a new low-waste primary industrial process for an old process to eliminate or drastically reduce the quantity of waste produced.

- Replacement of sulfuric acid in steel pickling with hydrochloric acid
- Replacement of liquid paints by powder coatings
- Replacement of solvent-based adhesives with water-based adhesives

Waste Minimization

The reduction of the quantity of waste through good house-keeping practices or by the application of concentration technologies. Also the reduction in the degree of hazard of waste through simple in-plant treatment.

- Separation of waste streams to permit recovery
- Application of countercurrent rinsing to minimize volume discharge
- Neutralization of wastes and precipitation of smaller-volume sludges
- Fixing leaky taps and nozzles

Waste Reuse

The direct reuse of a waste stream, as is, or with a very minor modification.

- Reuse of surplus or salvage chemicals
- Use of blast furnace slag as aggregate
- Use of solvents from electronics industry in paints manufacture
- Use of refinery-spent caustic in pulping wood
- Use of oil sludges in asphalt manufacturing
- Use of electronic circuit manufacturing plating baths in regular plating shops

Waste Recycle

The reclamation of value from waste streams through the application of reprocessing technologies such as distillation, etc.

- Oil refining
- Solvent distillation
- Recovery of iron salts from pickle liquor
- Recovery of heavy metals from sludges
- Recovery and reuse of spent foundry sands
- Recovery of scrap metal
- Regeneration and reuse of activated carbon
- Recycling of grease and fats to renderers

Reference: Varangu and Laughlin, 1988.

Table 4.5
WASTE EXCHANGES

Materials	Receivers
Acids	
Nitric Acid	Metal Reclaimer
Sulfuric Acid	Metal Reclaimer
Alkalis	
Calcium Hydroxide	Broker to New Business
Potassium Hydroxide	Chemical Company
Other Inorganic Chemicals	
Alumina	Abrasives Manufacturer
Asbestos (unused)	Manufacturer for Reblend
Foundry Sands	Asphalt Manufacturer
Solvents	
Degreasing Solvents	Replace with Biodegradable Solvent Substitute
Ink Wastes	Recycling and Recovery
Other Organic Chemicals	
Paints	Salvation Army
Latex Materials	Manufacturer for Reblend
Oils, Fats and Waxes	
Gasoline (Experimental)	Charity Organization
Oils (PCB-Free)	Oil Recycler
Plastics and Rubber	
Polystyrene (Water-Damaged Pack)	Plastic Recycler
Plastic Drums	Municipal Composting Programs

Reference: Varangu and Laughlin, 1988.

Figure 4.1
WASTE IDENTIFICATION FLOWCHART

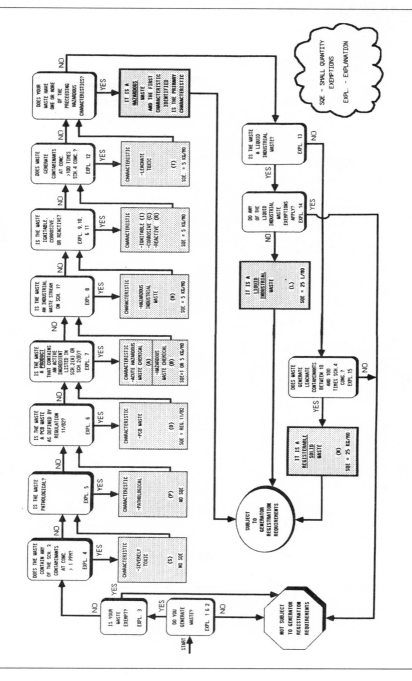

Figure 4.2
ENVIRONMENTAL PROTECTION ACT GENERATOR REGISTRATION REPORT

Ontario	Ministry of the Environment	Ministère de l'Environnement

Generator Registration Report
"Regulation 309, R.R.O. 1980, Form 2"

Rapport d'inscription du producteur
"Règlement 309, R.R.O. de 1980, formule 2"

NOTE: Regulation 309 requires generators of hazardous or liquid industrial wastes to submit a Generator Registration Report using this form respecting each waste generation facility and each hazardous or liquid industrial waste.

REMARQUE: Le règlement 309 exige que les producteurs de déchets industriels liquides ou dangereux présentent un Rapport d'inscription du producteur en se servant de la présente formule pour chaque lieu de production de déchets et chaque déchet industriel liquide ou dangereux.

Part I – Generator Identification / Partie I – Identification du producteur

This report is / Le présent rapport constitue:

Generator Registration Number
Nº d'inscription du producteur

1. ☐ an initial generator registration report / un premier rapport d'inscription du producteur

or / ou

2. ☐ a revision – enter Ontario Generator Registration No. / une révision – veuillez inscrire le numéro d'inscription du producteur de l'Ontario

3. For generators located outside of Ontario, enter Registration/Notification number assigned by your local environmental authority. / Si vous êtes un producteur de l'extérieur de l'Ontario, veuillez inscrire le numéro d'inscription/d'identification attribué par les autorités locales en matière d'environnement.

Name of Generator (Enter the corporate name or, if a partnership or proprietorship, the name of the principal(s). If the generator intends to carry on business under a separate name or style, this should also be entered.) / **Nom du producteur** (Veuillez inscrire la dénomination sociale ou, s'il s'agit d'une société en nom collectif ou d'une société à propriétaire unique, le nom du (des) principal (principaux) propriétaire(s). Si le producteur envisage d'exploiter une entreprise sous une dénomination ou un nom distinct, veuillez également le noter.)

4. Name /Nom

5. Address / Adresse

6. Municipality / Municipalité   Province/State Province/État   Postal Code / Code postal

7. Site location / Lieu des installations

8. Municipality / Municipalité   Province/State Province/État   Postal Code / Code postal

9. Name of contact / Nom de la personne à contacter   Tel. No. / Nº de tél.

10. Standard Industrial Classification Codes (SIC) for Site noted in Section 7. / Codes de la classification des activités économiques pour les installations décrites au nº 7

11. Total number of wastes to be registered with this report / Nombre total de déchets à inscrire au moyen de ce rapport

12. Name of Company Official / Nom du représentant autorisé de la compagnie

13. Position / Poste

14. Signature / Signature

15. Date / Date

·············· PENALTY ·············· ··············· PÉNALITÉ ···············

Contraventions may be punished by fines of up to $2,000 (higher if environmental damage may result). (Environmental Protection Act, sections 47 and 147)

Toute infraction peut être sanctionnée par une amende maximale de 2 000 $ (ou plus s'il peut en résulter une détérioration de l'environnement). (Articles 47 et 147 de la Loi sur la protection de l'environnement).

16. Ministry Use Only / Réserve au ministère

County Code / Code de comté	
Regional/District Code / Code de région/district	
Municipal Code / Code de municipalité	
Inter City Tie Line / Ligne privée interurbaine	

1487 (5/85) Page 1 of 2

Part 2 – Waste Identification / *Partie 2 – Identification des déchets*

1. Description of Waste / *Description des déchets*

2. Description of generating process / *Description du procédé de production*

3. Waste quantity generated or accumulated / *Quantité des déchets produite ou accumulée*

Continuous process / *Procédé continu*

or / *ou*

Batch process / *par lots*

kg/mo. / *kg/mois*

batches/mo. / *lots/mois*

kg/batch / *kg/lot*

4. Primary characteristic / *Caractéristique principale*

Analytical data (if applicable). If the data has been estimated, attach separate sheet outlining the basis for the estimate. / *Données analytiques (le cas échéant). Si les données sont estimatives, veuillez annexer une feuille à part pour décrire sur quoi reposent les estimations.*

Name of Laboratory (if applicable). / *Laboratoire (le cas échéant)*

Waste Class / *Catégorie des déchets*

Hazardous Waste Number / *Numéro des déchets dangereux*

Specific Gravity / *Gravité spécifique*

Physical State (Solid-S, Liquid-L, Gas-G) / *État physique (solide-S, liquide-L, gaz-G)*

For Ministry Use Only / *Réservé au ministère*

5. Secondary Characteristic / *Caractéristique secondaire*

Analytical data (if applicable) / *Données analytiques (le cas échéant)*

Part 3 – Waste Management / *Partie 3 – Gestion des déchets*

1. Principal Intended Receiver / *Réceptionnaire principal prévu*

Company name and address / *Nom et adresse de la compagnie*

Receiver No. / *Nº du réceptionnaire*

Municipality / *Municipalité*

Province/State / *Province/État*

Postal Code / *Code postal*

2. Principal Intended Carrier / *Transporteur principal prévu*

Company name and address / *Nom et adresse de la compagnie*

MOE Carrier No. / *Nº du M. de l'E. du transporteur*

A

Municipality / *Municipalité*

Province/State / *Province/État*

Postal Code / *Code postal*

1487 (5/85) Page 2 of 2

Figure 4.3
REGULATION 309 MANIFEST

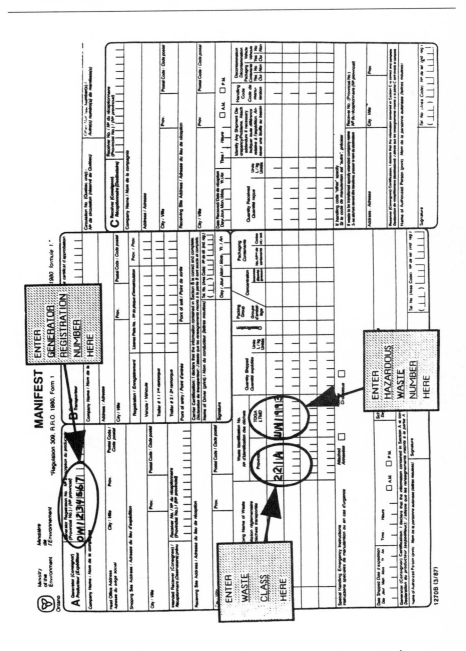

Figure 4.4
TDGA MARKING FOR CLASS 2—GASES

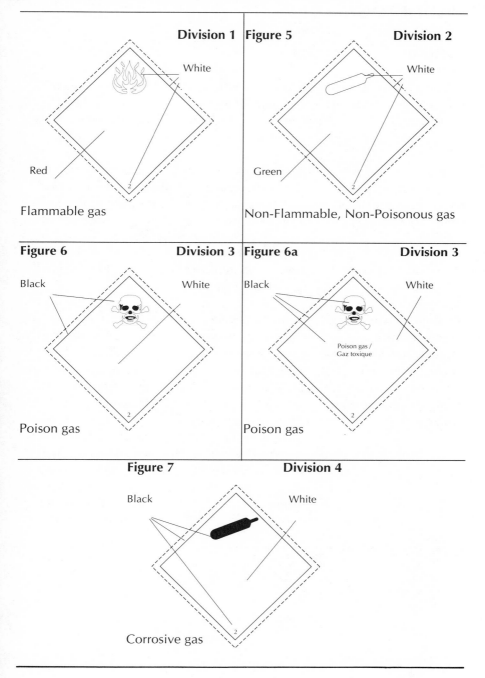

Division 1   Figure 5   Division 2

White

Red

Flammable gas

White

Green

Non-Flammable, Non-Poisonous gas

Figure 6   Division 3   Figure 6a   Division 3

Black   White

Black   White

Poison gas / Gaz toxique

Poison gas

Poison gas

Figure 7   Division 4

Black   White

Corrosive gas

Figure 4.5
RESPONSIBILITIES DURING TRANSPORTATION UNDER TDGA

Consignor	Carrier	Consignee
Obtain a provincial number in the province of registration	Obtain registration program number for the province in which the vehicle is based	Obtain a provincial number for the province in which the facility is located
Complete Section A of the Manifest and pass on all necessary documents to carrier	Complete Section B of the Manifest and pass on all necessary documents to consignee	Complete Section C of the Manifest and forward appropriate copies to prescribed persons
Identify the physical state of the waste, shipping name, waste identification number, classification, packing group, quantity shipped, number of packages and special handling and emergency instructions	Display appropriate safety marks in proper manner and location

Replace any safety marks that are damaged or lost while the consignment is in the carrier's charge

Refuse consignments of dangerous goods that are offered for transport which do not meet the requirements of the regulation | Identify the quantity of waste, any discrepancy, (e.g. leaking containers), whether the waste has been refused for any reason, and whether or not decontamination of the vehicle was required

Meet the requirements of a consignor when returning empty packages, containers or vehicles that are not purged or cleaned |

5.0

Decommissioning and Disposition of Contaminated Land

5.1 OVERVIEW

Past practices have resulted in conditions at many sites that are not environmentally acceptable today. There are thousands of sites in Ontario where toxic materials are used or hazardous wastes are generated, or which are contaminated as a result of past operations or waste disposal practices. Many of these sites are in areas where there are strong demands for redevelopment. These include port areas, rail lands, old factory sites, former metal foundries, refineries, etc.

Owners, prospective buyers, and sellers of property need to be aware of environmental legislation in Ontario that influences the suitability of sites for redevelopment, assigns responsibilities for site contamination, and outlines the extent to which clean-up efforts may be needed. At greatest risk are those who deal with properties that have a history of industrial or commercial use.

Several factors are contributing to the growing importance of this issue. Some are political or regulatory in nature. For example, the Environmental Protection Act illustrates the "no-excuse accountability" of new environmental legislation. It clearly places responsibility for making a site "acceptable" upon the current owner. (Previous owners also can be held responsible.) If a contaminated site is owned by a corporation or a site becomes contaminated as a result of the actions of a corporation, the individual officers of the corporation are liable. Conversely, some aspects of the regulatory framework are missing or incomplete as is the case for the procedures and/or criteria to be used to determine the environmental "acceptability" of site conditions or of clean-up efforts.

There also are social or cultural factors to consider. These reflect the general "greening" or sensitizing of public opinion and reaction to environmental concerns. The results range from growing expectations for information to calls for prompt remedial action at contaminated sites.

Finally, there are factors that are technological in nature. For example, many methods for remediating various types of site contamination are in the developmental and demonstration stages but very few of the methods have been approved for use in Ontario. This need for approved technologies is compounded by the rapidly declining availability of the frequently used options in the past such as excavation and off-site disposal. Steadily rising costs of clean-up activities are increasing the numbers of situations where clean-up costs exceed the value of the property.

Collectively, these conditions pose serious obstacles to the decommissioning, restoring, and transferring of property. They also clearly illustrate the need for current property owners to protect the environmental quality of their sites. While there are several initiatives in progress which will eventually clarify various facets of this issue, it is anticipated that site decommissioning, clean-up, and property transfer will continue to be hampered by uncertainty and lack of precedent for several years.

5.2 PROVINCIAL REGULATIONS AND LEGISLATION

While decommissioning and clean-up are often used interchangeably, it is helpful to differentiate between the two terms. **Decommissioning** most often involves permanently closing an industrial facility or part of a facility. It also can involve indefinitely suspending part or all of a facility. Other terms used to describe specific decommissioning activities include mothballing, partial dismantling, total dismantling, and closure.

Clean-up means restoring a site so that it is suitable for a prescribed use and does not pose any undue threat to human health or the environment. The aspects of a site that most often require attention are soil and/or ground water quality. While some form of clean-up is often necessary before redevelopment of a property can proceed, clean-up is not a mandatory component of decommissioning.

There is currently no legislation in Ontario which explicitly requires site decommissioning or which states clean-up requirements; however, there are several ways for decommissioning and/or clean-up to be intercepted by regulatory processes:

- If a project is the subject of the environmental assessment process, the MOE may make recommendations for conditions to be attached to the approval or exemption order of the project.
- If a project involves a change in land use or municipal plan amendment, the MOE may be asked by the municipality or the Ministry of Municipal Affairs to comment on the proposal. The MOE can request the approving authority to withhold approval unless certain conditions are met.

- Like municipalities, some conservation authorities and federal agencies will ask the MOE for opinions of environmental suitability of proposed projects and applications.
- At any site that has become contaminated, the MOE can impose an order or direction under the Environmental Protection Act (EPA) or the Ontario Water Resources Act to stop or reduce the contamination.
- Section 45 of the EPA requires the approval from the Minister for any sort of development to proceed at any site used within the past 25 years as a waste disposal site. In such cases, the MOE can make approval contingent upon whatever conditions it feels appropriate. If the Certificate for Approval to operate such a site included decommissioning or clean-up plans, those plans take precedence.

The MOE will often use provisions of the EPA to stipulate or enforce the actions and objectives that it feels are necessary. For example, Section 17 of the EPA (Director's Authority to Order Preventative Measures) can be used to issue orders to enforce the decommissioning or site clean-up process when proponents are unwilling to meet MOE objectives or time frames. As shown in Table 5.1, the same legislation described in Chapters 2, 3, and 4 concerning atmospheric emissions, liquid effluents, and waste management can be applied by the MOE to decommissioning and clean-up activities.

There are very few pieces of environmental legislation that explicitly apply to the transfer of property ownership or require an owner to inform a purchaser or lessee about site conditions. One exception is the Gasoline Handling Act which requires property owners to inform the purchaser or lessee of any underground storage tanks. In addition, the vendor must provide proof that the tanks comply with certain provisions of the regulation. These provisions, described in Sections 2, 6, and 7 of the Act, include:

- no person shall use storage tanks and related equipment that is not approved by the Director of the Energy Branch
- operators of such equipment may require licences
- no person shall install, repair, service or remove equipment unless he is in that business and registered as a contractor by the Director
- all tanks must meet specified design, construction, installation and operational requirements
- all tanks must be tested according to specified procedures

5.3 DECOMMISSIONING

5.3.1 Current Practice and Guidelines

The recent MOE publication entitled "Guidelines for the Decommissioning and Clean-up of Sites in Ontario" (MOE, 1989a) often is cited as the basic MOE reference when proponents start to discuss site decommissioning in Ontario. The guidelines apply to the closing of any provincially, municipally, and privately owned site or facility at which environmental contamination has occurred. The document can also be used, as appropriate, where remedial action may be necessary to clean up a site regardless of whether the facility is to be decommissioned. The MOE has also indicated that the guidelines be used when sites are offered for sale, even if a decommissioning is not anticipated or planned.

The guidelines do not apply to the closure of waste disposal sites or to other facilities if closure conditions have been stipulated in a Certificate of Approval issued for the site, or if terms and conditions have been attached to an exemption order issued under the Environmental Assessment Act, unless the approval or order identifies the guidelines as being applicable.

The MOE suggests that decommissioning typically consists of four phases:

Phase I—Planning the Decommissioning

- prepare initial documentation that describes the site, preliminary inventory of potential contaminants, current zoning, and the proposed decommissioning/clean-up schedule
- initiate public communications and consultation
- identify clean-up guidelines to be used or develop site-specific values

Phase II—Designing and Implementing the Decommissioning/Site Clean-up

- design the remedial work program
- implement the remedial work program

Phase III—Verifying Completion of a Satisfactory Decommissioning/ Clean-up

- verify that objectives have been met
- ongoing monitoring may be needed
- inform regulatory agencies that decommissioning has been completed

Phase IV—Signing off

- submit final comprehensive report to MOE and local municipal office
- register on title documents created in previous phases
- MOE can provide written statement of completion (but in no way will MOE accept liability for any future problems that may arise)
- affidavit may be deposited on title setting out remaining matters of concern

Each of these phases can be subdivided into tasks. The proper sequence of tasks is highly site-specific as is the timing of the overall process. A more detailed description of each phase is provided in the guidelines document.

There is no requirement to notify the MOE about decommissioning plans; however, there are several ways in which the MOE may become aware of such plans. The Employment Standards Act requires that the Ministry of Labour be informed of all employment terminations involving 50 or more employees. The Ministry of Labour will share this information with the Waste Management Branch of the MOE. Regional MOE staff usually will be aware of local decommissioning activities and plans. In many areas, concerned individuals or public organizations will inform the MOE.

Given the few precedents concerning decommissioning and clean-up and the need to demonstrate to the MOE and/or municipal agencies that the environmental conditions at a site are compatible and suitable for a proposed use, it is usually in a proponent's best interest to inform all of the agencies directly and to initiate an open exchange of information and concerns at an early stage of decommissioning.

5.3.2 The Role of Ambient (Background) Concentrations

In principle, remedial action is required wherever contaminants are present at concentrations above ambient (background) levels. The MOE defines ambient or background levels as the level of a substance in the local area. Often it is necessary to undertake a sampling program to determine these concentrations.

The MOE has established Upper Limit of Normal (ULN) concentrations for some parameters in soil (see Table 5.2). ULN values represent the expected maximum concentrations of substances in surface soil from areas not subject to the influence of point sources of emissions. "Urban" ULN values are based on samples collected from centres with a minimum population of 10,000. "Rural" values are based on samples collected from areas that have not been developed. The MOE stresses that ULN values are not guidelines but serve as levels which if exceeded should prompt further investigation on a case-by-case basis to determine their significance (MOE, 1989b).

The MOE guidelines suggest that background levels in water should be defined according to the objectives outlined in the MOE document entitled "Water Management: Goals, Policies, Objectives and Implementation Procedures" (MOE, 1984). This document will not provide much guidance for evaluating ground water quality, except perhaps at locations where ground water enters surface water.

In some situations, background levels of parameters in soil or ground water may be of concern because they are elevated throughout an area. This may be the case in urban areas which have been industrial in nature for many years or where the substances of concern are present as a result of sources such as traffic emissions. Where this is the case, it may be necessary to collect samples from locations outside the local area.

5.3.3 Communication and Public Participation

Communication of decommissioning activities to interested public groups and the media is an essential component of the overall process. Depending on the size and profile of the decommissioning, proper communication can include providing opportunities for public input at several occasions, making a file of information available to the public at one or more locations such as local libraries, distributing written material to local residents that describes the project, or establishing a public liaison committee.

If a decommissioning or clean-up project eventually will include a rezoning application or planning amendment, the Planning Act contains statutory requirements for public meetings. Some municipalities are requiring that area residents be consulted during the preparation and implementation of decommissioning programs.

The size and location of a facility to be decommissioned will greatly influence the amount of attention that the public or media pay to specific projects; however, it is increasingly unlikely that any decommissioning project in Ontario will not draw the attention of one or more groups. In the context of the overall process, it is always in a proponent's interest to consider the concerns and opinions of such groups.

5.4 CLEAN-UP GUIDELINES

5.4.1 The Three Options

Wherever soil has become contaminated and the contamination poses a threat to people or the environment, a series of questions inevitably emerges: Does the site need to be cleaned? When will the site be suitable for use? What level of residual contamination is acceptable? These and other concerns often are expressed by the simple phrase "How clean is clean?" Unfortunately, the answer is not so simply stated. At present, few jurisdictions have established soil quality or clean-up guidelines and those that have address relatively few types of substances.

As noted in Section 5.3.1, remedial action may be required wherever contaminants are present at concentrations above ambient (background) levels; however, the MOE offers a proponent three basic options for developing clean-up guidelines above background levels provided that they are protective of human health and the environment:

1 application of relevant MOE policies and guidelines;
2 application of clean-up criteria developed in other jurisdictions, where appropriate;
3 development and application of site-specific guidelines.

If clean-up guidelines above background levels are proposed, specific reference must be made to the future use of the site. The MOE typically considers five broad categories of land use: agricultural, residential, parkland, commercial, and industrial. Generally, more stringent clean-up requirements are need for agricultural, residential and parkland redevelopment.

5.4.2 Relevant MOE Policies and Guidelines

The most straightforward approach to selecting clean-up objectives is to use the guidelines and provisional guidelines presented in the MOE decommissioning guidelines document. The MOE has developed soil guidelines for the 22 parameters listed in Table 5.3. Initially recommended by the Phytotoxicology Section of the Air Resources Branch, most of the values are based primarily on phytotoxicological considerations. Some are based on human health or the health of grazing animals. The guidelines do not address specific organic compounds. As indicated in Table 5.4, the MOE has also adopted interim soil guidelines for dioxins and furans proposed by a federal/provincial technical committee (JCC-SHEO, 1989) and for PCBs based on the recommendations of the Canadian Council of Ministers of the Environment. (CCREM, 1987).

Other MOE policies that can be used to establish clean-up guidelines include:

- provincial objectives for surface water quality if contaminants are reaching surface waters such as a river or lake via ground water (see Section 3.2.1)
- provincial drinking water quality guidelines if contaminants are present in local ground water which is used as a drinking water source (see Section 3.2.1)
- the appropriate sewer use by-law if contaminants are reaching the local sewer system (for example, the MOE Model Sewer Use By-law or the Toronto Sewer Use By-law as described in Section 3.5)
- policies and guidelines related to resolving ground water quality problems and the application of the reasonable use concept to ground water management (see MOE, 1984)
- Regulation 308 concerning emissions to the atmosphere (see Section 2.2.1)

The MOE also may consider aesthetic qualities such as appearance and odours. The aesthetic guidelines used to assess soil quality during the recent decommissioning of two former petroleum refinery sites near Toronto included (Reades, 1989):

- absolutely no remaining refinery-related odours in the soil
- no discoloration or staining of soil
- no hydrocarbons or sheen if a soil sample is placed in water

5.4.3 Soil Guidelines Developed in Other Jurisdictions

To use clean-up guidelines or criteria from another jurisdiction, the methodology used to derive those values should be consistent with the overall MOE objective of establishing criteria that are fully protective of human health and the environment. Several agencies in Canada are investigating or developing soil guidelines. Some of these efforts are directed toward specific sites, others toward certain types of sites, and yet others are intended for broad application.

One of the most frequently cited efforts concerning soil quality guidelines are the "ABC" values developed by the Netherlands Ministry of Housing, Planning and the Environment (Moen *et al.*, 1985). To assess the severity of contamination and the urgency for further investigation of remediation, three levels of concentrations were identified for approximately 50 inorganic and organic substances:

- Level A is the reference value for "good" quality soil.
- Level B is the value above which there is potential for harmful effects on human health or the environment. Further investigation is required.
- Level C is the value above which soil is polluted and requires remedial investigations and clean-up.

The B and C levels were based upon information concerning toxicity, vapour pressure, solubility, mobility, accumulation, and corrosiveness but do not take into account site-specific factors. Since the first set of these guidelines was established in 1983, it has been recommended that they be used with caution and that other site-specific information be gathered prior to assessing specific situations. Federal agencies in the Netherlands are currently investigating ways to improve the basis for establishing soil and ground water clean-up guidelines. One possible option is to use some form of risk assessment/management.

In 1988, the Ministère de l'environnement du Québec (MENVIQ) issued soil and ground water guidelines modelled after the approach of the Netherlands (MENVIQ, 1988). Three levels (presented in Table 5.5) have been established for more than 90 substances:

- The A Value represents background concentrations for naturally-occurring substances and the analytical detection limit for man-made organic substances.
- The B Value marks the threshold above which a thorough site investigation is necessary.
- The C Value marks the threshold above which it may be necessary to take prompt remedial action.

Concentrations between A and B are considered to be slightly contaminated. Remedial action will not usually be necessary for soil. For sensitive land uses such as agriculture or residential development, measures such as excavation of surface soils or the addition of a layer of clean soil may be needed. Ground water quality does not meet the drinking water standards or criteria.

Concentrations between B and C are considered to be contaminated. Ground water should not be used for drinking. Restrictions on land use may be necessary. Uses such as commercial and industrial may not require remedial action.

Concentrations above C indicate serious contamination. All uses of the land will be restricted. Some form of restoration likely is needed.

MENVIQ clearly states that these values should be used strictly as indicators of environmental conditions and should not be regarded as standards (MENVIQ, 1988).

In 1988, the Canadian Council of Resource and Environment Ministers (CCREM; now the Canadian Council of Ministers of the Environment or CCME) issued interim guidelines for nine specific organic compounds at abandoned coal tar sites. Again, the ABC format was followed. The soil values are the same as those recommended by MENVIQ while the ground water values are slightly different. Also different are the definitions assigned to the three values:

- Value A is the approximate achievable detection limits for the compounds in soil. For ground water, the value is either the detection limit in water or a drinking water quality guideline recommended by the World Health Organization.
- Value B is an intermediate value five to ten times that of Value A.
- Value C is considered to be the level at which contamination is significant.

The interpretations of concentrations between A and B, between B and C, and above C are essentially the same as those assigned by MENVIQ. The CCREM document clearly indicates that the values are not based on considerations of human or environmental risk, that they are in large measure based on a best-guess, pragmatic approach, and intended for use until definitive values are developed (CCREM, 1988).

Both the MENVIQ and CCREM values have been interpreted as indicating that the B values represent maximum concentrations for residential and agricultural land use, while C values are suitable for commercial and industrial land use. Neither document explicitly expresses that sentiment and such interpretations should be approached with caution.

Several other sources of soil and ground water guidelines are listed in Table 5.6. Regardless of which sources are consulted, it is essential that the basis for the values be understood and that any statements from the developers of the guidelines concerning their application or interpretation be reviewed before values be adopted for a specific site.

To provide direction and guidance to decommissioning efforts across Canada, the CCME has recently undertaken several initiatives. One of these is the development of soil clean-up guidelines suitable for use at "orphan" sites (those for which a responsible party cannot be identified) across Canada. The development of scientifically defensible guidelines will be an ongoing process. If perceived as appropriate, such guidelines may come to be applied to a broader range of sites. It is possible that the CCME guidelines could be adopted by various agencies as the guidelines to be used at sites unless the owner or proponent chooses to develop site-specific values. This "two-tiered approach" (Tier 1 being the CCME guidelines and Tier 2 being site-specific values) is also recommended in a recent report prepared for the CCME Decommissioning Steering Committee concerning the decommissioning of industrial sites (Monenco, 1989).

5.4.4 Developing Site-Specific Guidelines

For situations where the MOE has not established clean-up guidelines, the party(s) responsible for the decommissioning or clean-up of a property can take the initiative and develop site-specific guidelines. Obviously, the onus is on the proponent to undertake whatever effort is required and to demonstrate that the proposed values are sufficiently protective of the environment and human health. Efforts in that regard should consider the following issues:

- environmental mobility of the contaminants of concern
- the pathways by which the contaminants of concern may impact on human health or the environment
- the risks posed to human health
- the risks posed to non-human site users such as terrestrial or aquatic species of plants and animals
- anticipated future uses of the site
- surrounding land uses
- possible synergistic or antagonistic effects of the contaminants of concern
- possible exposures to off-site receptors by pathways such as diet or water supplies
- physical features and environmental conditions of the site such as soil type, ground water regime, local meteorology
- background concentrations of contaminants
- possible phytotoxicological effects
- possible aesthetic considerations
- compatibility with other relevant environmental guidelines or criteria

5.4.5 Using Risk Assessment/Management Techniques to Develop Guidelines

As noted in previous sections, risk assessment and management techniques are likely to be a major component of future efforts to develop site-specific guidelines. Such techniques appear to offer a more defensible alternative to some of the methods that historically have been used such as basing guidelines on analytical detection limits, background conditions, or technological capabilities. Failure to consider risks can result in limited resources being used to reduce already low levels of risk at one situation while higher risks go unattended at other situations.

While the phrase "how clean is clean" often has been used in the past to discuss clean-up requirements, a more appropriate phrase might be "how clean is fair" when risk assessment and management techniques are to be used. In this context, the concept of fairness must address several aspects including the costs that will be incurred by those who will pay for the clean-up, the risks that will be experienced by site users and neighbours as a result of residual contaminants that may remain after clean-up, and the benefits that will be realized by the owners of the site (and possibly future site users or neighbours). Chapter 11 describes the way(s) in which risk assessment and management can be used to resolve environmental issues. While it would be misleading to present risk management as a panacea for resolving complex issues, it is equally true that risk management is critical to identifying cost-effective actions and ensuring that resources are used efficiently.

To date, site-specific guidelines have only been developed for a few sites in Ontario. Those efforts have focused on developing guidelines for organic compounds. Preliminary investigations undertaken on behalf of the CCME Decommissioning Steering Committee have led to the development of a computer model that can be used to help establish site-specific clean-up guidelines. The AERIS (Aid for Evaluating the Redevelopment of Industrial Sites) model combines information about the environmental behaviour of a contaminant, its toxicological properties, the way(s) in which a site is used, and environmental characteristics of a site to identify maximum acceptable soil concentrations of contaminants. The model can be used to evaluate a wide spectrum of contaminants, land use scenarios, and site characteristics (DSC, 1989).

5.5 CLEAN-UP METHODS AND STRATEGIES

5.5.1 Overview

There are literally dozens of methods and techniques that can be used to remove contaminants from soil and ground water. Many of the options have been developed in recent years and efforts are still underway to demonstrate their viability and to identify the conditions for which they are best suited. While much of this effort has been undertaken in the United States and Europe, there are also programs underway in Canada such as the National Groundwater and Soil Remediation Program (GASReP) at the Wastewater Technology Centre in Burlington, Ontario.

Programs like GASReP are designed to investigate, demonstrate, and test various clean-up technologies.

At complex sites, more than one technology may be needed to address contamination. It may also be necessary to clean certain portions of a site or specific contaminants before other problems can be addressed. The considerations of timing, sequencing, logistics, and combining (either in series or in parallel) various technologies all need to be taken into account in developing clean-up strategies. Also, it is not necessary for a strategy to consist only of technologies that remove contaminants. Other components of a strategy can include isolating contaminants (so that they are immobile in the environment), on-site or off-site storage, or pairing future use to clean-up efforts (for example, areas where clean-up to residential requirements is difficult may be designated for commercial/industrial use).

5.5.2 Specific Clean-up Technologies

The predominant approach to soil clean-up in the past has been to excavate and dispose off-site. Several factors are quickly removing this clean-up option. These include regulations that make it illegal to place severely contaminated soil at municipal or private landfills, dramatic increases in the tippage fees at disposal sites, and the growing realization that landfills are a precious resource best used for disposing municipal wastes. As a result, this option is becoming less available at the same time that the amount of material that might be taken to landfills is rapidly growing. To fill this widening gap, technologies are being developed for various types of contaminants and environmental conditions.

The following discussion only briefly touches upon specific clean-up technologies that are available or are in the process of being developed. There is extensive documentation for virtually each of the technologies and the amount of literature is growing rapidly as demonstrations and actual applications are published.

Thermal technologies include the use of rotary kilns, fluidized bed incinerators, circulating bed incinerators, multiple and fixed-hearth incinerators, plasma arc furnaces, oxidative and reductive infrared systems, molten salt or molten glass systems, and pyrolysis units. All of these utilize high temperatures to destroy organic compounds. The extent of destruction is largely influenced by the internal temperatures that are achieved and residence time. Principal concerns include the presence of incineration by-products in the exhaust. Various methods such as adsorption, scrubbing, and catalytic oxidation can be used to remove pollutants from the gases before being exhausted to the atmosphere. While some thermal technologies, such as rotary kilns, have been available for several years, none are currently approved for use in Ontario.

Physical-chemical treatment systems include the addition of chemicals to contaminated soil which subsequently solidify the soil and prevent the dissolving or leaching of contaminants. The solidified material can be left in place (which may be inconvenient at some sites) or can be excavated and disposed off-site. Physical-chemical treatment also includes the use of proprietary chemical mixtures to separate contaminants in processes such as soil washing, solvent extraction, and flotation. The chemical mixtures must be treated to remove the contaminants or will also need to be managed. Such treatment systems have not been approved for use in Ontario.

Biological processes include landfarming, composting, aerating, creation of bioreactors, or enhanced *in situ* bioremediation. All of these processes take advantage of naturally-occurring biological processes. Most organic compounds can be broken down by microbial organisms and techniques such as landfarms have been used for many years to manage organic wastes. Landfarming can require large amounts of land and, if used for hazardous wastes, the site cannot be reused for 25 years without the approval of the Minister. The enhancing of biological processes by controlling moisture content, nutrients, temperature and oxygen, offers promise for both soil and ground water contamination and may also be applied at some sites with minimal physical disruption. Conditions are easier to control in bioreactors but soil must first be excavated. Atmospheric emissions are difficult to control. It is expected that the MOE will soon approve the use of biological processes at a couple of Ontario sites.

Some treatment technologies address contaminated ground water. Typically these are referred to as **pump and treat** approaches. Treatment can include air stripping (enhanced volatilization), use of ultraviolet light, and ion exchange to remove the contaminants from the ground water. Such techniques are best suited to volatile organic compounds and sites where the soil is relatively permeable. Atmospheric emissions from a pump and treat system in Ontario would need to be monitored for volatile compounds and likely require treatment of the off-gases before release.

In addition to some forms of bioremediation, there are several non-biological **in situ technologies**. These include vitrification, heating with radio frequencies, and steam injection. These technologies have not yet evolved beyond the demonstration phase and have not been approved in Ontario.

5.6 LEGAL ASPECTS OF BUYING OR SELLING CON-TAMINATED PROPERTY

5.6.1 The Role of Common Law

A basic tenet of common law is that the onus is on buyers to protect themselves by an express warranty that premises are fit for their purpose and free from specified defects. The *caveat emptor* principle applies when a buyer purchases a property that has a defect which could have been discovered during a careful inspection. If the defect could not be discovered, the onus may be on the vendor; however, the purchaser must prove that the vendor knew of the latent defect. At many sites, it is difficult to prove that the owner knew of the contamination. Examples include ground water contamination resulting from a leaking tank or historical disposal activities that occurred before the owner took possession.

The *caveat emptor* principle may also be neglected if misrepresentation has occurred during the purchase of the contaminated property; however, the misrepresentation must be actual fraud to rescind the contract and recover out-of-pocket losses. If an innocent misrepresentation occurs (i.e. the owner believed they were acting in good faith), the contract may be rescinded but recovery of out-of-pocket losses may not be allowed. Several other torts (civil wrongs excluding breach of contract), may be applicable during a property transfer. These include negligence, nuisance, and trespass. Section 8.7 discusses common law as it pertains to torts.

Where responsibility for contamination is complicated by changes in ownership, the MOE can elect to issue an order to all parties that can be legally associated to the cause of the contamination. Because of the broad definitions in the EPA of "owner" and "operator", liability for past contamination can extend through unsuspecting parties (Hall, 1990). Where the transfer of property is concerned, the adage "let the buyer beware" is more applicable today than ever before.

5.6.2 The Role of Contract Law

To maximize protection from assuming a property that poses environmental liabilities, a **purchaser's offer** should contain the following provisions (Ruderman, 1989):

- The purchaser has the right to access files, documents, etc. pertinent to the property, inspect the property, and conduct environmental tests during a conditional period.
- The purchaser has the right to use agents, consultants, etc. to perform the above inspection, testing and/or review of records.
- If not satisfied with the inspection, the purchaser must be given the right to terminate the agreement or proceed with the agreement such that it is not deemed to be a waiver of non-compliance with any of the vendor's warranties.
- The vendor must provide an absolute warrant that there are no noxious, dangerous, toxic substances or conditions on the property (including urea formaldehyde, asbestos, PCBs, or any radioactive substance).

- The vendor must provide an absolute warrant that the vendor has not received notice or has knowledge of any judicial or administrative action or action by adjacent or affected land owners related to the use of the property or the presence or discharge of noxious, dangerous or toxic substances.
- The vendor must provide an absolute warrant that all necessary licences to operate the business have been obtained and the business is in compliance with all government laws and regulations.
- The vendor must inform the purchaser promptly in writing if any of the aforementioned warranties are untrue or if the vendor has knowledge of any event or likely event which may result in the warranty no longer being true.
- A statement that the warranties will survive closing.
- The purchaser has the right to terminate if warranties are found to be untrue and potential recovery of inspection costs.
- The requirement that the vendor rectify the breach of warranty prior to closing and that a portion of the purchase price is held back as security on the completion of the work.
- The purchaser has the right to obtain information on all government files related to the property, a right to cause various government departments to inspect the property, and a requirement that the vendor sign consents permitting such release and inspection.

The decision to include any or all of the above points will depend upon many factors including the extent of potential contamination and the value of the property.

In recent years, the rights of a purchaser to claim damages arising from non-disclosure of facts relating to the condition of the property has been progressively expanding. Therefore, if a vendor has any knowledge of potentially hazardous conditions he may not be protected by an offer which contains no warranties. The knowledge portion of this liability can extend to a corporation's officers, directors and agents.

The **vendor's counter-offer** may contain the following (Ruderman, 1988):

- A requirement that the purchaser acknowledge the previous uses of the property which may have resulted in the existence of hazardous, noxious, or toxic conditions or substances in the soil and structures.
- That the purchaser conduct a thorough inspection, including soil test, at its own expense and that the purchaser is buying on an "as is" basis. The vendor makes no representation or warranties regarding the presence or absence of toxic or hazardous substances or conditions, especially urea formaldehyde, asbestos, PCBs, or radioactive materials.
- If the purchaser does not terminate the agreement during the

inspection period, the purchaser is deemed to have accepted the conditions of the property and the existence of any toxic or hazardous substances or conditions. As such, the purchaser is solely responsible for any remedial action.

- The purchaser is to indemnify the vendor during and after closing from all claims, liabilities, and obligations respecting such substances or conditions.
- If the purchaser terminates the agreement following the inspection, the purchaser will be responsible for all costs and will not be entitled to make any claim for damages arising out of breach of warranty.

Such clauses will not fully protect the vendor from liability if there is an actual concealment of conditions relating to the property, a direct false statement about the condition of the property, or an intentional withholding of facts (Ruderman, 1988).

The above counter-offer terms may conflict with those described in the offer to purchase and may scare off a purchaser. It is best to have a lawyer knowledgeable in the field of environmental law involved in the transaction to ensure that the appropriate steps are being taken, especially if there is the possibility that the property is contaminated. Land is no longer a risk-free investment.

Note that the various types of **professional advisors** (such as engineers, lawyers, real estate agents, etc.) that may participate during the transfer of ownership have a duty to act with a reasonable degree of care. A person under contractual duty to make an inspection may be liable for breach of contract and/or negligence by his failure to perform the task properly (Sefton, 1988).

5.7 AVOIDING CONTAMINATED PROPERTY

5.7.1 Overview

An ever-increasing number of properties are being classified as contaminated due to the presence of organic, inorganic and/or radioactive materials. The improper storage, use, or disposal of raw materials or waste products can contaminate soil and ground water at any type of site but most often this occurs during operations at industrial sites. In Canada, it is estimated that there are more than 30,000 industrial/commercial sites where toxic materials are used or hazardous waste are generated. In addition, there are many thousands of properties which have been contaminated as a result of past industrial operations or waste disposal practices (Ibbotson et al., 1988).

Recent case law involving contaminated property suggests that the courts consider health risk to be central in the determination of liability. In one case, the Court held that even though radioactive material found in the backyard of a house and in the general area did not constitute an immediate risk or hazard to the owners, it was sufficient to be a potential risk or hazard. The Court based this opinion on the fact that the Atomic Energy Control Board had a policy to remove material with the same degree of contamination that the soil had on and near the plaintiffs, property (Willms, 1988).

It also appears that the perception of risk posed by contaminants is often as significant or more significant than the risk itself, and can form the basis of judicial and legislation decisions (Sefton, 1988).

During the past few years, several court actions involving contaminated real estate in Ontario have been publicized widely:

McClure Crescent—This subdivision in Toronto was built on land contaminated with radioactive waste. A group of homeowners successfully sued the Province for $2.5 million plus interest.

Ottawa-Carleton Coal Tar Site—The Regional Municipality of Ottawa-Carleton has launched a $12 million suit against five former tenants of a property contaminated with coal tar, including the vendor who allegedly contaminated the site, the subsequent owners and the engineers who designed the works (Shier, 1989).

South Riverdale—Contamination from a nearby metal recovery plant has resulted in elevated levels of lead in the soil of a Toronto neighbourhood. Contaminated soil has been removed from the properties and the inside of houses cleaned as part of the remedial efforts.

In addition to the legal aspects of property transfer, there are several actions that can be taken to alert the parties involved to cautionary items or "red flags" before a transaction is completed. Responses to finding red flags can include environmental monitoring, performing a detailed environmental audit and/or risk assessment, or site clean-up. Chapters 10 and 11 provide in-depth discussions of environmental audits and risk assessments, respectively. Many of the investigatory actions described in the remainder of this section also can be referred to as a "real estate" audit or inspection.

5.7.2 Review Historical Information

The history of a site can offer clues as to the types of contaminants that might be at a site and the sections of a site where contamination is most likely be found. The history of a site also can be used as a starting point for investigating potential environmental concerns and may help explain why certain conditions exist. The MOE recommends that a site history be prepared at an early stage of the site decommissioning process.

Transfers of ownership can greatly complicate an assessment of past contamination. With each new owner, the clues by which contamination can be identified may become more difficult to uncover.

The title search that often is a legal prerequisite for a transfer of ownership can identify previous owners of a property and possibly potential activities which may have occurred on the site. Past land uses that merit special caution or concern include:

- metal foundries
- metal plating operations
- leather tanneries
- coal gasification works
- wood preserving facilities
- scrap yards
- petroleum refining, blending, storage, or distribution facilities
- chemical producers
- pesticide manufacturing or formulating
- paint and ink manufacturing

5.7.3 MOE Files

Under the Freedom of Information Act, MOE files on a company may be reviewed by a citizen. Information regarding processes/chemicals, the names of individuals registered on complaints, and information used in a current court proceeding may be confidential or unavailable for review.

An MOE "approval" file may contain Certificates of Approval for air emissions, water discharges and waste treatment and/or disposal systems. The approvals for solid waste stored on-site should be critically reviewed for the types of chemicals stored, volumes and the abatement technology employed to stop ground water contamination, if any.

An approval file should also contain violation notices, control orders and the recently initiated tickets under the EPA. The violations may identify atypical releases of contaminants onto the property, spills and/or improper waste disposal.

The MOE also maintains "complaint" files. For contaminated property, these files will provide little information as they often are focused on issues such as odour or noise. Some complaints, however, can suggest conditions that warrant further investigation.

5.7.4 Company Files and Records

If accessible, company files and records are a key source of information on the environmental performance of a facility. Files to review include:

- environmental audits and plant inspection reports
- incident reports
- waste manifests for Regulation 309
- compliance reports
- chemical inventories and purchases

The environmental audit files, if available, should provide an account of the status of the company's environmental compliance and/or risk.

Care must be taken, in that one must first assess the type of audit performed and the detail involved. A superficial audit carried out by auditors with little experience is not to be trusted and in some cases can be misleading.

Also misleading is an audit which only addresses compliance and therefore may ignore significant environmental risks at a facility, e.g. inadequate spill containment or prevention at a discharge adjacent to a sensitive fish habitat.

The files on waste manifests and chemical inventories/purchases should allow a list of chemicals used on the site to be compiled. Such a list can be used to identify hazardous chemicals which are used, stored or produced at the facility.

Ground water is a special concern wherever it is used as a drinking water supply. Attention should always be paid when reviewing historical information that pertains to possible off-site migration of contaminated ground water. The legal and financial consequences of off-site contamination and the difficulties of remediating it are often greater and more complicated than any on-site contamination.

5.7.5 Interviews

Interviews with plant personnel or former employees, especially retired employees, can allow information to be collected regarding on-site contaminants which may not have been recorded. Informal discussions with plant personnel, although unlikely, may lead to the identification of improper waste disposal practices. Statements like "waste oil used to be dumped in the back field" or "there was that big spill several years ago" may be very important and should be investigated further.

Neighbours, especially in recent years, have become much more aware of local industrial operations. Important pieces of information on the operations of the facility from their perspective can round out an assessment. Some judgement, however, may be required to separate fact from fiction.

5.7.6 Site Visits or Inspections

A site visit is a prerequisite for most property transfers. The site visit for an industrial facility should include most or all the following steps:

- review of chemical inventory
- assess waste streams
- review of storage facilities, especially underground tanks and piping
- assess lagoons, pits, ponds or standing water, piles and vegetation
- inspect all emission/discharge locations
- become aware of industries adjacent to the site
- preliminary sampling

An initial opinion as to the site's likelihood to pose environmental liabilities can be drawn by responding to the questions presented in Table 5.7. A positive response to any of the questions should raise a red flag and hence require a more detailed inspection or audit. The more red flags, the greater the need to consult with environmental specialists.

5.7.7 On-Site Conditions to Note

The **topography** or physical layout of the property, including lagoons, pits, ponds or standing water, and piles may help in the assessment of past disposal practices. Areas with sparse vegetation should be checked for the presence of contaminants that impede plant growth.

The presence of **hazardous chemicals** can greatly complicate the restoration of a site due to the increased cost of off-site disposal of any soil that needs to be excavated, potential ground water treatment, and on-site worker health and safety.

Chemicals such as halogenated aliphatic hydrocarbons (i.e. trichloroethylene), halogenated aromatic hydrocarbons (such as PCBs), or mixtures such as coal tar and creosote all require special care and consideration.

PCBs were formerly used in electrical equipment, such as transformers and capacitors, and as a fire retardant insulator. PCBs by themselves are not considered extremely toxic to humans by the scientific community, but contamination that can be caused during PCB-related fires can be (see Section 7.1).

Asbestos is a generic term that applies to naturally occurring hydrated mineral silicates that are separable into flexible, incombustible fibres. It was used extensively for ceiling and floor tiles, pipe insulation, cement and insulating materials. The presence of asbestos will complicate and increase the costs of decommissioning or clean-up efforts. If asbestos is suspected of being present, a sample should be taken during the site visit. Visual inspection of fireproofing insulation materials is unreliable.

Formaldehyde is an important industrial chemical used to produce synthetic urea- and phenol-formaldehyde resins. These resins in turn are used as adhesives in particle board, fibreboard, plywood and laminates, coating processes, paper products, foam for insulation and in some fabrics. Some people may become sensitized to formaldehyde and experience severe reactions when re-exposed. Hence, it is important to identify the insulation material and if required obtain a written statement indicating the absence of this material.

Storage tanks and piping can be the source of leaks which contaminate soil and/or ground water. Contamination may go undetected for several years. It is estimated that there likely are several thousand leaking tanks in Canada (Singh and Viswanathan, 1988).

A knowledge of **activities in the surrounding area** is essential when evaluating a property. Contaminants know no bounds. Besides environmental concerns, there are cases on record where employees of a company have walked off the job because of odorous emissions from a nearby facility.

5.7.8 Preliminary Sampling

Preliminary sampling efforts should be based on information about historical and current operations at the site, observations made during a site visit, the results of previous sampling, and the future use of the site.

If the proposed or anticipated use of a site is to change from industrial to residential, the investigation must be thorough enough to ensure that contamination could not be encountered by activities such as excavations for gardens or swimming pools.

Monitoring wells can be used to study the hydrogeology of a site and the potential extent of ground water contamination. Monitoring wells are required for determining water levels, ground water flow directions and ground water quality and/or contamination.

Boreholes are one of the most commonly used ways to investigate the physical and chemical quality of soil strata. **Test pits** can often give a more complete picture of the real extent of contaminant migration than a large number of boreholes, when contamination is shallow (less than 3 m), visually identifiable and associated with fill, buried structures or past superficial spills. Test pits may not reveal contamination that occurs in thin layers or involves low concentrations (Reades, 1989).

Geotechnical investigations for building extensions may provide data regarding the extent of any contamination at a site. In addition, observations made during excavation for building additions, the installation of utilities or for the removal of pipelines or underground structures not only are relevant, but provide an indication of the potential extent of contamination (Reades, 1989).

Non-disruptive investigations using **geophysical techniques** such as near-surface conductivity surveys and total field (proton) magnetometer surveys can be used to delineate buried metallic objects such as tanks, drums, pipelines, and debris. All of the anomalies should be examined prior to excavating since anomalies can be induced by nearby objects such as buildings, fences, and storage bins.

On-site monitoring for organic compounds using an organic vapour analyzer is becoming a common technique during site inspections. Vapours can be analyzed quickly in surficial soils or by analyzing the headspace of the sample jars of the soil samples obtained from the site during drilling investigation. Such analysis can greatly assist in delineating the vertical extent of contamination in boreholes and whether contamination detected in adjacent boreholes is similar.

For a preliminary investigation, it may be cost-effective to analyze samples for a few indicator parameters such as total organic carbon, total organic halogens, total oil and grease, or Analytical Test Group 9 (metal scan). The results of these analyses should indicate if further sampling is required.

Off-site sampling of adjacent surface water into which a facility's direct discharge or storm water flows may be appropriate in some cases. In addition, surface water should also be sampled at locations where ground water emerges.

5.8 SUMMARY

Owners, prospective buyers, and sellers of property need to be aware of environmental legislation in Ontario that influences site redevelopment, decommissioning, clean-up, and the assignment of liabilities. At greatest risk are those who deal with properties that have a history of industrial or commercial use. Past practices have resulted in conditions at many sites that are not environmentally acceptable today.

The Environmental Protection Act clearly places responsibility for making a site acceptable upon the current owner but previous owners or site operators can also be held responsible. Where responsibility for contamination is complicated by changes in ownership, the MOE can elect to issue an order to all parties that can be legally associated to the cause of the contamination. Where the transfer of property is concerned, the adage "let the buyer beware" is more applicable today than ever before.

There currently is no legislation in Ontario which explicitly requires site decommissioning or which states clean-up requirements; however, there are several ways in which regulatory agencies can effect the decommissioning and/or clean-up of a site. The recent MOE publication entitled "Guidelines for the Decommissioning and Clean-up of Sites in Ontario" is often cited as the basic reference when proponents consider site decommissioning in Ontario; however, that document is only a guideline and many issues concerning decommissioning and clean-up are not addressed.

There is a growing body of information and cases which are setting precedents, procedures, and/or criteria for determining the environmental "acceptability" of site conditions or of clean-up efforts; however, "approved" technologies and methods to achieve acceptable levels of clean-up are generally lacking. Many methods for remediating sites or addressing various types of contamination are in the developmental and demonstration stages but very few of the methods have been approved for use in Ontario.

Given the gaps in regulatory guidance and the need to demonstrate to the MOE and/or municipal agencies that the environmental conditions at a site are compatible and suitable for a proposed use, it is usually in a proponent's best interest to inform all of the agencies directly and to initiate an open exchange of information and concerns at an early stage of decommissioning.

Collectively, these conditions pose serious obstacles to the decommissioning, restoring, and transferring of property. They also clearly illustrate the need for current property owners to protect the environmental quality of their sites.

REFERENCES

Canadian Council of Resource and Environment Ministers (CCREM), 1987. "Interim Guidelines for PCBs in Soil". Prepared by J.D. Clarke, M. Richardson, B. Hanna Thorpe, and M. Bealieu.

Canadian Council of Resource and Environment Ministers (CCREM), 1988. "Proposed Interim Guidelines for PAH Contamination at Abandoned Coal Tar Sites". Prepared for the Waste Management Committee, Toxic Substances Advisory Committee by the Ad Hoc Federal-Provincial Working Group on Interim PAH Guidelines.

Decommissioning Steering Committee, 1989. "The Development of Soil Clean-up Criteria in Canada. Volume 2—Report on the 'Demonstration' Version of the AERIS Model (An Aid for Evaluating the Redevelopment of Industrial Sites)". Prepared for Environment Canada, Conservation and Protection.

Hall, A., 1990. "Decommissioning and Cleanup - Regulatory Framework". Presented at Cleaning Up Contaminated Sites, Toronto, Ontario, 23 January.

Ibbotson, B.G., Phyper, J.D., and Powers, B.P., 1988, "Using an Expert System to Facilitate the Development of Clean-up Guidelines". Presented at the Annual SETAC Conference, Arlington, Virginia, 13 to 17 November.

Joint Consultative Committee of Senior Health and Environment Officials (JCCSEO), 1989. "Accepted Interim Apportionment of Exposure and Guidelines for Polychlorinated Dibenzo-P-Dioxins (PCDD) and Polychlorinated Dibenzofurans (PCDF)".

Ministère de l'environnement du Québec (MENVIQ), 1988. "Contaminated Sites Rehabilitation Policy".

Moen, J.E.T., Cornet, J.P., and Evers, C.W.A, 1985. "Soil Protection and Remedial Actions: Criteria for Decision Making and Standardization of Requirements". Contaminated Soil, pp. 441-448.

Monenco Consultants Limited, 1989. "National Guidelines for Decommissioning Industrial Sites"—DRAFT. Prepared for Environment Canada, Conservation and Protection. DOE 8505-5.

Ontario Ministry of the Environment (MOE), 1984. "Water Management: Goals, Policies, Objectives and Implementation Procedures of the Ministry of the Environment".

Ontario Ministry of the Environment (MOE), 1989a. "Guidelines for the Decommissioning and Clean-up of Sites in Ontario", February.

Ontario Ministry of the Environment (MOE), 1989b. "Upper Limit of Normal Contaminant Guidelines for Phytotoxicology Samples". Phytotoxicology Section, Air Resources Branch. ARB-138-88-Phyto.

Reades, D.W., 1989. "Hydrogeological Investigation During Environmental Audits". Presented at the Regulatory Compliance Workshop, Toronto, 11 October.

Ruderman, J.C., 1988. "Negotiating the Agreement of Purchase and Sale to Reduce Risk of Environmental Hazards". Presented at the Environmental Real Estate Transaction Conference, Toronto, 19 September.

Sefton, C.R.C., 1988. "Remedies: Litigation the Toxic Real Estate Case". Presented at the Environmental Real Estate Transaction Conference, Toronto, 19 September.

Shier, D.S.K., 1989. "Negotiating Environmental Provisions in Real Estate Transactions to Avoid Costly and Unnecessary Disputes". Presented at Environmental Management, Toronto, 4, 5 April.

Singh, J., and Viswanathan, S., 1988. "Reducing Environmental Risks in Real Estate Transactions". Presented at the Environmental Real Estate Transaction Conference, Toronto, 19 September.

Willms, J.R., 1988. "Welcome and Opening Remarks from the Chair". Presented at the Environmental Real Estate Transaction Conference, Toronto, 19 September.

Table 5.1
EXAMPLES OF REGULATIONS THAT CAN BE APPLIED TO DECOMMISSIONING AND SITE CLEAN-UP

A—ONTARIO ENVIRONMENTAL PROTECTION ACT

Part II General Provisions
Section 5 -   Prohibition of exceeding regulatory limits
Section 6 -   Controls orders for emissions and discharges
Section 13 -   Prohibition of discharging contaminant which causes an adverse effect
Section 16 -   Minister's authority to order preventive measures
Section 17 -   Study and reporting of preventative measures

Part V Waste Management
Section 27 -   Approvals for waste management systems or disposal site
Section 39 -   Prohibition on depositing waste except at approved sites
Section 45 -   Prohibition of using former waste disposal site

Part IX Spills
Section 81 -   Restoration of environment

Part X Control Orders and Stop Orders

Part XIV Miscellaneous
Section 143 - Enforcement of required actions
Section 147A -   Duty to take reasonable care

REGULATION 308 - Air Pollution
REGULATION 309 - Waste Management
REGULATION 11/82 - PCB Wastes

B—ONTARIO WATER RESOURCES ACT
Section 16 -   Prohibition of discharges that adversely impact water quality
Section 18 -   Director's authority to require alleviating impairment of water quality

C—ENVIRONMENTAL ASSESSMENT ACT
Section 14 -   Approval by Minister to proceed with an undertaking
Section 20 -   Effect of a decision by the Environmental Assessment Board

D—GASOLINE HANDLING ACT

Section 2/6 - Approval of storage tanks and licences to operate

Section 7 - Specifications for installing, testing, and operating underground storage tanks

Section 8 - Responsibilities for possible leaks

Table 5.2
UPPER LIMIT OF NORMAL (ULN) VALUES
FOR SOILS

Parameter	Urban Soil	Rural Soil
antimony	8	1**
arsenic	20	10
boron	15	10**
cadmium	4	3, 4*
calcium	hv	hv
chromium	50	50
cobalt	25***	25
copper	100	60
iron	3.5%***	3.5%
lead	500	150
magnesium	ne	1%
manganese	700	700, 1000*
mercury	0.5	0.15
molybdenum	3	2**
nickel	60***	60
selenium	2	2
sulfur	ne	0.1%
vanadium	70	70
zinc	500	500

Notes

All values in ug/g (unless indicated otherwise) on dry weight basis and apply to soil in the top 5 cm.

* - The first value is based mainly on data from southern Ontario. The second is based on northeast region data.

** - Provisional value estimated from range of results, pending additional data.

*** - Rural results higher than urban results; urban guideline based on rural results.

ne - not established

hv - highly variable, not established

Table 5.3
MOE SOIL CLEAN-UP GUIDELINES

| Parameter | Agricultural/Residential and Parkland | | Commercial/Industrial | |
| | Type of Soil[2] | | Type of Soil | |
Guidelines:	Medium & Fine	Coarse	Medium & Fine	Coarse
pH	6 to 8	6 to 8	6 to 8	6 to 8
EC (mS/cm)	2	2	4	4
SAR	5	5	12	12
nitrogen (%)[3]	0.5	0.5	0.6	0.6
oil & grease (%)[4]	1	1	1	1
arsenic	25	20	50	40
cadmium	4	3	8	6
chromium (VI)	10	8	10	8
chromium (total)	1000	750	1000	750
cobalt	50	40	100	80
copper	200	150	300	225
lead	500	375	1000	750
mercury	1	0.8	2	1.5
molybdenum	5	5	40	40
nickel	200	150	200	150
selenium	2	2	10	10
silver	25	20	50	40
zinc	800	600	800	600
Provisional Guidelines:				
antimony	25	20	50	40
barium	1000	750	2000	1500
beryllium	5	4	10	8
vanadium	250	200	250	200

Notes

All values in ug/g unless indicated.

1 For comparison with these guidelines, analyses for metal and metalloids must be conducted using an approved strong, mixed-acid digestion procedure.

2 Defined as greater than 70% sand and less than 17% organic matter

3 If nitrogen levels exceed the guidelines, the mineralization of the soils should be evaluated. Additions of nitrogen-based fertilizer may be counterproductive.

4 Guideline is for fresh oil; for weathered oil (minimum of 2 years exposed on site), the guideline is 2%.

Table 5.4
MOE INTERIM SOIL QUALITY GUIDELINES

Polychlorinated Dibenzo-p-dioxins and Polychlorinated Dibenzofurans:

1 ug TEQ/kg (1 part per billion)

- where the TEQ (toxicity equivalent quantity) of dioxins and furans in soil is the sum of the concentrations of each isomer group times the toxicity equivalent factors (TEF) for each group. TEF values range from 1 for 2,3,7,8-tetrachlorodibenzo-p-dioxin to 0.001 for octachlorodibenzo-p-dioxin and octachlorodibenzofuran.

- assumed to apply to all types of soil and land use

Polychlorinated Biphenyls (PCBs):

0.5 ug/g for agricultural land

5 ug/g for residential and park land

50 ug/g for commercial and industrial land

Table 5.5
SOIL AND GROUND WATER GUIDELINES RECOMMENDED BY MENVIQ

	Soil (mg/kg)			Ground Water (ug/L)		
	A	B	C	A	B	C
I—Heavy Metals						
arsenic	10	30	50	5	50	100
barium	200	500	2000	50	1000	2000
cadmium	1.5	5	20	1	5	20
chromium (total)	75	250	800	15	40	500
cobalt	15	50	300	10	50	200
copper	50	100	500	25	500	1000
lead	50	200	600	10	50	100
mercury	0.2	2	10	0.1	0.5	1.0
molybdenum	2	10	40	5	20	100
nickel	50	100	500	10	250	1000
selenium	1	3	10	1	10	50
silver	2	20	40	5	50	200
tin	5	50	300	10	30	150
zinc	100	500	1500	50	5000	10,000
II—Mineral Pollutants						
NH_4	na	na	na	200	500	1500
Br (dissolved)	na	na	na	100	500	2000
Br (free)	20	50	300	na	na	na
CN (free)	1	10	100	40	200	400
CN (total)	5	50	500	40	200	400
F (dissolved)	na	na	na	300	1500	4000
F (free)	200	400	2000	na	na	na
PO_4	na	na	na	50	100	700
NO_3 (as N)	na	na	na	10	10,000	—
NO_2 (as N)	na	na	na	20	1000	—
H_2S	na	na	na	10	50	500
S (total)	500	1000	2000	—	—	—
III—Monocyclic Aromatic Hydrocarbons						
benzene	0.1	0.5	5	0.5	1	5
ethylbenzene	0.1	5	50	0.5	50	150
toluene	0.1	3	30	0.5	50	100

chlorobenzene	0.1	1	10	0.1	2	5
1,2-dichlorobenzene	0.1	1	10	0.1	2	5
1,3-dichlorobenzene	0.1	1	10	0.1	2	5
1,4-dichlorobenzene	0.1	1	10	0.1	2	5
xylene	0.1	5	50	0.5	20	60
styrene	0.1	5	50	0.5	40	120

IV—Phenolic Compounds

non-chlorinated[1] (each)	0.1	1	10	1	3	20
chlorophenols[2] (each)	0.1	0.5	5	1	2	5
chlorophenols (total)	0.1	1	10	1	4	10

V—Polycyclic Aromatic Hydrocarbons (PAHs)

acenaphthene	0.1	10	100	0.5	20	30
acenaphthylene	0.1	10	100	0.5	10	20
anthracene	0.1	10	100	0.2	7	20
benzo(a)anthracene	0.1	1	10	0.1	0.5	2
benzo(a)pyrene	0.1	1	10	0.1	0.2	1
benzo(b)fluoranthene	0.1	1	10	0.1	0.2	1
benzo(c)phenanthrene	0.1	1	10	0.1	0.5	2
benzo(g,h,i)perylene	0.1	1	10	0.1	0.2	1
benzo(j)fluoranthene	0.1	1	10	0.1	0.2	1
benzo(k)fluoranthene	0.1	1	10	0.1	0.2	1
chrysene	0.1	1	10	0.1	1	5
dibenzo(a,h)anthracene	0.1	1	10	0.1	0.2	1
dibenzo(a,h)pyrene	0.1	1	10	0.1	1	5
dibenzo(a,i)pyrene	0.1	1	10	0.1	1	5
dibenzo(a,j)pyrene	0.1	1	10	0.1	1	5
7,12-dimethyl benz(a)anthracene	0.1	1	10	0.1	0.2	1
fluoranthene	0.1	10	100	0.1	2	10
fluorene	0.1	10	100	0.1	2	10
indeno(1,2,3-c,d)pyrene	0.1	1	10	0.1	1	5
3-methylcholanthrene	0.1	1	10	0.1	0.2	1
naphthalene	0.1	5	50	0.2	10	30
phenanthrene	0.1	5	50	0.1	1	5
pyrene	0.1	10	100	0.2	7	30
PAHs (total)	1	20	200	0.2	10	50

VI—Chlorinated Hydrocarbons

aliphatics[3] (each)	0.3	5	50	1	10	50
aliphatics (total)	0.3	7	70	1	15	70
chlorobenzenes[4] (each)	0.1	2	10	0.3	2	5

chlorobenzenes (total)	0.1	4	20	0.3	4	10
hexachlorobenzene	0.1	2	10	0.1	0.5	2
PCBs[5]	0.1	1	10	0.1	0.2	1

VII—Pesticides

aldrin + dieldrin	—	—	—	0.05	0.7	2
chlordane	—	—	—	0.05	0.7	2
DDT	—	—	—	0.05	30	60
Endrin	—	—	—	0.05	0.2	0.5
Heptachlor Epoxide	—	—	—	0.05	3	5
Lindane	—	—	—	0.05	4	10
Methoxychlor	—	—	—	0.05	100	200
Carbaryl	—	—	—	0.05	70	150
Carbofuran	—	—	—	0.05	70	150
2,4-D	—	—	—	0.05	100	200
2,4,5-TP	—	—	—	0.05	10	20
Diazinon	—	—	—	0.05	14	30
Fenitrothin	—	—	—	0.05	7	20
Parathion	—	—	—	0.05	35	70
Parathion-methyl	—	—	—	0.05	7	20
Diquat	—	—	—	0.05	50	100
Paraquat	—	—	—	0.05	7	20
Picloram	—	—	—	0.05	1	2
Pesticides (total)	0.1	2	20	0.05	100	200

VIII—Indicator Parameters

phenolics (colorimetric)	0.1	1	10	1	2	5
gasoline	100	150	800	1000	1500	3000
mineral oil and grease	100	1000	5000	100	1000	5000

Notes

na - not applicable
— - value not established

1 -non-chlorinated phenolic compounds include:
    2,4-dimethylphenol
    2,4-dinitrophenol
    2-methyl 4,6-dinitrophenol
    nitrophenol (2- 4-)
    phenol
    cresol
2 - chlorophenols include:
    chlorophenol isomers (ortho, meta, para)
    dichlorophenols (2,6- 2,5- 2,4- 3,5- 2,3- 3,4-)

trichlorophenols (2,4,6- 2,3,6- 2,4,5- 2,3,5- 2,3,4- 3,4,5-)
tetrachlorophenols (2,3,5,6- 2,3,4,5- 2,3,4,6-)
pentachlorophenol

3 - aliphatic chlorinated hydrocarbons include:
chloroform
dichloroethane (1,1- 1,2-)
dichloroethene (1,1- 1,2-)
dichloromethane
1,2-dichlorpropane
1,2-dichloropropene (cis and trans)
1,1,2,2-tetrachloroethane
tetrachloroethene
carbon tetrachloride
trichloroethane (1,1,1- 1,1,2-)
trichloroethene

4 - chlorobenzenes include:
all trichlorobenzene isomers
all tetrachlorobenzene isomers
pentachlorobenzene

5 - PCBs include:
isomers 1242, 1248, 1254 and 1260

Table 5.6
OTHER SOURCES OF CLEAN-UP GUIDELINES

Bell, C.E., Kostecki, P.T., and Calabrese, E.J., 1989. "State of Research and Regulatory Approach of State Agencies for Cleanup of Petroleum Contaminated Soils". *In* Petroleum Contaminated Soils - Volume 2. E.J. Calabrese and P.T. Kostecki, editors.

British Columbia Ministry of the Environment, 1990. "British Columbia Standards for Managing Contamination at the Pacific Place Site".

Fitchko, J., 1989. "Criteria for Contaminated Soil/Sediment Cleanup". Pudvan Publishing Co., Inc.

Monenco Consultants Limited, 1989. "The Development of Soil Clean-up Criteria in Canada. Volume 1 - Methods and Strategies Currently Used to Develop Clean-up Criteria for Contaminated Sites". Prepared for Environment Canada, Conservation and Protection.

Inter-Departmental Committee on the Redevelopment of Contaminated Land, 1987. "Guidance on the Assessment and redevelopment of Contaminated Land". ICRCL 59/83 (second edition). United Kingdom.

Siegrist, R.L., 1989. "International Review of Approaches for Establishing Clean-up Goals for Hazardous Waste Contaminated Land". Institute for Georesources and Pollution Research, Norway.

Table 5.7
PRELIMINARY GUIDE TO ASSESSING
ENVIRONMENTAL LIABILITIES

Q1.   Were significant volumes of persistent toxic chemicals used at the site?

Q2.   Were hazardous waste materials disposed on-site?

Q3.   Are there any tanks or pipelines (above or below ground) which are suspected of leaking or have leaked in the past?

Q4.   Are there unexplained earthworks or vegetation damage?

Q5.   Is there stained soil or concrete, foul or unusual odours, oily sheens or discoloration of surface waters?

Q6.   Are there facilities in the immediate vicinity which may pose a health or environmental risk or nuisance problem because of their current or past operation?

Q7.   Have halogenated hydrocarbons (e.g. PCBs), asbestos and/or formaldehyde been used or produced at the facility?

Q8.   Is ground water used by nearby residents and/or does ground water discharge to a nearby surface water course?

6.0

Noise and Vibration

6.1 OVERVIEW

Noise is defined as unwanted or disturbing sound. The types of situations where noise is an issue most often involve commercial or industrial facilities in proximity to residential areas. The effect that a sound has on the surrounding environment (i.e. the extent to which it can be considered to be noise) depends on many variables including the acoustic characteristics of the sound itself, the path the sound must travel, characteristics of the areas around the source and the receiver, and the effects of other ambient sound levels.

Vibrations involve the flow of energy through the ground. As energy travels further from its source, it decreases in strength at a rate which is dependent upon distance, soil conditions and mode of transmission. Depending on the amount of energy involved and its duration, vibration can be merely perceived, be annoying, or, in the extreme, cause structural damage.

Both sound and vibration are defined as environmental contaminants in the Environmental Protection Act (EPA) and should be treated no less seriously than an atmospheric emission or liquid effluent. In Ontario, residents can file complaints with various agencies including the MOE, local municipality, city, or township. There are many examples where noise abatement actions have been instigated as a result of the complaints of neighbours. There are also instances in which noise has been the source of initial aggravation and prompted those being disturbed to investigate and complain about other environmental issues concerning the source of the noise.

Some of the factors that influence community tolerance to noise include (Thumann and Miller, 1986):

- the presence of clearly visible noise sources, such as outdoor cooling towers, vents, stacks, etc.

- an obvious change or fluctuation in sound level
- pure tones or discrete-frequency sounds
- noises which interfere with sleep or communications
- unusually low background noise levels
- low frequency noise which induces vibrations (e.g. rattling windows) in residences
- impulses or startling noises
- noise which conveys displeasing information (e.g. glass breaking)

The units of measurement for sound and vibration span several orders of magnitude when used to describe conditions typically found in the environment. For example, the frequencies of sound in the environment can range over one million hertz (cycles per second). Even larger ranges can be encountered for sound intensity and sound pressures. To preserve constant-percent accuracies in measuring or describing noise, and to avoid large exponents in the numbers involved, logarithmic scales are used for several noise and vibration parameters (Beranek, 1971). The logarithmic parameter most commonly associated with acoustics is the decibel. The logarithmic nature of sound is illustrated in Table 6.1 which provides examples of sound pressures (decibels) and sound power levels of several common sources.

6.2 PROVINCIAL REGULATIONS

6.2.1 Environmental Protection Act

Sound and vibration are defined as contaminants under the Environmental Protection Act (Section 1(c)). As noted in Section 2.2, the EPA contains a general prohibition against the discharge of a contaminant into the natural environment that causes or is likely to cause an adverse effect. The EPA definition of "adverse effect" includes:

- impairment of the natural environment for any use that can be made of it,
- harm or material discomfort to any person,
- loss of enjoyment of normal use of property, and
- interference with the normal conduct of business.

In the context of sound and vibration, key parts of the definition, especially with respect to complaints from neighbours, include the loss of enjoyment of normal use of property and material discomfort.

In Ontario, the courts have stated that when a person with average sensibilities is bothered by noise impinging on his property, the person is entitled to complain and the courts will assist in having the bothersome noise checked. In addition, the courts have also stated that one cannot acquire a right to inflict noise on another's property unless the other property owner is actually there, suffering the noise, and taking no action to prevent it (Working Group on Noise Control, 1989).

Section 138(1) of the EPA provides local municipalities with the power to pass sound and vibration by-laws, subject to the approval of the Minister.

6.2.2 Municipal Noise By-Laws and Guidelines

Municipalities can establish by-laws for several aspects of sound and vibration:

- to regulate or prohibit the emission of sounds or vibrations
- to provide for the licensing of persons, equipment, and premises with respect to the emission of sounds or vibrations
- to prescribe maximum permissible levels of sounds or vibrations that may be emitted
- to prescribe procedures for determining the levels of sounds or vibrations that are emitted

By-laws may make different provisions for different areas of a local municipality and may make provisions for exempting any person, equipment, or premises from any provision of the by-law for such period of time and subject to such terms and conditions as may be set out or provided for in the by-laws.

To assist municipalities develop noise by-laws, and provide a consistent basis for noise control across Ontario, the MOE issued the Model Municipal Noise Control By-Law in 1978. Table 6.2 lists various MOE Noise Pollution Control (NPC) publications that support the Model Municipal Noise Control By-Law. Table 6.3 lists noise guideline documents issued in recent years by the Ontario Ministry of Housing and the MOE.

Several of the MOE publications listed in Table 6.2 address sound level limits from specific types of sources or in specific situations. For example, the MOE guidelines with respect to sound level limits for stationary sources are provided in NPC-105 and NPC-131. Publication NPC-105 uses road traffic noise background as the standard allowable sound level for **stationary noise sources**. Sound measurements are to be recorded using one-hour equivalent energy sound level (L_{eq}) in A-weighted decibels (dBA). The document also lists limits for various types of impulsive sources.

Publication NPC-115 sets out sound emission standards for various items of **construction equipment** according to the date of manufacture. It includes limitations for excavation equipment, dozers, loaders, backhoes, pneumatic pavement breakers, portable air compressors, and tract drills.

Publication NPC-131 specifies the sound level limits for the assessment of **proposed residential land developments** and alterations to or conversion of any existing developments or construction. Quantitative sound level limits for use in land use planning decisions include:

$$L_{eq} = 55 \text{ dBA} \quad 7:00 \text{ am to } 11:00 \text{ pm in outdoor recreational areas}$$
$$L_{eq} = 50 \text{ dBA} \quad 11:00 \text{ pm to } 7:00 \text{ am at bedroom windows}$$

Publication NPC-133 provides information for the assessment of **planned stationary sources**. The guidelines provided apply to new sources of sound as well as expansion, alteration, or conversion of existing sources. The information required in the document can be used to obtain a Certificate of Approval (C of A) for the source from the MOE. The document includes measurement standards and procedures as well as sound level limits for urban and rural areas.

Publication NPC-134 provides information for the assessment of **planned new land uses**. Guidelines are provided for changes to official plans, rezoning, applications for subdivision approval, and all new land uses adjacent to major transportation and energy corridors, industries and airports. The document also provides measurement standards and procedures.

6.2.3 Vibration Guidelines

Acceptable levels of vibration are based upon perceptibility. One method of evaluating the perceptibility of vibration has been developed by the Canadian National Railroad (CNR). The CNR approach is based on the premise that vibrations with frequencies between 4 and 200 hertz have the potential to cause annoyance at a sensitive residential receptor location if the velocity exceeds 0.14 mm/s during an averaging time of one second. Below this speed, vibration is not a concern; above it, consideration should be given to mitigation measures. The MOE has adopted the same values in draft form but has not yet included them in official guidelines.

Stronger vibration levels are usually needed to produce annoyance or inconvenience in commercial or industrial areas than those at a sensitive residential location; however, there are no guidelines for acceptable vibration levels in commercial or industrial spaces. If complaints arise, each situation is assessed individually according to the activities occurring in the space and the perceptibility of the vibration intrusion.

6.3 OBTAINING APPROVALS

As outlined in Section 8(1) of the EPA, a C of A must be issued by the Director to any person who intends to:
- construct, alter, extend, or replace any plant, structure, equipment,

apparatus, mechanism, or thing that may emit or discharge or from which may be emitted or discharged a contaminant into any part of the natural environment other than water; or

- alter a process or rate of production with the result that contaminant may be emitted or discharged into any part of the natural environment other than water or the rate or manner of emission or discharge of a contaminant into any part of the natural environment other than water may be altered.

Failure to obtain a C of A, especially for an industrial operation, may result in prosecution.

Exemptions to the C of A requirements with respect to noise and vibration include:

- routine maintenance carried out on any plant, structure, equipment, apparatus, mechanism or thing
- any equipment, apparatus, mechanism or thing in or used in connection with a building or structure designed for the housing of not more than three families where the only contaminant produced by such equipment, apparatus, mechanism or thing is sound or vibration
- any plant, structure, equipment, apparatus, mechanism or thing used in normal agricultural practice
- any motor or motor vehicle that is subject to the provisions of Part III of the EPA

It is current MOE policy to approve development applications even if the sound levels described in Section 6.2 for outdoor recreation and at bedroom windows are exceeded provided that appropriate mitigative measures can be taken.

6.4 MONITORING

6.4.1 Estimating Noise Levels

Sound pressure levels are measured in A-weighted decibels (dBA). The term "A-weighted" indicates that factors are assigned to specific frequencies to approximate the relative sensitivity of the normal human ear to different frequencies (pitches of sound). Sound pressure level is defined according to the equation (Thumann and Miller, 1986):

$$L_p = 20 \log P/P_o \qquad (6.1)$$

where L_p = sound pressure level (dBA)
P = sound pressure (micropascals)
P_o = reference pressure = 20 micropascals

The reference pressure is the pressure equivalent to 10 to 12 watts/m^2, the threshold of human hearing.

To estimate sound pressure levels outdoors, the basic power formula can be used (Thumann and Miller, 1986):

$$L_p = L_w + 10 \log [Q/(4 \pi R^2] + 0.02 \qquad (6.2)$$

where

L_w = sound power level (dBA)
  = $10 \log (W/10^{-12})$
R = distance from the source (m)
Q = directivity factor of the source
W = acoustic power (watts)
10^{-12} = standard reference power (watts)

The parameter Q takes into account the directivity of the source and the reflecting surfaces:

Q = 1 for point sources radiating uniformly in all directions with no reflecting surfaces
Q = 2 for sources radiating from flat surfaces
Q = 3 for noise source radiating from corners

A simple formula can be used to predict noise levels at a plant boundary based on measurements taken adjacent to the source (Thumann and Miller, 1986):

$$L_{p,X} = L_{p,Y} - 20 \log (X/Y) \qquad (6.3)$$

where

X = distance at which noise is being estimated for (m)
Y = distance at which noise monitoring data are available (m)

Equation 6.3 will result in a level decrease of 6 dBA when the distance is doubled, i.e. the inverse square law, in free space. The above relationship does not apply directly adjacent to the noise source (also referred to as the "near field"). Sound measurement should be measured at a minimum distance of two machine dimensions and at least one wavelength. If information on the wavelength is unavailable a good rule of thumb is to monitor at a distance of several times the equipment dimensions (Thumann and Miller, 1986).

When more than one source exists, the overall noise level is not the additive of each acoustic power level (W). Two equal sound sources result in the overall noise level being 3 dBA higher than either source alone.

Noise within a community fluctuates with time; thus a single measurement of sound level is insufficient for an assessment. The statistical method which is most commonly used to describe environmental noise is the equivalent sound level (L_{eq}). The L_{eq} is a time-weighted, mean square, A-weighted sound pressure.

To present the random fluctuation of community noise, especially where traffic is present, values for L_{90}, L_{50}, L_{10} and L_1 should be used. These are the noise levels that exceed 90% of the measurements (also referred to as background or ambient), 50% (median), 10% (intrusive), and 1% (the "peak" noise levels).

6.4.2 Noise Measurement

Sound measuring devices typically consist of a microphone, electronic amplifier, filters and a readout meter. When measuring noise, the microphone should be located at least 1.2 m above the ground and 3 m away from significant sound-reflecting surfaces. Average wind speeds of greater than 15 km/h may invalidate the data. Short-term (less than 5 minutes) wind gusts up to 20km/h are acceptable. Steady precipitation can also invalidate monitoring.

It is essential that the device be calibrated in the laboratory and in the field. Field calibration should be conducted prior to and after each set of sound level readings. Table 6.4 lists several helpful publications concerning the measurement of sound.

To be qualified to assess noise as it relates to land use planning, a certificate of competency in environmental acoustic technology should be obtained from the MOE. The MOE conducts certification courses and provides manuals based on the guidelines available from the Model Municipal Noise Control By-Laws and other documents. MOE publication NPC-135 lists the requirements of certification.

6.4.3 Vibration Measurement

Sources of vibration include road traffic, rail traffic (including streetcars), and large-scale industrial equipment. Vibration can be measured using instruments similar to those used for monitoring noise.

The results of vibration surveys can be used to identify locations where remedial actions are warranted or to identify appropriate setback distances to avoid excessive vibration levels.

6.5 SUMMARY

Noise should be treated as any other pollutant which may cause the loss of enjoyment of normal use of property. As such, it is important that a company be aware of its contribution to the surrounding noise levels and reduce noises which are having a detrimental impact on local residents.

Noise control for the most part is regulated by municipal by-laws. The MOE has published a Model Noise Control By-Law as a means of providing a uniform base for noise control across Ontario. The Model By-Law includes Noise Pollution Control documents which describe guidelines for noise levels, assessments, monitoring and abatement.

REFERENCES

Beranek, L.L (Ed.), 1971. "Noise and Vibration". McGraw-Hill Book Company, New York.

Ontario Ministry of Environment (MOE), 1978. "Model Municipal Noise Control By-law". Final Report, August.

Thumann, A., Miller, R., 1986. "Fundamentals of Noise Control Engineering". The Fairmont Press Inc.

Working Group on Environmental Noise, 1989. "National Guidelines for Environmental Noise Control". Federal-Provincial Advisory Committee on Environmental and Occupational Health, March.

Table 6.1
REPRESENTATIVE SOUND SOURCES AND LEVELS

Source	Decibels (dB)	Power (in Watts)
human breath	10	0.00000000001
rustling leaves	20	0.0000000001
soft whisper	30	0.000000001
small electric clock	40	0.00000001
ventilation fan	60	0.000001
conversation	70	0.00001
shouting	90	0.001
blaring radio	110	0.1
small aircraft engine	120	1
large pipe organ	130	10
turboprop aircraft at takeoff	150	1000

Table 6.2
PUBLICATIONS WITHIN THE MOE MODEL MUNICIPAL NOISE CONTROL BY-LAW

NPC-101	Technical Definitions
NPC-102	Instrumentation
NPC-103	Procedures
NPC-104	Sound Level Adjustments
NPC-105	Stationary Sources
NPC-106	Sound Levels of Road Traffic
NPC-115	Construction Equipment
NPC-116	Residential Air Conditioners
NPC-117	Domestic Outdoor Power Tools
NPC-118	Motorized Conveyances
NPC-119	Blasting
NPC-131	Guidelines for Noise Control in Land Use Planning
NPC-132	Guidelines for Noise Control in Rural Areas
NPC-133	Guidelines on Information Required for the Assessment of Planned Stationary Sources of Sound
NPC-134	Guidelines on Information Required for the Assessment of Planned New Uses with Respect to Sound and Vibration Impacts
NPC-135	Certificates

Table 6.3
INDEX OF NOISE GUIDELINES

Ministry of Housing:

- Land Use Policy Near Airports (1978)

- Guidelines on Noise and New Residential Development Adjacent to Freeways (1979)

Ministry of the Environment:

- Ontario Hydro Protocol for Community Noise Control (1981)

- Noise Level Guidelines (1984)

- Guidelines for Landfill SItes (1979)

- Ontario Road Traffic Noise Prediction Methodology—"ORNAMENT" (1989)

- Guidelines for Noise Impact Assessment for Off-Site Vehicular Traffic (1988)

- Low Frequency Noise Criteria

- Guidelines for Quarries (1986)

- Manual for Certificate Course—Environmental Noise (1989)

- Environmental Noise Assessment in Land Use Planning (1989)

Table 6.4
SELECTED REFERENCES CONCERNING SOUND MEASUREMENT

American Society for Testing and Materials (ASTM), 1984. "Standard Method for Measurement of Outdoor A-Weighted Sound Levels". ASTM Standard E1014-84.

Canadian Acoustical Association (CAA), 1985. "Industrial Noise Control Manual".

Canadian Standards Association (CSA), 1983. "Recommended Practice for the Prediction of Sound Levels Received at a Distance from an Industrial Plant". CSA Standard Z107.55.

International Organization for Standarization (ISO), not dated. "Assessment of Noise with Respect to Community Response". Publication #1996.

Ontario Ministry of the Environment (MOE), 1983. Procedures for the Measurement of Sound". Publication NPC-203.

7.0

Special Materials

7.1 POLYCHLORINATED BIPHENYLS (PCBs)

7.1.1 Overview

"Polychlorinated biphenyls" (PCBs) refers to a class of 209 compounds. Each consists of two benzene rings on which are located one or more chlorine atoms. The physical, chemical, and toxicological properties vary widely among PCB compounds but all are stable at elevated temperatures, are non-volatile, and sparingly soluble in water. These characteristics make PCBs suitable for various uses including dielectric fluid in electrical equipment and in hydraulic fluids, paints, and inks. PCBs came into commercial use in the late 1920s. The major Canadian use was in dielectric fluid for industrial electrical equipment.

In 1973, the Organization for Economic Cooperation and Development urged all member countries to limit PCBs to enclosed uses and to develop control mechanisms to eliminate the release of PCBs into the environment. In 1977, PCBs became the first class of substances to be regulated under the Canadian Environmental Contaminants Act and subsequently most non-electrical uses of PCBs were prohibited in Canada. Since that time, regulations have been issued by the MOE as well as federal agencies that address virtually every aspect of the use, management, and disposal of PCBs. These are summarized in Table 7.1.

The PCBs that have been released in the environment have become widely dispersed. Airborne transport probably is an important method in their environmental distribution.

PCBs can accumulate in living organisms and have been found in animals in remote areas of Canada and at low levels in the fatty tissue and blood of Canadians (CCREM, 1986). Table 7.2 presents physical characteristics for a few PCB compounds. The octanol-water partition coefficient (K_{ow}) is a good indicator of the potential for bioaccumulation.

Birds, aquatic invertebrates, and most species of fish are particularly sensitive to PCBs. Effects which have been observed include the reduction in litter sizes of otters and minks, and birth defects, such as crossed beaks in birds (CCREM, 1986). It was these effects on wildlife, the persistence of PCBs, and their ability to bioaccumulate which prompted the federal government to regulate PCBs.

PCBs were identified as a suspected human health hazard approximately 20 years ago. Recent research indicates that, except for causing skin rashes (chloracne), many PCBs do not pose any outstanding health risks to human beings. PCBs with relatively high numbers of chlorine atoms are considered capable of causing some cancers in laboratory animals if exposure is high and prolonged. PCBs with high numbers of chlorine atoms are found in minuscule amounts in the PCBs supplied to the electrical industry.

Long-term occupational exposure to PCBs has not been shown to result in any statistical increase in cancer. No direct evidence has been found to link PCBs to birth defects or chromosomal changes in humans (Environment Canada, not dated). According to the American Council on Science and Health, there have been no reported cases of deaths attributed to PCB (Miller, 1989).

PCBs must be handled, stored, and transported as if they were highly toxic because of the requirements that recent legislation has imposed. Although PCBs may be less hazardous to humans than previously suspected, PCBs can be converted to dioxins and furans if heated sufficiently. The oily soot produced at fires involving PCBs can be hazardous.

7.1.2 Definitions and Classifications

All PCBs have the molecular formula $C_{12}H_{10-n}Cl_n$ where "n" represents the number of chlorine atoms. For the purpose of waste classification, Ontario defines PCBs as having $n \geq 1$ while the federal government defines PCBs as having $n \geq 2$.

Askarel is a generic name for synthetic electrical insulating materials that also are called PCB liquids or PCB fluids. Askarels range from crystal clear to pale yellow in colour and are denser than water. Environment Canada defines askarel as any fluid mixture that contains PCBs in excess of 30% by weight (Environment Canada, not dated).

Ontario Regulation 11/82 (amended 1984) defines several specific PCB terms. A **PCB material** is defined as a material that contains more that 50 ppm by weight of PCB regardless of whether the material is liquid or not.

A **PCB liquid** originally was defined as:

(i) liquids, other than liquids used or proposed for use for road oiling, containing PCBs at a concentration of more than 50 ppm by weight,

(ii) liquids used or proposed for use for road oiling, containing PCBs at a concentration of more than 5 ppm by weight, and

(iii)	liquids made by diluting liquids referred to in subclause (i) or (ii).

Section (ii) subsequently was rescinded and only new oil can be used for control of road dust except at coal fields where used oil may be employed if generated at the facility, and if a Certificate of Approval (C of A) has been obtained.

PCB waste includes PCB liquid and any equipment that contains PCBs and is no longer in use. The definition of PCB wastes *does not* include the following:

(iv)	PCB material or PCB equipment that has been decontaminated pursuant to guidelines issued by the MOE or instructions issued by the Director,

(v)	PCB equipment that is

(A)	an electrical capacitor that has never contained over 1 kilogram of PCBs,

(B)	electrical, heat transfer or hydraulic equipment or a vapour diffusion pump that is being put to the use for which it was originally designed or is being stored for such use by a person who uses such equipment for the purpose for which it was originally designed, or

(C)	machinery or equipment referred to in sub-subclause (vi)(A), or

(vi)	PCB liquid that

(A)	is at the site of fixed machinery or equipment, the operation of which is intended to destroy the chemical structure of PCBs by using the PCBs as a source of fuel or chlorine for purposes other than the destruction of PCBs or other wastes and with respect to which a certificate of approval has been issued under the Ontario Environmental Protection Act (EPA),

(B)	is in PCB equipment referred to in sub-subclause (v)(B).

7.1.3 Environmental Guidelines and Allowable Release Rates

The MOE has issued guidelines for concentrations of PCBs in water, air, soil, and discharges for PCB wastes as well as used concentrations as a basis for defining PCB wastes. These guidelines are summarized in Table 7.3.

Federal agencies have recommended guidelines for concentrations of PCBs in ambient water, air and soil. The Interim Order Respecting Chlorobiphenyls (20 February 1989) issued under the Canadian Environmental Protection Act (CEPA) prohibits the release of more than 1 gram per day of PCBs from any one piece or package of equipment in the course of operation, servicing, maintenance, decommissioning, transportation or storage of this equipment. It also prohibits the use of oils that contain more than 5 ppm by weight for the application to road surfaces, and the release of PCBs from all sources, except those discussed above, in excess of 50 ppm by weight.

The Fisheries Act prohibits the deposition of deleterious substances into water frequented by fish except as may be permitted by regulations. This Act applies to water frequented by fish or waters leading to fish-frequented waters and takes precedence over Section 5 of the Interim Order.

Although it was repealed in June 1988, the regulations issued under the former Ocean Dumping Control Act still govern the disposal of PCBs at sea, including incineration, through permits and regulations which specify environmental operating requirements. These regulations will eventually come under the jurisdiction of CEPA (CCME, 1989).

7.1.4 Manufacture, Importation, and Use

PCBs were first synthesized in 1881, but not manufactured on a commercial scale until 1929. Most PCBs used in Canada were imported from the United States either in pure form or as askarel. In 1977, production in the United States was terminated voluntarily. In Canada, most non-electrical uses of PCBs were prohibited under the former Canadian Environmental Contaminants Act and a national inventory of PCB-filled equipment was undertaken by Environment Canada.

While the major Canadian use of PCBs was in dielectric fluid for industrial electrical equipment, they also were used in waxes, adhesives, heat exchange fluids, vacuum pump oil, paints, de-dusting agents, hydraulic fluids, specialized lubricants, painting inks, pesticides, cutting oils, sealants, plasticizer, and carbonless copying paper. Some of the trade names under which PCB fluids were sold include Aroclor, Askarel, Chlorinol, Diachlor, Hyvol, Inchlor, Inerteen, Pyranol, and Sovol.

The manufacture, importation, sale and use of PCBs and any products, machinery, or equipment containing PCBs are regulated under the CEPA. The CEPA Interim Order Respecting Chlorobiphenyls prohibits the following:

- use of PCBs in electrical transformers and capacitors other than those that existed in Canada or were imported before 1 July 1980
- use of PCBs in heat transfer equipment, hydraulic equipment, electromagnets and vapour diffusion pumps that were designed to use PCBs other than those that were in use in Canada before 1 September 1977
- the use of PCBs in the operation of electromagnets that are operated over food or animal feed or anything intended to be added to food or animal feed
- use of PCBs as new filling or as make-up fluid in the servicing or

maintenance of electromagnets or electrical transformers and associated electrical equipment

- importing, manufacturing or knowingly offering for sale any equipment listed above which contains more than 50 ppm of PCBs by weight
- use of oils containing in excess of 5 ppm by weight for the application to road surfaces

Exemptions to these prohibitions include the sale of PCB-filled equipment as a necessary and integral part of an immovable building, plant or structure that is offered for sale, the sale of PCB-filled equipment for destruction or for storage awaiting destruction of the PCBs contained therein, or the importation of PCB-filled equipment for destruction of the PCBs contained therein. The latter exemption was required to develop a reciprocal agreement between Canada and the United States for the use of PCB-destruction facilities (CCME, 1989).

This Interim Order includes all of the requirements previously stipulated in regulations issued under the former Environmental Contaminants Act with some modifications. The Order is scheduled to be replaced shortly by a regulation under CEPA.

Electrical or other **equipment in service** that contains PCBs does not need to be registered with the MOE or Environment Canada; however, labelling of in-service equipment will assist in inventory control as well as during handling, storage and disposal. Figure 7.1 presents a label that should be used on large pieces of equipment such as transformers. Once the label is affixed, it should only be removed if the equipment has been decontaminated and the MOE and/or Environment Canada is satisfied that the PCB concentration is less than 50 ppm.

For smaller items, the label presented in Figure 7.2 can be used. If several smaller pieces of PCB equipment are found together, one label may be sufficient. The label should have an Environment Canada registration number at the bottom. The registration numbers allow Environment Canada to keep track of the amounts and locations of askarel equipment and liquids.

Figure 7.3 presents a general warning label that should be placed in a clearly visible position at the entrances to locations where PCB equipment is found.

Both the MOE and Environment Canada maintain inventories of askarel and PCB-contaminated equipment that has been labelled. Both agencies should be informed as to the status of a piece of PCB equipment, e.g. if it is taken out of service, re-located, stored, decontaminated, or disposed. Environment Canada recommends that owners of PCB equipment retain inventory records for five years after equipment is removed from service.

7.1.5 Decommissioning PCB Equipment

When PCB equipment is to be taken out of service, whether through failure, retrofit or redundancy, it must be decommissioned carefully. The following suggested procedures are taken from guidelines issued by the CCME (1989).

Notification and Record Keeping—Prior to decommissioning equipment, the MOE must be notified and both the site and material must be registered. Before the equipment is decommissioned, the following information should be recorded: nameplate data, serial numbers, dates of decommissioning and shipment, destination of equipment, and names of decommissioning personnel, as well as the Environment Canada label identification number, if applicable.

Planning—All persons assigned to handle the PCB equipment should be thoroughly instructed in the proposed procedures, particularly with respect to safety precautions, the use of safety equipment and the applicability of federal and provincial regulations. Prior to decommissioning, aspects such as containment, ventilation and working space available should be examined. The type, condition, and level of PCBs in the equipment dictate the extent of precaution to be taken. The maximum allowable emission rate from a piece of equipment during decommissioning is one gram per day.

If the equipment is located in an open area, suitable curbs, barriers and/or metal pans should be provided to prevent the release of PCBs in the case of a spill during handling operations. All floor drains should be plugged and air ducts leading to other parts of the building should be closed. If cracks or leaks are apparent, liquids should be removed from the equipment prior to movement. The area of work should be appropriately identified and unauthorized persons prohibited from entering.

Protective Clothing and Apparatus—The required protective clothing will depend upon the individual circumstances, such as concentration, quantity of PCBs and whether the material is in solid or liquid form. If workers are to come into direct contact with askarel, protective clothing impervious to PCBs should be worn. Federal and provincial regulations pertaining to the wearing of protective clothing and equipment must be observed at all times.

Procedures—Sealed capacitors should be placed into 205 L, No. 18-gauge steel drums fitted with removable steel lids and gaskets made of PCB-resistant material, such as nitrile rubber, cork, or Teflon. Capacitors should be stored with the terminals up to prevent leakage from the capacitor bushings. As many capacitors as space allows may be placed in each drum. Drums or containers smaller than 205 L may be used when the size or quantity of capacitors does not justify the larger container.

Leaking capacitors should be drained and then placed in heavy duty polyethylene bags before storing in a drum (one capacitor per bag). The drum should be packed with adsorbent material to adsorb PCBs which may escape from the bags.

Non-leaking capacitors that are too large to fit into a 205 L drum should be wrapped in heavy gauge polyethylene and crated for transfer to a storage area. If the capacitor is leaking it should be drained and stored in a drip pan containing sufficient adsorbent to adsorb any remaining liquid.

Small transformers may be stored or transported in leakproof containers, without draining, in a manner similar to that for capacitors. Transformers stored on-site need not be drained as long as they are structurally sound, external parts are protected from the weather, and spill containment is provided. Where large askarel transformers are being stored pending transportation or disposal, the askarel should be removed or stored in double-bung No. 16-gauge steel drums. PCB liquids may be stored in tanks rather than drums provided the tanks are above ground and are sound, properly labelled, regularly inspected, protected from the weather, and provided with spill containment.

7.1.6 Decontamination of PCB Equipment

The removal of PCBs from equipment or mineral oil is termed decontamination. There are two general types of decontamination: solvent cleaning and retrofilling.

Depending upon the level of contamination, size of equipment, transportation regulations, and draining, decontamination can take place at the point of removal from service, or at some other location prior to transportation. Decontamination can also take place at a disposal site.

Like decommissioning, decontamination must be undertaken carefully. The following suggested procedures are taken from guidelines issued by the CCME (1989).

Non-electrical Equipment Filled with Askarel—Non-electrical equipment which contained askarel can be decontaminated by triple rinsing. This approach is considered suitable for metal recovery.

Electrical Equipment Filled with Askarel—For electrical equipment that contains askarel, the procedure is complex and the success of the retrofilling is dependent on the type of transformer.

Equipment Filled with Contaminated Mineral Oil—Equipment which contained mineral oil contaminated with PCBs at concentrations < 500 ppm may be drained and refilled with clean oil for reuse. Scrapping for metal recovery is considered acceptable once all free liquid is removed from the hulk by an approved method. The drained oil is a PCB waste.

Containers—Askarel-contaminated containers, such as drums or tanks, should be decontaminated by triple rinsing with an appropriate solvent. Containers that held PCB-contaminated mineral oil or solvent should be rinsed in a manner appropriate to the degree of contamination and the intended use of the empty container or to the disposal method.

Solvent Disposal—Solvents used for PCB decontamination are classified as PCB waste if they contain more than 50 ppm of PCB by weight. It is acceptable, however, to use rinse solvent contaminated with greater than 50 ppm PCB as the first rinse when more than one PCB article is being decontaminated and the article being rinsed is more highly contaminated than the rinse solvent.

Retrofill Procedures—Equipment is drained, decontaminated and refilled with an appropriate replacement fluid. PCB-contaminated mineral oil equipment can usually be decontaminated by replacement of the oil. If the mineral oil is highly contaminated (i.e. PCBs concentration > 500 ppm), two or more rinsings may be required to reduce the level of contamination below 50 ppm. It is necessary to operate the equipment for several weeks to establish equilibrium before draining a second time.

There is also an *in situ* method for refilling in which the decontamination unit is connected directly to the piece of equipment (often a transformer). The oil is continuously recycled through the unit until the PCB concentration is reduced to an acceptable limit.

Once a piece of equipment, mineral oil, container, pump, hose, etc. is decontaminated it may be recycled, sold or disposed.

To decontaminate or dilute liquid PCB wastes, a valid Certificate of Approval specifically applicable to PCB wastes is required.

7.1.7 Storage of PCB Waste

Ontario Regulation 11/82 (amended 1984) requires approvals or Director's instructions for storage facilities, and addresses various aspects of licensing, operations, and record keeping.

Section 7 of Regulation 11/82 requires that every person storing PCB waste shall ensure that the PCB waste is in a safe and secure location so as to prevent waste coming into contact with any person and so that any liquid containing PCBs that may escape can be readily recovered and will not discharge, directly or indirectly, into a watercourse or ground water.

The owner of site where PCB wastes are stored must be registered as a hazardous waste generator under Regulation 309 and must meet various requirements for safety, storage of waste, and maintaining records.

Regulation 309 includes a small-quantity exemption for electrical capacitors that have never contained more than one kilogram of PCBs. These types of capacitors do not need to be registered. However, as a matter of MOE policy, large-scale generators of PCB-containing capacitors

have been asked to voluntarily collect them in order that they may ultimately be disposed in an environmentally acceptable manner (Crump,
1987).

The MOE is currently developing a regulatory amendment which
would attempt to define a "small" generator on a rational basis, e.g. total
square footage of fluorescent lighting. Until such an amendment is
gazetted, owners of more than one waste PCB-containing capacitor are
required to store them on their own property until such time as an
approved method of disposal becomes available.

Waste capacitors which are placed in a suitable container are then considered collectively. That is, the individual capacitors may be exempt but
collectively they qualify as either a PCB waste or a PCB-related waste,
and are therefore subject to the provisions of Regulation 11/82. The location at which the collected capacitors may be stored also must be defined
as a "PCB Waste Disposal Site", as defined in the regulation and subject
to all its provisions.

Regardless of the size of the storage facility, several concerns should
be addressed. Table 7.4 presents a list of appropriate storage requirements. These cover ventilation, fire control, emergency response training,
and spill containment equipment.

One of the Interim Orders made under CEPA with respect to the management of PCBs is the Interim Order Respecting the Storage of Wastes
Containing PCBs (16 September 1988) and amended (20 February 1989).
The Order stipulates that a maximum of one gram per day of PCBs is
allowed to be discharged into the environment during storage.

Equipment that contains material contaminated with PCBs should bear
the label presented in Figure 7.4. The label allows for the entering of the
PCB concentration, date of analysis, company name, and the signature of
an authorized company official. This type of label should be used to
identify drums, tanks or packaging where contaminated mineral oils, rinsing fluids, or other low-level PCB wastes are stored.

Drums or other containers that contain PCB liquids in concentrations
above 10,000 ppm require special identification to alert people to separate these liquids from low-level wastes in the storage area and also that
special disposal requirements may be necessary. The label presented in
Figure 7.5 can be used.

Environment Canada recommends that the owner of PCB wastes retain
an inventory record for five years after removal or disposal of the last of
their PCBs.

7.1.8 Transportation

The movement of PCB wastes in Ontario is governed by Regulation 309.
The requirements specified by Regulation 309 are described in Chapter 4.

Federally, the transportation of equipment and wastes that contains PCBs is governed by the Transportation of Dangerous Goods Act (TDGA) as described in Chapter 4. Under the TDGA regulations, PCBs or articles containing PCBs have a primary classification of 9.1, a subsidiary classification of 9.2 and a Product Identification Number (PIN) of 2315.

All equipment and wastes that contain PCBs at concentrations greater than 50 ppm should be labelled. **Safety marking and documentation** requirements are set out under TDGA regulations. When PCB wastes or equipment is offered for transport, it must be labelled as shown in Figures 7.5 and 7.6. All containers, articles, or equipment must clearly show the shipping name and the PIN number. When PCBs are transported in a large container or transport unit a Class 9 placard (see Figure 7.7), must be displayed. An exception to this rule is for road vehicles travelling solely on land and when the gross quantity of PCB goods is less than 500 kg. No such exception applies for PCB wastes.

PCB equipment requires a TDGA shipping document. PCB waste requires a manifest. People involved in shipping must be trained and certified in accordance with the TDGA or under direct supervision of a trained, certified person.

Recent amendments to the TDGA regulations provide certain **exemptions for small-quantity items** such as samples, articles of wastes, and some types of electrical equipment containing PCBs. Securely packaged (including adsorbent) samples, solids in quantities less than 10 kg gross weight, and liquids when their net quantity is the lesser of 2 L or 2 kg are exempt. When a waste is a PCB mixture containing less than 50 ppm of PCBs, or an article containing PCB or electrical equipment containing a PCB mixture, it is also exempt if the quantity of PCB mixture is not greater than 500 g. PCB articles in leak-free condition and containing not greater than 500 g of PCB mixture are exempt from all TDGA regulations.

The **documentation requirements** of the TDGA include:

- 60-day advance notification for PCB shipments destined for or imported from any international location
- the Canadian party must forward a letter to Environment Canada and Transport Canada confirming that arrangements have been made by the Canadian party, when dealing with a party outside of Canada, to receive completed copies of the Waste Manifest
- 30-day prenotification of interprovincial shipments and a seven-day prenotification for inspection by the appropriate authority.

The advance notification for international shipments can cover a series of consignments over a twelve-month period if estimated shipping dates for each consignment are provided. However, seven days before the intended shipping date of the second and each subsequent consignment, the shipper must again notify both Transport Canada and Environment Canada.

The TDGA regulation requires that articles containing PCB mixtures be securely enclosed in leak-proof **containers and packaging** suitable for PCBs. Serviceable electrical equipment used as emergency replacement for stationary equipment must be permanently mounted on a railway or road vehicle. This type of equipment, if it is drained, must have any remaining PCB mixture contained in the base below the drain opening. When transportation occurs by road vehicles, the equipment must be inspected by the carrier every two hours or every 200 km, whichever is more frequent.

The Ontario Dangerous Goods Transportation Act adopts the TDGA requirements for provincially regulated modes of transportation.

The U.S. banned the importing of PCB waste in 1980 and most European sites will no longer accept international shipments. Proposed federal PCB Waste Export Regulations under CEPA will ban overseas export of PCB wastes. The regulations will help Canada meet its international obligations under the United Nations Basel Convention to minimize hazardous wastes imports and exports, or place strict environmental controls if they cannot be avoided.

7.1.9 Destruction

The most widely used technology in Europe and the United States for the destruction of askarel liquids or askarel-contaminated wastes is that of high-temperature incineration. In Canada, the only high-temperature incinerators approved for the destruction of PCB wastes are located at Swan Hills, Alberta, Canadian Forces Base, Goose Bay, Labrador, and Smithville, Ontario. The latter was recently allowed to incinerate the province's largest stockpile of PCBs. Other sites should be available within the next few years in other provinces.

Ontario has given approval-in-principle to mobile destruction units and has passed a regulation specific to their establishment and control. The Mobile PCB Destruction Facilities Regulation (Regulation 148/86) describes siting, operation, environmental control, monitoring, and bonding requirements for two types of mobile PCB destruction technologies: mobile incineration and mobile chemical destruction facilities. The regulation outlines the requirements for record keeping and record retention at disposal facilities.

The Federal Mobile PCB Treatment and Destruction Regulations were recently introduced to govern the operation of mobile PCB destruction units at federal facilities. The regulations require that the destruction system must have a minimum PCB destruction efficiency of 99.9999%.

7.1.10 Disposal

Disposal of PCB wastes in Ontario and the operation of disposal sites are addressed in Regulation 11/82 (amended 1984). To receive PCB wastes at a disposal site, written instructions are required from the Director or the site must be operated under a Certificate of Approval that specifies the circumstances under which PCB waste may be accepted.

Once accepted at a site, the PCB waste cannot be disposed, decontaminated, or otherwise managed or diluted if in the form of a liquid unless the conditions are specified in the Certificate of Approval or in accordance with written instructions of the Director.

Section 7 of Regulation 11/82 requires that the PCB waste is in a safe and secure location so as to prevent waste coming into contact with any person and so that any liquid containing PCBs that may escape can be readily recovered and will not discharge directly or indirectly, into a watercourse or ground water.

A PCB waste disposal site is exempt from Sections 27, 39 and 40 of the EPA which deal with the requirement for a Certificate of Approval or provisional Certificate of Approval for a waste management system or waste disposal site (Section 5(1)). However, the exemption is subject to the following conditions (Section 5(2)):

- Record keeping (as discussed below) must be provided.
- Either written instructions from the Director prior to the removal of PCB waste are required or the waste management system or waste disposal site must have a Certificate of Approval which states that PCB wastes may be stored, handled, treated, collected, transported, processed or disposed.
- If the waste being removed contains over 50 L of PCB liquid the removal must be in accordance with written instructions of the Director, regardless of its destiny.
- PCB liquid must not be removed from equipment or a container except to transfer the liquid from a leaking container (after notifying the Director of the transfer) or pursuant to instructions of the Director.

If a Certificate of Approval or provisional C of A has been issued which specifies the manner in which the PCB waste may be stored, handled, treated, collected, transported, processed or disposed, the conditions of EPA Sections 27, 39 and 40 apply.

Certain conditions apply if a PCB waste disposal site is offered for sale or lease. The prospective purchaser, tenant or person taking possession of the site must be made aware of the existing legal requirements of the site in addition to notifying the Director of the change. The Director must be notified ten days after the sale, lease or change in possession of the location of the site and the nature and quantity of PCB waste.

The record keeping requirements of Regulation 11/82 for waste disposal sites include:

- method and time of PCB delivery to and from the site

- the source of the PCB waste and/or destination and the contact person
- description of the nature and quantity of PCB waste at the site
- the location of the waste disposal site
- the method of storage of the PCB waste at the site
- notification to the Director immediately by telephone, and in writing within three days, after PCB waste first comes on the site
- notification to the Director within 30 days after any other PCB waste is taken to or from the site

The operator must maintain the records until two years following written notice to the Director that he has ceased to be a holder of PCB wastes.

7.1.11 Summary

Polychlorinated biphenyls (PCBs) are a family of compounds which bioaccumulate in the food chain. Birds, aquatic invertebrates and most species of fish are particularly sensitive to PCB. Recent research indicates that, except for causing skin rashes, many PCBs are not harmful to human beings.

PCBs came into commercial use in the late 1920s. The major Canadian use was in dielectric fluid for industrial electrical equipment. All non-electrical uses of PCBs were prohibited in Canada in 1977. There remain many pieces of electrical equipment in service that contain PCBs.

The storage, transportation, decommissioning and destruction of PCBs are strictly regulated by several acts including the EPA (Regulation 309 and Regulation 11/82), the CEPA, and the TDGA. These pieces of legislation specify allowable air emissions, water discharges, interim soil guidelines and waste classification. Regulation 11/82 specifies material that contains more than 50 ppm of PCBs as PCB waste.

7.2 ASBESTOS

7.2.1 Overview

Asbestos is a generic term that applies to naturally occurring, hydrated mineral silicates that are separable into flexible, incombustible fibres. The family of asbestos minerals can be subdivided into serpentine and amphibole fibres. Chrysolite is the most common fibrous serpentine and accounts for more than 90% of the world's production of asbestos.

Asbestos has been used for ceiling and floor tiles, pipe insulation, cement and insulating materials. In addition, asbestos is incorporated into cement construction materials (roofing, shingles, and cement pipes), friction material (brakes linings and clutch pads), venting and gaskets, asphalt coats, and sealants (Mossman *et al.*, 1990).

Canada, specifically Thetford, Quebec, with its mines has been a major producer of asbestos for more than 100 years. Canada was the world's largest producer of chrysotile (white) asbestos, accounting for over 40% of world production.

Around the turn of the century, asbestos was shown to cause asbestosis (a fibrotic lung disease). The association with the causation of lung and pleural tumours in asbestos miners and workers was demonstrated in the 1950s and 1960s, respectively (Mossman *et al.*, 1990). The inhalation of asbestos fibres has been shown to produce asbestosis, lung cancer, and mesothelioma (a cancer of the lining of the lung and chest cavities). Epidemiological research in the 1960s revealed that insulation workers who had dealt with asbestos for twenty years or more were dying of lung cancer and the complications of asbestosis at alarming rates, particularly those who smoked (Zurer, 1990).

7.2.2 Removal Versus Management

Asbestos-containing materials (ACM) had been used widely in public buildings such as schools and hospitals and has become the focus of both fear and anger in Canada and the United States. Asbestos in buildings does not spontaneously shed fibres, but physical damage to ACM by decay, renovation, or demolition can lead to the release of airborne fibres.

Public pressure, fuelled by unsupported concepts such as the "one fibre theory" which maintains that one fibre of inhaled asbestos will cause cancer, has resulted in the removal of asbestos from schools and public building even though most ACM is in boiler rooms and other areas which are inaccessible to students or residents. The improper removal of previously undamaged or encapsulated asbestos can lead to increases in airborne concentrations of fibres in buildings, sometimes for months afterwards, and can result in problems with safe removal and disposal (Mossman *et al.*, 1990).

The concern led to many buildings owners having to implement expensive abatement programs to prevent the potential release of fibres from buildings containing asbestos. In large commercial properties, asbestos removal programs may cost million of dollars for a single building. At some commercial properties, leaving the asbestos in place may decrease revenues as companies choose to locate in buildings that are asbestos-free (Singh and Viswanathan, 1988).

In the United States, the 1986 Asbestos Hazard Emergency Response Act (AHERA) provides the Environmental Protection Agency (U.S. EPA) with the mandate to require schools to develop plans to manage (not necessarily remove) asbestos. It also requires asbestos-removal consultants and workers to have some minimal training and requires that asbestos be taken out of buildings before they are demolished or renovated (Zurer, 1990).

The U.S. EPA has published several documents to help school owners identify and control asbestos hazards in buildings:

- Guidance for Controlling Friable Asbestos-Containing Materials in Buildings, 1983 (EPA-560/5-83-002)
- Guidance for Controlling Asbestos-Containing Materials in Buildings, 1985 (EPA-560/5-85-024)
- Measuring Airborne Asbestos Following an Abatement Action, 1985 (EPA-600/4-85-049)

In 1984, a panel of the U.S. National Research Council (NRC) concluded that breathing the asbestos present in ambient air may be hazardous and that some cancers will result. The NRC panel reached that conclusion by extrapolating from high occupational doses to low doses of asbestos (Zurer, 1990). A recent publication by Mossman *et al.* (1990) stressed two points which have become clear since the NRC report of 1984. The first is that chrysotile asbestos, the asbestos which predominates in buildings, is not nearly so dangerous as other forms of asbestos. By lumping all kinds of asbestos together, the risk assessments undertaken by NRC, U.S. EPA, and the Occupational Safety and Health Association (OSHA) have exaggerated the risk from chrysolite. The second point is that the estimates of the amount of asbestos that buildings' occupants inhale have been too high. Fibre concentrations from recent studies in buildings are comparable to levels in outdoor air.

If asbestos is suspected of being present, the following actions can be taken:

- samples of fire proofing materials cans be taken (visual inspection is unreliable)
- the type(s) of asbestos present should be identified; chrysotile asbestos forms curly fibres while amphibole types of asbestos including crocidolite and amosite crystallize as sharp needles
- indoor air monitoring should be conducted
- if levels are unacceptable then a detailed assessment of physical damage to ACM should be conducted by experienced personnel
- repair and/or encapsulate damaged areas
- if conditions warrant that the ACM be removed, trained individuals should be employed and the material disposed of as per Section 14 of Regulation 309
- prior to stripping, the asbestos should be wetted to suppress dust
- individuals involved in the removal must wear appropriate protective clothing including respirator, coveralls and gloves

7.2.3 Management of Asbestos Waste

Section 14 of Ontario Regulation 309 specifies various aspects of managing asbestos waste. The management of asbestos waste must be carried out in accordance with the provisions outlined in Table 7.5. Section 3 of Ontario Regulation 175/83 specifically requires that every precaution must be taken to avoid the asbestos waste from becoming airborne.

The definition of asbestos waste (Section 1.4 in Regulation 309) includes an exemption for work that contains a "trivial amount" of asbestos; however, there is no definition of a trivial amount. Asbestos waste from commercial and domestic sources is specifically included under those categories (Sections 1.7 and 1.15 of Regulation 309).

Asbestos waste does not require registration in accordance with Regulation 309 as it is specifically identified as non-hazardous solid industrial waste (Section 1.42 of Regulation 309). It therefore does not require manifesting and can be disposed of at a non-hazardous landfill site; however, TDGA does require that the asbestos be manifested.

In addition to the Regulation 309 requirement that the word "caution" be present on both sides of the vehicle and all rigid containers, the TDGA requires that labels and placards be present during shipment.

7.2.4 Acceptable Concentrations in Air

Under Regulation 308, the half-hour point-of-impingement guideline for total asbestos is 5 fibres per cm^3 of length greater than 5 um. The ambient air quality criterion is 0.04 fibres per cm^3 of length greater than 5 um (MOE, 1989).

A more detailed discussion of air emissions is provided in Chapter 2.

7.2.5 Summary

At the turn of the century, asbestos was shown to cause asbestosis. The link to lung and pleural tumours in asbestos miners and workers was not demonstrated until the 1950s and 1960s. Research has demonstrated that the inhalation of asbestos fibres may produce asbestosis, lung cancer, and mesothelioma.

Asbestos-containing materials (ACM) have been used widely in public buildings, including schools and hospitals, as well as commercial and industrial establishments. Asbestos in buildings does not spontaneously shed fibres, but physical damage to ACM by decay, renovation, or demolition can lead to the release of airborne fibres. It is therefore important that an assessment be made by experienced personnel of the condition of ACM in a building. If the material is damaged it should be repaired and/or encapsulated, or if conditions warrant be removed. The removal being done by trained individuals.

In Ontario, the management of asbestos is specified by Regulation 309. The regulation covers the storage, removal, transportation, and disposal of asbestos. Only a waste management system operating under a certificate of approval that specifically authorizes the transportation of asbestos in bulk can be employed to transport bulk asbestos.

REFERENCES

Canadian Council of Ministers of the Environment (CCME), 1986. "The PCB Story". August.

Canadian Council of Ministers of the Environment (CCME), 1989. "Guidelines for the Management of Wastes Containing Polychlorinated Biphenyls (PCBs)". CCME-TS/WM-TRE008, Manual EPS 9/HA/1 (revised), September.

Crump, D.R., 1987. "Personnel Communications", Explanation of MOE position on the subject of PCB-containing ballast. December 16.

Environment Canada, not dated. "Handbook on PCBs in Electrical Equipment". Third edition, Commercial Chemicals Branch, Conservation and Protection.

Environment Canada, 1989. "Environment Canada Release Regulations on the Operation of Mobile PCB Incinerators". PR-HQ-089-37.

Miller, J., 1989. "Myth or Menace?" Toronto Star, p. D1, 2 September.

Miller, M.M., Stanley, P.W., Huany, G.L., Shiu, W.Y, and Mackay, D., 1985. "Relationships Between Octanol-Water Partition Coefficient and Aqueous Solubility". Environ. Sci. and Technol., Vol. 19, No. 6., pp. 522-528.

Ontario Ministry of the Environment (MOE), 1984. "Water Management: Goals, Policies, Objectives and Implementation Procedures of the Ministry of the Environment". Revised May.

Ontario Ministry of the Environment (MOE), 1989. "List of Ambient Air Quality Criteria, Standards, Interim Standards, Tentative Design Standards, Guidelines and Provisional Guidelines". May 19.

Mossman, B.T., Bignon, J., Corn, M., Seaton, A., and Gee, J.B.L., 1990. "Asbestos: Scientific Developments and Implications for Public Policy". Science, Vol. 24, January.

Sing, J, and Viswanathan, S., 1988. "Reducing Environmental Risks in Real Estate Transactions: Conducting a Pre-Purchase Site Assessment". Presented at the Environmental Real Estate Transaction Conference, 19 September, Toronto.

Zurer, P.S., 1990. "Many Asbestos Removal Projects Cited as Needless, Costly, and Risky". C & EN, February, 5.

Table 7.1
SUMMARY OF PCB REGULATIONS

Definitions	Ontario EPA Regulation 11/82
Environmental Guidelines	Ontario Drinking Water Objectives
	MOE Air Quality Criteria and Standards
	MOE Soil Quality Guidelines
	CCME Ambient Water Quality Guidelines
	CCME Interim Soil Quality Guidelines
	Ocean Dumping Control Act
Environmental Releases	CEPA Interim Order
	Fisheries Act
	Mobile PCB Incinerators Release Regulation
Importation, Manufacture, and Use	CEPA Interim Order
Decommissioning Equipment	MOE Notification
	CCME Guidelines
Decontaminating Equipment	CCME Guidelines
Equipment Storage	MOE and Environment Canada Notification
Waste Storage	Ontario EPA Regulation 11/82
	CEPA Interim Order
Movement/Transportation	Ontario Regulation 309
	Transportation of Dangerous Goods Act
	Dangerous Goods Transportation Act
Labelling	Transportation of Dangerous Goods Act
	Dangerous Goods Transportation Act
Mobile Destruction Units	Ontario Regulation 148/86
	Federal Mobile Destruction Unit Regulation
Disposal	Ontario EPA Regulation 11/82
Disposal Facilities	Ontario EPA Regulation 11/82
Record Keeping	Ontario EPA Regulation 11/82
Import/Export	CEPA Waste Export Regulation

Table 7.2
PHYSICAL PARAMETER VALUES OF SELECTED PCBs

Compound	Molecular Wt. g/mol	Solubility mol/m³	Log K_{ow}
biphenyl	154.2	4.35×10^{-2}	3.76
2-	188.7	2.68×10^{-2}	4.50
2,6-	223.1	6.23×10^{-3}	4.93
2,4,6-	257.5	8.76×10^{-4}	5.51
2,3,4,5-	292	7.17×10^{-5}	5.72
2,3,4,5,6-	326.4	1.68×10^{-5}	6.3
2,2',4,4',6,6'-	360.9	1.13×10^{-6}	7.55
2,2',3,3',4,4',6-	395.3	5.49×10^{-6}	6.68
2,2',3,3',5,5',6,6'	429.8	9.15×10^{-7}	7.11
2,2',3,3',4,5,5',6,6'-	464.2	3.88×10^{-8}	8.16

Reference: Miller *et al.*, 1985

Table 7.3
ALLOWABLE CONCENTRATIONS OF PCBs

Water

3 ug/L in drinking water	Ontario Drinking Water Objectives (MOE, 1984)
1 ng/L in ambient water	(CCME, 1989)
5 ug/L in discharges	Regulation for Mobile PCB Incinerators (Environment Canada, 1989)

Air

35 ng/m^3 (annual average)	(CCME, 1989)
150 ng/m^3 (24-h average)	(CCME, 1989; MOE, 1989)
450 ng/m^3 (0.5-h average)	(MOE, 1989)

Soil

0.5 ppm - agricultural soil	MOE and CCME Interim Guideline (CCME, 1989)
5 ppm in non-agricultural (residential and public access)	MOE and CCME Interim Guideline (CCME, 1989)
25 ppm - industrial/ commercial	MOE Interim Guideline (CCME, 1989)
50 ppm - industrial/ commercial	CCME Interim Guideline (CCME, 1989)

Waste

50 ppm by weight	Regulation 11/82

Release Rate

1 g/d	CEPA

Table 7.4
PCB STORAGE FACILITY REQUIREMENTS

1 Spill containment (have a collection system for rain water if storage is outdoors; can place PCB-adsorbent material in drain lines)

2 Fire alarm system and suitable portable or flood-type fire extinguishers

3 Emergency response training for personnel

4 separation of storage facility from processing and manufacturing operations

5 Restricted access to site

6 Isolated room (else a 2 m high woven mesh fence with lockable gate)

7 Placement of personnel protection equipment and clean-up kits within easy access

8 Adequate ventilation (air intake and exhaust outlets should be on the exterior walls of buildings)

9 If storage site is equipped with a mechanical exhaust system that exhausts into a building, the system must be provided with a smoke sensory control to stop the fan and close the damper(s) in the event of a fire

10 Ventilation switch placed outside of storage room if mechanical ventilation (the system should allow for several minutes of ventilation prior to entry)

11 Floors should be made of steel, concrete, or similar durable material

12 Area should have continuous curbing (designed to accommodate the larger of two times the largest piece of equipment or 25% of the total volume of PCB liquid at the location; or for a single unit 125% of the container's volume)

13 Concrete should be sealed with a PCB-resistant sealant

14 All floor drains, pumping systems and sumps leading from the storage location should be sealed

15 Located and engineered so that no PCBs will be released in the event of flood, storm, or runoff from firefighting

16 Appropriate storage containers as outlined in Section 7.1.5 of the Interim Storage Order

17 Drums or other portable containers should be placed on skids or pallets

18 stacking should be limited to two containers high, unless special shelving, bracing, strapping, etc. is provided

19 If equipment containing liquid PCBs is stored outside, equipment and containment should be covered by a weatherproof roof or barrier that protects the equipment or liquids and the curbing or drip pans under them

20 Solids, including drained PCB equipment, may be stored outside without being covered by a roof or other secondary covering providing the drained equipment and containers are structurally sound

21 Bulk containers, e.g. large international shipping containers or approved commercially manufactured metal storage containers or structures, may be used for either primary or secondary containment for outdoor storage

22 Requirement to have an emergency fire plan which has been approved by the local fire department

Table 7.5
REQUIREMENTS FOR MANAGING ASBESTOS WASTES

1 If asbestos leaves a site, it must be sent to a waste disposal site where the operator has previously agreed to accept the material and has been advised of its arrival time

2 Unless transported in bulk, the asbestos waste must be stored in a rigid, impermeable, sealed container capable of accommodating the weight of the material

3 Sign required during transportation

4 Only a waste management system operating under a certificate of approval that specifically authorizes the transportation of asbestos in bulk can be employed to transport bulk asbestos

5 If a cardboard box is used for storage, the asbestos must be sealed in a polyethylene bag six mil thick placed within the box and must be transported within a closed vehicle

6 The external surfaces of the container and the vehicle or vessel used for transporting the asbestos must be free of asbestos waste

7 Shall not be transported in a compaction-type waste haulage vehicle

8 Both sides of the vehicle transporting the asbestos wastes and every container (see item 2) must display in large, easily legible letters that contrast in colour with the background the word "caution" in letters not less than ten centimetres in height

9 The driver must be trained in the management of asbestos waste

10 Shall not be transported with any other cargo in the same vehicle

11 Vehicle must be equipped with emergency spill equipment

12 Asbestos waste may be deposited at a landfilling site only while the depositing is being supervised by the operator of the site or a person designated by him for the purpose and the person supervising is not also operating machinery or the truck involved

13 If deposited in a landfill, the location within the site must have been adapted for this purpose and at least 125 cm of garbage or cover material must be place forthwith over the deposited asbestos waste

14 Protective clothing and respiratory equipment must be worn

Figure 7.1
PCB LABEL FOR LARGE EQUIPMENT

ATTENTION

PCB   BPC

CONTAINS   CONTIENT DES

POLYCHLORINATED BIPHENYLS   BIPHÉNYLES POLYCHLORÉS

A TOXIC SUBSTANCE SCHEDULED UNDER THE CANADIAN ENVIRONMENTAL PROTECTION ACT. IN CASE OF ACCIDENT, SPILL OR FOR DISPOSAL INFORMATION, CONTACT THE NEAREST OFFICE OF ENVIRONMENTAL PROTECTION, ENVIRONMENT CANADA.	SUBSTANCE TOXIQUE MENTIONNÉE DANS L'ANNEXE DE LA LOI CANADIENNE SUR LA PROTECTION DE L'ENVIRONNEMENT. EN CAS D'ACCIDENT, OU DE DÉVERSEMENT, OU POUR SAVOIR COMMENT L'ÉLIMINER, CONTACTER LE BUREAU DE LA PROTECTION DE L'ENVIRONNEMENT, MINISTÈRE DE L'ENVIRONNEMENT LE PLUS PRÈS.

OR 26900

Figure 7.2
PCB LABEL FOR SMALL EQUIPMENT

CAUTION   ATTENTION

CONTAINS   CONTIENT DU

PCB BPC

A   UNE

TOXIC   SUBSTANCE

SUBSTANCE   TOXIQUE

OR 12882

Figure 7.3
PCB GENERAL WARNING LABEL

ATTENTION
PCB   BPC

CONTAINS   CONTIENT

POLYCHLORINATED   DES

BIPHENYLS   BIPHENYLES POLYCHLORES

A TOXIC SUBSTANCE SCHEDULED UNDER THE CANADIAN ENVIRONMENTAL PROTECTION ACT. IN CASE OF ACCIDENT, SPILL OR FOR DISPOSAL INFORMATION, CONTACT THE NEAREST OFFICE OF ENVIRONMENTAL PROTECTION, ENVIRONMENT CANADA.

SUBSTANCE TOXIQUE MENTIONNÉE DANS L'ANNEXE DE LA LOI CANADIENNE SUR LA PROTECTION DE L'ENVIRONNEMENT. EN CAS D'ACCIDENT, OU DE DÉVERSEMENT, OU POUR SAVOIR COMMENT L'ÉLIMINER, CONTACTER LE BUREAU DE LA PROTECTION DE L'ENVIRONNEMENT, MINISTÈRE DE L'ENVIRONNEMENT LE PLUS PRÈS.

Figure 7.4
PCB WARNING LABEL FOR CONTAMINATED EQUIPMENT

Figure 7.5
TDGA PCB LABEL

Black

ATTENTION

PCB-BPD

CONTAINS
POLYCHLORINATED BIPHENYLS

CONTIENT DES
DIPHÉNYLES POLYCHLORÉS

A TOXIC SUBSTANCE SCHED-
ULED UNDER THE CANADIAN
ENVIRONMENTAL PROTECTION
ACT. IN CASE OF ACCIDENT,
SPILL OR FOR DISPOSAL
INFORMATION, CONTACT THE
NEAREST OFFICE OF ENVIRON-
MENTAL PROTECTION, ENVI-
RONMENT CANADA.

SUBSTANCE TOXIQUE MENTION-
NÉE DANS L'ANNEXE DE LA
LOI CANADIENNE SUR LA PRO-
TECTION DE L'ENVIRON-
NEMENT. EN CAS D'ACCIDENT,
OU DE DÉVERSEMENT, OU
POUR SAVOIR COMMENT
L'ÉLIMINER, CONTACTER LE
BUREAU DE LA PROTECTION
DE L'ENVIRONNEMENT, MINI-
STÈRE DE L'ENVIRONNEMENT
LE PLUS PRÈS.

Figure 7.6
TDGA CLASS 9 LABEL

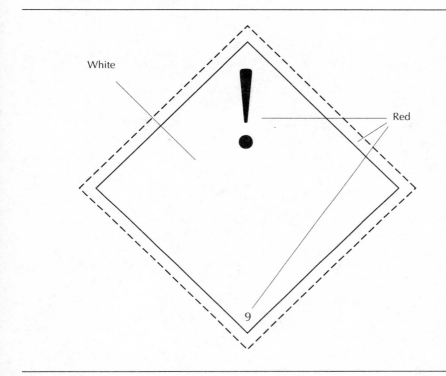

Figure 7.7
TDGA CLASS 9 PLACARD

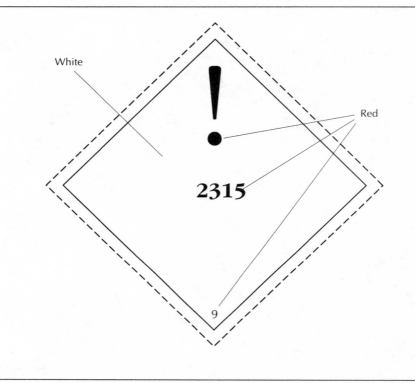

8.0

Enforcement

8.1 BACKGROUND

Prior to 1985, the enforcement activities of the MOE were seen by some as being somewhat lethargic and ineffective. The majority of non-compliance issues were resolved through discussions between the MOE regional personnel and industry. Approximately 50 cases per year went to court, convictions were few, and penalties did not seem to be adequate deterrents. Since 1985, several events have occurred that are causing those perceptions to change:

- Since the formation of the Investigations and Enforcement Branch (IEB) in 1985, the number of cases going to court has increased every year. In 1988, the number of cases in court reached 280.
- The rate at which violators are being prosecuted has tripled since 1985.
- The Environmental Enforcement Statute Law Amendment Act of 1986 extended liabilities to directors and officers of companies that do not comply with MOE requirements and greatly increased the penalties possible for violations.
- Individuals can be fined $2000 to $100,000 and issued jail terms and made responsible for other costs. The fines for corporations range from $2000 to $2,000,000.

As a result of these changes and the importance that regulatory agencies (including the MOE) are placing on enforcement, companies and their employees face the increasing likelihood of being inspected or interviewed. If violations are observed or suspected, regulatory agencies can be expected to pursue corrective actions actively and, if necessary, seek convictions.

Figure 8.1 presents an organization chart of the MOE. In terms of enforcement the key group is the Administrative Operations Division which includes the IEB and regional abatement personnel.

8.2 INSPECTIONS

8.2.1 Authority and Responsibilities of Provincial Officers

Provincial acts that provide designated representatives (referred to in this discussion as Provincial Officers) with the right to inspect sites or premises as part of investigations include the Environmental Protection Act (EPA) and the Ontario Water Resources Act (OWRA). Analogous powers of inspection are provided in federal legislation including the Canadian Environmental Protection Act (CEPA) and the Transportation of Dangerous Goods Act (TDGA).

In broad terms, a Provincial Officer administers the acts by attempting to identify, contain, cleanup, and prevent emissions or spills being repeated. In addition to administering the acts, the Provincial Officer is also responsible for obtaining evidence for prosecution. Table 8.1 lists the powers of a Provincial Officer under the EPA.

A Provincial Officer must have **reasonable cause** before exercising the prescribed powers. It may be difficult to determine if the Provincial Officer is restricting his activities to those reasonably related to the administration of the EPA and its regulations, or whether, in fact, an investigation is taking place to obtain evidence for a prosecution (Cotton, 1989).

In addition to the authority granted by legislation, Provincial Officers may in certain circumstances be required to obtain an Order of the Justice of the Peace or a Search Warrant. The latter is obtained by making a sworn declaration to the Justice of the Peace concerning the offence that has been committed and the items being sought (McKenney, 1989).

Recent court case law on the Canadian Charter of Rights and Freedoms strongly suggests that Provincial Officers should not search premises to seize or obtain evidence of an offence without a search warrant or order of a court (Jetten and Smith, 1989).

The powers of a Provincial Officer are defined less broadly under Section 10(1) of the OWRA than under the EPA and only cover the entry into lands or buildings by an inspector for the purpose of surveys, examinations, investigations, inspections or other arrangements he or she considers necessary.

8.2.2 Timing of Inspections

A Provincial Officer may enter a business premise at any **reasonable time** to check for compliance with the EPA. What constitutes a reasonable time may vary with the circumstances. It is generally accepted that routine inspection should be conducted during normal business hours. In contrast, a search based on the suspicion of an offence may be reasonable even if carried out at other times of the day.

In most cases, the MOE will give a company notice of any incident or situation into which they are investigating. The company and government representatives should attempt to establish procedures for conducting any investigation such as when and where interviews are to be conducted.

If the time suggested by a Provincial Officer is not convenient, an alternative time may be requested by the company. It is not unreasonable to request that an inspection be delayed to allow the company to consult a lawyer.

If prearrangements have not been made and an inspector or officer arrives to investigate a situation, he should be treated courteously and the concerns addressed without delay. Some companies, fearing that incriminating evidence or practices may be uncovered, may refuse entry or assume an uncooperative attitude. This type of conduct may give rise to a charge of obstructing a Provincial Officer in the execution of his duty.

If an inspector or officer arrives unannounced, he should be asked to show his credentials or badges, etc., to indicate the department he represents and then asked questions concerning:

- the purpose of the investigation and/or the nature of the problem
- whether there is a specific date or series of dates that are of concern
- whether a specific location or source is under investigation
- the section of which act or regulation may have been violated

If the responses indicate that the inspection is with regard to an investigation into a possible violation, copies of the responses should be sent to a lawyer.

Some facilities have a lawyer meet the inspector at the gate. The lawyer may ask the aforementioned questions and/or act as an intermediate between the inspector and other personnel. This procedure may be beneficial in some cases, but may be impractical as well as expensive.

8.2.3 Obligations of Those Being Inspected

Some legislation contains sections that, in effect, impose obligations on individuals to cooperate when an investigation by an inspector is launched. Sections 126(1), 127, and 129 of the EPA prohibit an individual from hindering, obstructing or providing false information to a Provincial Officer in the lawful performance of his or her duties. In addition, an individual may not refuse any **reasonable request** for information for the purposes of the Act or regulation.

Under Section 14(4) and (5) of the federal Transport of Dangerous Goods Act (TDGA), specified individuals are required to give an inspector all reasonable assistance so that he can carry out his duties and functions. The Act also specifies that no person shall provide false or misleading information to the inspector or remove, alter or interfere in any way with anything seized or removed by the inspector.

If the search is requested because of a suspicion that an offence has been committed, the company should object to any search before legal counsel is consulted.

8.2.4 Information Gathering

An inspector may take photographs, conduct tests, or inspect equipment as long as the requests are reasonable. Non-related pictures should not be taken. To protect confidential business information, and prevent the inclusion of extraneous information, the company should have the right to approve pictures used in reports.

All testing and sampling procedures should be reviewed to ensure that they were done properly and allow for a fair conclusion. It may be appropriate to take a duplicate sample and have the sample analyzed by an independent laboratory.

A list should be kept of all documents or photocopies provided to the MOE. Documents which have been passed to the MOE should be numbered to avoid confusion.

It is preferable to designate one company representative to show the inspector the facility and coordinate responses to questions. The individual should be familiar with the legal implications of the inspection and should have a working knowledge of the facility. In addition, the employee should take careful notes of what is seen and photographed, who is interviewed, what is said, and sampling procedures and locations.

8.2.5 Confidentiality

One approach to the unwanted disclosure of documents is to use the concept of solicitor-client privilege. In most cases, information passing between a lawyer and client is privileged if it is secured for the purpose of obtaining legal advice.

To claim this privilege the following conditions must be met:

- the information/study must be requested by the corporation and/or officers and directors
- the request must be in anticipation of litigation
- the information must be delivered by the lawyer to the corporation and/or officers and directors
- the information must be kept confidential

A more detailed discussion of the confidentiality as it can pertain to environmental audits is presented in Section 10.6. If the question of confidentiality does arise during an investigation, especially over a potentially sensitive document, legal counsel should be sought.

8.3 INTERVIEWS

A company should try to prearrange the procedures used for interviews. Individuals should be briefed by the company in advance of an interview on their individual rights and what is required of them. In cases where this is not possible, or for some other reason the prearrangement has not been made, individuals should be made aware of their individual rights at the beginning of the interview.

Individuals should approach interviews with the attitude that **statements made may be used in a court of law** whether or not the individual being interviewed is charged or not. Some guidelines to remember during an interview include (Rovet, 1988):

1 Stick to the facts; do not speculate.
2 Make sure you understand the question, or ask for clarification or a repeat of the question.
3 Take your time answering the questions.
4 Do not wander off the topic.
5 Do not volunteer information.
6 If you do not know an answer, say so.
7 Take notes during the interview.

If the sole purpose of the questioning is to obtain evidence of an offence for the purpose of prosecution, a person may refuse to answer. An inspector cannot force a person into self-incrimination. If the Provincial Officer has reasonable or probable grounds to believe that the individual being interviewed has committed an offence, the officer must recognize the rights against self-incrimination and give a warning (McKenney, 1989). During the interview, an individual is required to give only the information that is pertinent to the investigation. Most MOE officers have been trained as interviewers and may try to get an individual to be open. This may reveal information which in some cases is not pertinent to the investigation.

A company can be incriminated and convicted through statements made by an employee during the course of an inspection. Damaging statements given by employees must be made voluntarily without threat, promise, or inducement. Any threat to prosecute the individual employee if he or she doesn't give a statement would remove the voluntary nature of the statement (Rovet, 1988).

A Provincial Officer may write a narrative of the answers while interviewing a person and ask the person to sign it as his or her own statement. The statement will be paraphrased in words selected by the inspector to highlight issues which the officer feels are important. The statement may omit salient facts (Rovet, 1988). None of the laws or regulations require individuals to sign or initial anything. The choice of whether to sign or not sign the document is up to the individual being interviewed.

An inspector may suggest the use of a tape recorder for interviewing purposes. There is no statutory authority or obligation which would require an individual to participate in tape-recorded interviews, and therefore it is entirely up to the individual to object to the use of tape recorders. A person should not feel embarrassed or be afraid to refuse to participate in recorded interviews.

Whenever possible, a company representative not related to the incident but familiar with the particular act under which the investigation is being conducted should be present at all meetings and interviews during the investigations. If this has not been prearranged, the person being interviewed can request the right to have someone present. The inspector has the legal right to disallow a third party to be present during the interviews (Section 126(4) of the EPA) unless the third party is the person's legal counsel.

In some cases, a company lawyer may wish to sit in and represent the corporation. If a company's lawyer indicates that he will represent both the company and the employee, the investigator may indicate to the person being interviewed the following warnings (McKenney, 1989):

- Any information that the corporate lawyer learns, may not be held confidential from the person's employer.
- There may be a conflict of interest between the corporate client and the individual. Should a conflict occur, corporate counsel may be unable to represent the employee.
- The employee is not obligated to accept the corporation's lawyer and may obtain his own legal counsel.
- It is an offence, under environmental law, to dismiss or discipline any person because he or she has given information to the MOE or a Provincial Officer.
- An employee can ask if the company will pay for the services of an independent lawyer.

8.4 RESPONSES TO VIOLATIONS

8.4.1 MOE Responses

Enforcement officials, whether, municipal, provincial, or federal, are expected to respond to violations according to the sufficiency of the evidence and predetermined response criteria. In May 1986 the MOE adopted a "uniform enforcement policy" based on the following considerations (McKenney, 1989):

- Was the incident something prohibited by EPA, OWRA or the Environmental Assessment Act (EAA)?
- What efforts were made to prevent or reduce effects?
- What is this company/person's history of violations?
- Was the discharge deliberate or because of negligence?
- Have warnings or orders gone unheeded?
- Was there concealment of evidence or false information provided?
- Was there real or potential harm done to people, property, animals or plants?

The degree to which the policy fosters uniform enforcement remains to be seen.

The MOE views the laying of charges as only one of many remedies to reduce or eliminate pollution. Other remedies include voluntary compliance, warnings and control documents. A control document is any written instrument which covers statutory authority. These include Minister's reports, orders, licences, permits, certificate of approvals, requirements and directions, and program approvals.

In general, a control document will require that intermediate steps in a control order be completed in a timely and regular fashion, that pollution control equipment be installed by the specified date, and that pollution control equipment be properly maintained and operated. The control document will also specify the allowable emissions or discharges, and the monitoring requirements that must be met.

The EPA provides for various types of orders that can be issued. When a discharge or emission is found to be in non-compliance, the Minister can issue a control order under Section 6 of the EPA. A **control order** may specify directions or the manner of discharge, additional studies of the discharge, and implementation of procedures.

Section 7 of the EPA allows a Director to issue a **stop order** to immediately cease polluting activities. There must be an immediate danger to human life or health or property for a stop order to be issued.

Under Sections 16 and 85 of the EPA, the Minister may issue a **clean-up order** to any individual or company who caused or permitted a discharge or spill of a contaminant compelling the individual or company to take necessary steps to repair the injury or damage. This can include the restoration of the environment.

Section 17 of the EPA empowers the Minister to issue a **prevention order** for the discharge of a contaminant if it is believed that the discharge likely will cause an adverse environmental effect. This type of order may require specific facilities, equipment, or procedures to be followed. A prevention order may also require monitoring or the study of the effects of the contaminant (Shier, 1989).

Under the Municipal, Industrial Strategy for Abatement (MISA) program the MOE has outlined the following steps which are to be taken if a company is found to be in non-compliance:

1) An Occurrence Report outlining the nature of the non-compliance will be completed.
2) This would be followed up by abatement action which would involve communication with the company as the first step. The Ministry may contact the company by telephone or in person, then follow up with a letter to confirm that the violation has occurred and to request that the company respond. It is essential that response to the Ministry is made promptly and that every reasonable effort is made to return to

compliance. If there is no response or a poor response, the occurrence would then be referred to the IEB.

3) If the violation is deliberate, involves an attempt to conceal, or is a repeated occurrence of an earlier violation, then the Occurrence Report would be referred directly to the IEB. The IEB investigation could result in a recommendation for prosecution.

The IEB was created in 1985 to clearly separate the roles of abatement work from environmental enforcement. It has two primary objectives (McKenney, 1989):

1) Conduct investigations and make recommendations regarding the appropriate legal remedies against polluters.

2) Supply information in support of those prosecutions.

The IEB visits facilities primarily to determine whether or not a law has been broken. In a typical year, the IEB is involved in approximately 1500 investigations. Staff members come from a broad background. Many have extensive experience in environmental science while others are former members of police forces.

Under both the EPA and OWRA proceedings may *not* be brought for an offence if a period of two years has passed since the date on which the alleged offence occurred. Recent changes, however, provide that such proceedings may not be commenced later than two years after the later of

• the day on which the offence was committed
• the day on which the evidence of the offence first came to the attention of the MOE.

This change will not apply to offences committed more than two years before the amendment came into force.

8.4.2 Federal Responses

When a violation of the Canadian Environmental Protection Act (CEPA) is discovered, enforcement officials consider the nature of the violation, the desired response by the violator, and consistency in enforcement when deciding what action to take (Environment Canada, 1988).

The **nature of the violation** concerns the seriousness of the harm or potential harm, the intent of the alleged violation, whether the occurrence has been repeated, and if there were attempts to conceal information or otherwise subvert the objectives and requirements of the Act.

The desired result of any response is compliance with the Act within the shortest possible time and with no further occurrence of violation. The violator's history of compliance, willingness to cooperate with enforcement officials, evidence of corrective action already taken, and the existence of enforcement actions by other federal or provincial authorities as a result of the same activity may be considered.

To achieve **consistency in enforcement**, officials will consider how similar situations were handled when deciding what enforcement action is taken.

Like the MOE, Environment Canada has various types of responses available to deal with violations of CEPA and its regulations (Environment Canada, 1988).

A **warning** may be issued if it is believed that a violation is continuing or has occurred, and the degree of harm or potential harm to the environment, human life, or health appears to be minimal. A warning may be issued if the violator has a record of compliance and/or made reasonable efforts to remedy or mitigate the consequence of the offence.

In response to a release of a substance in contravention of the CEPA, an inspector may give **directions** to remedy a dangerous condition or reduce any danger to the environment, human life, or health that results from the release of a substance.

When there is a minimal threat to the environment or human life or health, a **ticket** may be issued. Ticketable offences include failure to provide information on a new substance, or failure to provide, within the allowable time, a pre-shipment notice. For any offence that is designated as ticketable, inspectors will always issue a ticket except when a warning is considered appropriate.

The Minister may issue four types of **orders**: prohibiting activities involving new substances to Canada; a recall of substances and products; requirements for additional information on, or testing of, substances suspected of being toxic, and to prohibit their manufacture or importation, or to limit these two activities until the expiration of the assessment period to determine the risk that they present to the environment; or interim orders for immediate action to prevent a significant danger to the environment, human life or health.

Under the CEPA, the Minister has the authority to seek **injunctions** to stop or prevent violations. If an individual or company is not complying with the injunction, the Minister can return to the court to seek a contempt of court ruling. A contempt of court ruling may carry fines or imprisonment terms beyond those stipulated in the CEPA.

Inspectors can lay a charge and seek a **prosecution** for every violation under CEPA, except where warnings, tickets, and/or orders are considered to be more appropriate. If a violation involved death or bodily harm, serious harm or risk to the environment or human health, false information/concealment of information, or less than all reasonable measures being taken to comply with Environment Canada responses, prosecution can be expected.

If there is no prosecution, or prosecution has resulted but an order to recover cost was not obtained, or the prosecution did not result in a conviction, the Crown may seek a **civil suit** to recover the cost of a clean-up (including the hiring of third parties) or action taken to prevent an unauthorized release of a regulated substance.

8.4.3 Municipal Responses

Like their provincial and federal counterparts, municipalities can respond to environmental violations with various informal and formal actions. Informal actions include: informal notice (e.g. a telephone conversation), meeting, warning letter and/or meeting to show cause. At the latter, the municipality would present the facts concerning the non-compliance and request the violator to show cause as to why the municipality should not proceed with one or more formal enforcement actions. Formal actions include the issuance of a compliance program, civil action, an order of prohibition, and/or contempt of court.

Where a by-law of a municipality or local board, passed under the authority of the Municipal Act or any other general or special act, is contravened and a conviction entered, the court in which the conviction has been entered (or any court of competent jurisdiction), may make an order prohibiting the continuation or repetition of the offence by the person convicted (Section 326 of the Municipal Act).

Table 8.2 presents a typical example of enforcement strategy that a municipality may follow a when ensuring compliance of the Municipal Model Sewer Use By-law.

8.5 PENALTIES AND LIABILITIES

8.5.1 Ontario Environmental Protection Act

Subsection 146f of the EPA equates the actions and omissions of an officer, official, employee or agent of a corporation in the course of his or her employment, or in the exercise of his or her powers or the performance of his or her duties, with the actions or omissions of the corporation.

It is up to the discretion of the Crown prosecuting a case whether the individual employee will be charged along with the corporation. Often the Crown is not interested in convicting individuals except those with considerable corporate authority.

Prior to 1986, the liability of officers and directors was limited to persons who could be said to be the directing minds and wills of the corporation. This artificial distinction between those who make policy and those who implement it no longer exists. Officers and directors must now communicate adequate information and specific instructions through the management structure and arrange for the training, supervision and monitoring so that adverse effects to the environment are prevented (Petrie, 1989).

Subsection 147a(1) of the EPA clearly states that every director or officer of a corporation that engages in an activity that may result in the discharge of a contaminant into the natural environment contrary to the Act has a **duty to take all reasonable care** to prevent the corporation from causing or permitting such unlawful discharge. Furthermore, it is an offence for anyone who fails to carry out that duty and permits a prosecution and conviction of an officer or director despite the fact that the corporation has not been prosecuted or convicted for the offence (Petrie, 1989).

The EPA has created a positive duty to educate and instruct employees to prevent environmental damage, and that duty is a personal one assumed by directors and officers of a company. The officers must implement environmental policy, ensure that an adequate system for environmental protection is set up, and act upon the findings of environmental compliance reports.

In one particular court decision (*Queen v. the City of Sault Ste. Marie*), the minimum duty of officers and directors was expressed to be (Glenn *et al.*, 1988):

1) Officers report back periodically to the board on the operation of the company's environmental system.

2) Officers report substantial non-compliance to the board in a timely manner.

Table 8.3 presents a summary of EPA penalties. There are penalties for individuals and corporations. The financial penalties can be levied for each day a violation occurs. In addition to the fines, there is an allowance for violators being required to pay an amount equal to the monetary benefit accrued due to the violation. There are provisions for imprisonment (terms of up to one year) for violations of specific sections or subsections of the Act.

In July, 1990 an eastern Ontario businessman was sentenced to six months' imprisonment on three counts under the EPA and OWRA. He is believed to be the first person in Canada to be sent to jail for an environmental offence. The man's company was fined $30,000 on each count for a total of $90,000. The charges were laid after excavation revealed more than 180 drums of industrial solvents on the company's property which had contaminated nearby drinking-water wells.

When there is minimal or no threat to the environment or human life or health, a Provincial Officer may issue a **ticket**. Table 8.4 presents examples of ticketable offenses and the corresponding fines. The fines themselves may not be large but the conviction will affect a company's compliance record—a record that may be used against the company should they be charged and/or convicted of a more serious offence.

8.5.2 Ontario Water Resources Act

Like the EPA, Section 75 of the OWRA addresses the concept of personal duty of care in that every director or officer of a corporation that engages in an activity that may result in the discharge of any material into or in any waters or on any shore or bank or that may impair the quality of the water has a duty to take all reasonable care to prevent the corporation from causing or permitting such unlawful discharge.

The penalties for the contravention of any part of the OWRA are presented in Table 8.5. In addition to fines, a conviction under Section 68 (the protection of public water supplies) may result in imprisonment for not more than one year.

8.5.3 Canadian Environmental Protection Act

The offence sections of CEPA refer to "every person". Therefore, individual employees of the company may be prosecuted where they had care and control of the deleterious substance which escaped into the natural environment and caused damage.

Section 122 states that where a corporation commits an offence, any officer, director or agent of the corporation who directed, authorized, assented to, acquiesced in or participated in the commission of the offence is a party to and guilty of the offence, and is liable, whether or not the corporation has been prosecuted or convicted.

Subsection 124(1) goes one step further in that an employee may not necessarily be prosecuted but his actions may implicate an officer, director and/or company.

Table 8.6 presents a summary of penalties under CEPA. The Act provides for maximum fines of $1 million, five years in jail and taxing of profits perceived to have been gained by polluting. The CEPA also provides a civil cause of action to any person who has suffered loss or damage as a result of conduct contrary to the Act or the regulations, including the right to seek injunctive relief.

8.5.4 Transport of Dangerous Goods Act

Under the Transport of Dangerous Goods Act (TDGA), any officer, director, or agent of a corporation who directed, authorized, or consented to the commission of an offence is guilty of the offence and liable to conviction whether or not the corporation is prosecuted. Penalties for violations under the TDGA are presented in Table 8.7. The Act provides for maximum fines of $100,000 a day for a summary conviction and imprisonment for up to two years if the conviction is on indictment.

Amendments have recently been proposed that would increase maximum penalties to $1 million and jail terms of up to five years. Changes are also being considered as to what constitutes an offence and broadening the definition of responsible parties to include corporate directors and executives.

8.5.5 Fisheries Act

To be prosecuted under the Fisheries Act, the Ministry does not have to prove that fish were actually harmed, only that a "deleterious" substance was deposited into waters frequented by fish, or that the fish habitat was harmed. Special regulations made under the Act allow for specific material to be discharged under certain circumstances. Such regulations have been developed for chloro-alkali effluents, liquid mercury effluents, petroleum refinery effluents, and pulp and paper effluents.

The penalties prescribed under the Fisheries Act are presented in Table 8.8. The penalties cover the addition of a deleterious substance, the harmful alteration of a fish habitat and throwing material overboard. The first carries a maximum fine of $100,000 a day, plus the cost of mitigative action and income lost by commercial fishermen.

8.5.6 Municipal Act

Table 8.9 presents the maximum penalties under the Model Sewer Use By-law. The penalties range from a maximum of $5000 a day for a first offence to $50,000 a day for a second offence.

The Municipal Act allows a municipality or a local board to obtain an order prohibiting the continuation or repetition of a contaminant discharge to a sewer by a person convicted of an offence. If the offender knowingly acts in contravention of the order of prohibition, an application can further be brought for an order citing the offender in contempt of court and committing the offender to jail (MOE, 1988).

A recent court case involved a metal plating company and the Municipality of Metropolitan Toronto. After 40 convictions for violating Metropolitan Toronto sewer use by-laws, the court granted a prohibition order under Section 326 of the Municipal Act against the plating operation. Following the making of the order there were four further convictions. Metropolitan Toronto commenced contempt proceedings against the company and its president. Both were found in contempt. The company was fined $100,000 and its president was sentenced to six months in jail and levied a $25,000 fine. The fine was levied to cover in part the legal fees of Metropolitan Toronto (Vialanic, 1989).

8.6 DEFENSES AND MITIGATIVE FACTORS

8.6.1 Criminal Offences

For offences under the Criminal Code or other statutes with significant penal sanctions, the burden of proof to be overcome by the prosecution is: proof beyond a reasonable doubt; strict proof as to the identification of accused; and proof of causal connection to the offence (Petrie, 1989).

The prosecution must show that the source of the pollution was a specific company or individual, or at least demonstrate that there is no reasonable likelihood of another source of the pollution. This can be demonstrated by the use of photographs showing the plume of smoke dispersing from the stack on the roof of the plant, by testimony of witnesses who saw effluent pouring from the drain pipe into a stream, by scientific methods of "fingerprinting" the chemical and matching that fingerprint to a product known to be used by the accused, or by eliminating other likely sources (Petrie, 1989).

Once the accused has been positively identified, a causal connection to the environmental damage must be made. Neighbours may testify that they could smell, taste, or feel the pollutant settling on their properties. Experts may testify as to the probable health effects of the pollution. Alternatively, it may be sufficient to prove that the regulatory standards or performance standards in a Certificate of Approval (C of A) were exceeded. Types of technical defenses, although rare, may include (Petrie, 1989):

- improper service of court documents
- lapse of the limitation period (usually two years)
- unreasonable delay in reaching trial
- failure of investigating officer to inform you of your rights to retain and instruct counsel upon detention or arrest

8.6.2 Quasi-Criminal Offences

Absolute liability offences must be specified as such in the statute. Absolute liability means that, once the Crown proves that the accused has committed the offence, the accused cannot raise a defense such as mistake of fact, due diligence, or Act of God. The defendant may be free of fault and yet liable under an absolute liability offence (Petrie, 1989). An example is failure to obtain a C of A.

The CEPA and EPA offences are **strict liability** offences. An example is in Section 125(1) of the CEPA which states that "no person shall be guilty of an offence under this act, if the person established that he exercised all **due diligence** to prevent its commission."

To establish a defense based on due diligence, the onus of proof is on the defendant to establish that **reasonable care** was taken. The defendant must show that the care taken was consistent with general standards of care common to the business activity in question. If special circumstances of the case indicated a different level of care than that of the standard practice was required, that indeed it was achieved.

The standard of care will depend on all the circumstances of the case, including the magnitude of the damage that could occur in the event of a mistake and the likelihood of there being a mistake. If the defendant proves a degree of precaution sufficient to prevent the foreseeable, he may be considered duly diligent (Petrie, 1989).

A due diligence offence cannot stand on the acquiescence or inaction of government officials. Acquiescence of government is only relevant where it directly or indirectly caused the accused to reasonably believe that appropriate care had been taken.

In cases where reasonable care does not afford a full defense of due diligence, the efforts may still be used as a mitigating factor in determining sentence. Best efforts to remedy the situation after a pollution event is another mitigating factor (Petrie, 1989).

Part IX of the Environmental Protection Act (commonly known as the "Spills Bill") lists several possible defenses:

- due diligence
- an act of war, terrorism, insurrection, or hostile act of a foreign government
- a natural phenomenon of an exceptional, inevitable and irresistible character
- an act or omission of a person for whom the owner or contractor of the pollutant is not responsible under the law

8.7 THE ROLE OF COMMON LAW

Sections 8.4 (Responses to Violations) and 8.5 (Penalties and Liabilities) cover environmental statutory law. In recent years, especially in the United States, there has been a significant increase in private lawsuits for pollution-related activities such as clean-up activity, contaminated property transfers, and elevated exposures to nearby residents from various types of activities. However, the statutory context in the United States (e.g. Comprehensive Environmental Response Compensation and Liability Act—CERCLA) is substantially different from that in Canada. In essence, fault does not have to be proven in the United States and all related parties must bear a share of the responsibility and financial burden.

Common law has its origins in the morals, traditions, and business practices of England. The law has evolved over the centuries through the decisions of judges interpreting these norms and legislation which codified society's standards. Torts are part of common law. They are civil wrongs other than breach of contract. Courts may remedy a wrong by awarding damages or injunctive relief (prohibitive or mandatory orders) to compensate the injured property and prevent further wrongs. Tort causes of action may include negligence, nuisance, trespassing, and riparian rights (Petrie, 1989).

Negligence occurs when a person's conduct falls below the standard regarded as reasonable among his peers. To prove negligence, one must show that the standard of reasonable care was breached and that the defendant should have foreseen the damage that resulted.

Nuisance is the unreasonable interference with the comfort or enjoyment of property, or causing damage to another's property. Noise, odours, vibrations, and actual physical intrusions of deleterious substances can create a cause of action in nuisance.

The law recognizes both private and public nuisances. Private nuisance involves the interference with an interest in land, such as the occupier's interest in the use and enjoyment of the land. Public nuisance is the interference with the public in its exercise of public rights. A nuisance against the public is normally pursued by the Attorney General. An individual does not have to be negligent to be found liable in nuisance.

Nuisances can be continued or adopted by the subsequent owner of property who, with the knowledge or presumed knowledge of the nuisance, allows it to continue after a reasonable period of time available to stop the nuisance.

A long-standing example of the role of common law in environmental matters is the 1868 decision of the British House of Lords in the case of *Rylands V. Fletcher.* The decision supported the proposition that a party who brings onto his land a non-natural use is answerable for the damages which the thing causes if it escapes or is discharged from that party's land. A water reservoir constructed on land which contained an abandoned mine shaft ruptured through the shaft flooding the neighbouring coal mine. The degree of care exercised by the defendant was not an issue. Liability was a direct consequence of proof of the physical damage resulting from the non-natural use of the land. Liability was imposed even if there is no negligence.

Trespass is a direct, unauthorized interference with private property. Liability for trespass can occur where there is no actual damage suffered by the person in actual possession of the property. The discharge of pollution onto another's property is a form of trespass.

The owner of land which borders on a watercourse has a **riparian right** to the continued flow of the water in its natural quantity and quality subject to the ordinary, reasonable use of owners upstream along the watercourse. The right to sue for damages and injunctive relief is created not only with diminished quantity or quality of water; one can also sue if surface water flow is altered so that another's property is flooded.

8.8 SUMMARY

The enforcement activities of the MOE have changed in recent years from that of cooperation between MOE regional personnel and industry to prosecution. Under various environmental acts, Provincial Officers have a wide variety of powers which allow them to inspect sites or premises as part of investigations. Provincial Officers must have reasonable cause, however, before exercising their statutory powers.

Some environmental legislation impose obligations on individuals to co-operate with an investigation. As part of the information-gathering the inspector may take photographs, conduct tests, or inspect equipment as long as the requests are reasonable. It is important that employees be made aware of their individual rights prior to being interviewed. If the sole purpose of the question is to obtain evidence of an offence for the purpose of prosecution, a person may refuse to answer. An inspector cannot force a person into self-incrimination.

Enforcement officials may respond to violations by issuing an order (e.g. control order, clean-up order) or lay charges. The laying of charges may result in anything from a small fine for a ticketable offense to a substantial fine ($2,000,000) and/or imprisonment if environmental impairment occurs.

REFERENCES

Cotton, R., 1989. "101 New Liabilities Under MISA: Your Rights and Responsibilities". Presented at Effluent Management for the 1990s, 5 and 6 June, Toronto.

Environment Canada, 1988. "Canadian Environmental Protection Act (CEPA): Enforcement and Compliance Policy". May.

Glenn, W., Shier, D., Sisson, K. and Whilms, J., 1988. "Toxic Real Estate Manual". Corpus Information Sources, June.

Jetten, B., and Smith, B., 1989. "When the Environmental Police Call ... It Could Become a Corporate Nightmare". Environmental Science and Engineering, November.

McKenney, M., 1989. "Environmental Enforcement in Ontario". Presented at the Environmental Auditing Workshop, 10 and 11 October, University of Toronto.

Ontario Government, 1989. "Penalties Adjustment Act", S.O. 90, 6.72. Statutes of Ontario.

Ontario Ministry of the Environment (MOE), 1987. "Short Form Wordings and Set Fines; Pursuant to Part 1, Provincial Offences Act, Schedule 55". August.

Ontario Ministry of the Environment (MOE), 1988. "Model Sewer Use By-Law". ISBN 0-7729-4419-9, August.

Ontario Government, 1990. "Environmental Protection Statute Law Amendment Act".

Petrie, P., 1989. "What Management and Staff Should Know About Environmental Laws to Minimize Personal and Corporate Liability". Presented at the Environmental Auditing Workshop, 10 and 11 October, University of Toronto.

Rovet, E., 1988. "Canadian Business Guide to Environmental Law". International Self-Counsel Press Limited.

Shier, D.S., 1989. "Negotiating Environmental Provisions in Real Estate Transactions to Avoid Costly and Unnecessary Disputes". Presented at the Environmental Auditing Workshop, 10 and 11 October, University of Toronto.

Vialanic, M. (Ed.), 1989. "Municipality of Metropolitan Toronto v. Siapas". Canadian Environmental Law Reports, Carswell Legal Publications, Vol. 1, Part 3, March.

Table 8.1
POWERS OF PROVINCIAL OFFICERS UNDER EPA

A Provincial Officer can:

- enter any place where it is believed that a contaminant has been discharged or may be discharged into the natural environment;

- enter any place where it is believed that relevant documents are likely to be found;

- take samples and record or copy any information by any method;

- make inquiries of any person, orally or in writing;

- detain or remove anything, including a vehicle or vessel, that is discharging or is likely to discharge a contaminant into the natural environment which causes or is likely to cause an adverse effect; and

- seize anything that is produced, or that is in plain view, during an inspection if the officer reasonably believes that there has been a contravention of the Act or the regulations and the thing being seized will afford evidence of the contravention.

Reference: Jetten and Smith, 1989

Table 8.2
EXAMPLES OF MUNICIPAL ENFORCEMENT STRATEGY USING THE MODEL SEWER USE BY-LAW

Sample Violations	Responses
Informal Actions	
Minor exceedance of discharge limit—one-time violation	Informal meeting
Minor exceedance of discharge limit on an infrequent basis	Warning letter
Failure to notify about a one-time minor spill into sewage works	Show cause meeting
Major exceedance of discharge limit—one-time violation	Show cause meeting
Formal Actions	
Exceeding of discharge limits on a regular basis	Civil action
Failure to notify municipality of a major spill into the sewage works	Civil action
Exceeding discharge limit with known damage to sewage treatment plant or failure to comply with compliance program	Order of prohibition
Exceeding discharge limits with known damage to sewage treatment plant on a regular basis	Order of prohibition
Failure to comply with order of prohibition to stop discharging sewage exceeding by-law limits and causing sewage treatment plant damage	Contempt of court

Reference: MOE, 1988

Table 8.3
PENALTIES UNDER THE ONTARIO EPA

Offence	Occurrence	Maximum Daily Penalty	
		Individual	Corporation

Section 146
Contravention of any part of
the Act or regulations
   OR
Failure to comply with an order
or a C of A under Sections 8 or 14

	First*	$10,000	$50,000
	Second*	$25,000	$100,000

Subsection 146a
Discharge of contaminant to the
environment (Section 13(1))
   OR
Disobedience of a stop order (Section 119)

	First**	$10,000	$2000-$200,000
	Second**	$25,000	$4000-$400,000

Section 147
Contravention of the Act or
regulations with respect to
hauled liquid industrial waste
or hazardous waste

a) which may result in environmental impairment:

	First***	$2000-$10,000	$2000-$100.000
	Second***	$4000-$25,000	$4000-$200,000

b) which results in environmental impairment:

	First***	$2000-$50,000	$2000-$1,000,000
	Second***	$4000-$100,000	$4000-$2,000,000
		Plus imprisonment for one year	

Notes:

* Additional penalties can include:
- amount equal to the monetary benefit accrued due to the violation
- court can order action to prevent or eliminate effects on the environment
- any other conditions the court thinks appropriate
- changes to conditions can be made as court sees fit
- must comply even if in jail
- suspension of one or more existing or pending licences if fines are not paid

** Additional penalties can include those above plus:
- imprisonment for one year
- prevent repetition of offence

*** same as above, but excludes prevention of the repetition of the offence.

References: Ontario, 1989 and Ontario, 1990

Table 8.4
EXAMPLES OF TICKETABLE OFFENCES UNDER EPA

Regulation	Activity	Penalty

I) Regulation 309*

Operate a Landfilling Site:

	• allow use by unauthorized persons	$103.75
	• allow access while attendant not on duty	$103.75

Operate Waste Management System:

	• vehicle valves not locked with driver absent	$78.75
	• fail to clearly mark vehicle	$103.75
	• fail to keep certificate of approval in vehicle	$103.75

Asbestos Handling:

	• permit asbestos waste to leave location in inadequate containers	$153.75
	• asbestos waste not covered with suitable tarpaulin or net in unenclosed vehicle	$153.75

Transporting Waste:

	• carrier - fail to promptly transport subject waste to proper receiving facility	$103.75
	• carrier - fail to complete Section B of manifest	$78.75

Regulation	Activity	Penalty
	• carrier - fail to give manifest to generator at time of transfer	$78.75
	• generator - fail to complete Section A of manifest	$78.75
	• generator - fail to retain copy 2 of manifest for two years	$78.75
II) **Regulation 308 ****		
	• cause or permit visible emission - obstruct passage of light more than 20 percent	$153.75
	• burn or permit burning in combustion unit of type of fuel or waste for which unit not designed	$153.75
	• emit contaminants beyond property limits from prescribed activities	$153.75
III) **Reg. 11/82 PCB *****		
	• operation - fail to keep records of all PCB waste held	$103.75
	• fail to report required information to Director in writing within 3 days	$103.75

References:

*	MOE, 1987
**	Amendment to Regulation 817/80: Schedule 37
***	Amendment to Regulation 817/80: Schedule 83

Table 8.5
PENALTIES UNDER THE OWRA

Offence	Occurrence	Maximum Daily Penalty	
		Individual	Corporation
Section 67: Contravention of any part of the Act or regulations			
	First	$10,000	$50,000
	Second	$25,000	$100,000
Section 68: Discharge of contaminant into a public water supply (Sec. 16(1) or 19(2)(b))			
	First	$10,000	$4000-$100,000
	Second	$25,000	$8000-$200,000
	Plus imprisonment for not more one year		

Reference: Ontario, 1989

Table 8.6
PENALTIES UNDER THE CEPA

Type of Offence	Conviction	Maximum Penalty
Sections 111 and 112 Failure to notify or provide information to an inspector OR Providing misleading information OR Hindering an investigation (Sections 16, 26, 27, 50, 102 and 103)		Maximum fine of $200,000 Up to six months in prison
Section 113 Failure to properly store, handle, register and/or dispose of a hazardous chemical	Summary Conviction	Maximum fine of $300,000 and/or Up to six months in prison
Failure to properly import a hazardous chemical (Sections 17, 18(1)(c), 29(1)(a), 29(1)(b), 26(1)(b), 27, 29(2), 34(1), 35, 36, 40, 42, 43, 46, 54, 56, 57, 64, 65, 68(4), 69 and 70)	Indictment	Maximum fine of $1 million and/or Up to 3 years in prison
Section 114 Providing Minister with false information (Sections 16, 17, 18(1)(a), 18(1)(b), 26, 27, and 29(1)(b))	Summary Conviction	Maximum fine of $300,000 and/or Up to six months in prison

Type of Offence	Conviction	Maximum Penalty
	Indictment	Maximum fine of $1 million and/or Up to 5 years in prison
Section 115 Every person in contravention of the Act who intentionally or recklessly causes loss of environment or risk of death or harm to others		
	Indictment	Liable to a fine and/or Up to 5 years in prison
	If death or bodily harm	Subject to prosecution and punishment under the Criminal Code (Section 203 and 204)
Section 133 The contravention or failure to comply with an order or direction once convicted of an offence (Sections 127, 128, 130 and 132)		
	Summary Conviction	Maximum fine of $200,000 and/or Up to six months in prison
	Indictment	Maximum fine of $1 million and/or Up to 3 years in prison
Section 116 Contravention of any regulation not already covered		
		Maximum fine of $200,000 and/or Up to six months in prison

Table 8.7
PENALTIES UNDER THE TDGA

Type of Offence	Conviction	Maximum Penalty
Subsection 6(1) Failure to provide proper safety requirements (Sections 4 and 5) OR Failure to obey a directive to cease or alter the activity (Section 28)		
	Summary Conviction	First $50,000 Second $100,000
	Indictment	Imprisonment for a term not exceeding two years
Subsection 6(2) Failure to comply with any provision of the Act or regulations		
	Summary Conviction	$10,000
	Indictment	Imprisonment for a term not exceeding one year

Table 8.8
PENALTIES UNDER THE FISHERIES ACT

Type of Offence	Conviction	Maximum Daily Penalty
Subsection 33(5)(b) The deposit of a deleterious substance (Section 33(2))		
	First	$50,000
	Second	$100,000
	Plus cost for mitigative measures, and liable for loss of income by any licensed commercial fisherman	
Subsection 31(1) Harmful alteration, etc. of fish habitat		
	First	$5,000
	Second	$10,000
Subsection 33(3) Throwing overboard certain substances		
	First	$5,000
	Second	$10,000

Table 8.9
PENALTIES UNDER THE MODEL SEWER USE BY-LAW (SECTION 321 OF THE MUNICIPAL ACT)

	Individual	Corporation
First Offence	$5000/day	$25,000/day
Second Offence	$10,000/day	$50,000/day

Reference: MOE, 1988

Figure 8.1
MOE ORGANIZATIONAL CHART

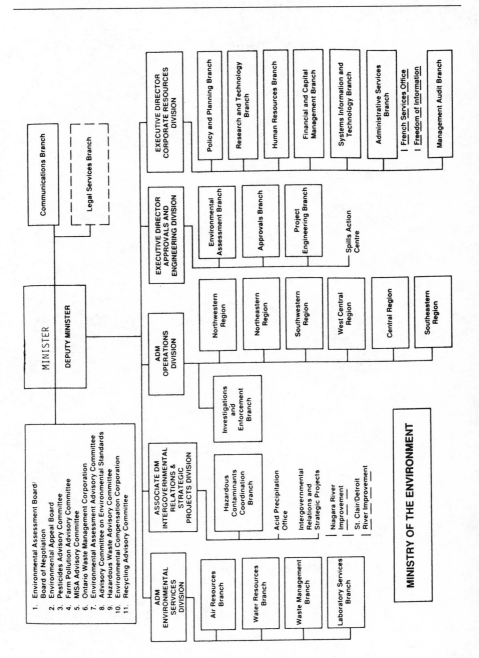

MINISTER

DEPUTY MINISTER

Communications Branch

Legal Services Branch

1. Environmental Assessment Board/ Board of Negotiation
2. Environmental Appeal Board
3. Pesticides Advisory Committee
4. Farm Pollution Advisory Committee
5. MISA Advisory Committee
6. Ontario Waste Management Corporation
7. Environmental Assessment Advisory Committee
8. Advisory Committee on Environmental Standards
9. Hazardous Waste Advisory Committee
10. Environmental Compensation Corporation
11. Recycling Advisory Committee

EXECUTIVE DIRECTOR CORPORATE RESOURCES DIVISION
- Policy and Planning Branch
- Research and Technology Branch
- Human Resources Branch
- Financial and Capital Management Branch
- Systems Information and Technology Branch
- Administrative Services Branch
- French Services Office
- Freedom of Information
- Management Audit Branch

EXECUTIVE DIRECTOR APPROVALS AND ENGINEERING DIVISION
- Environmental Assessment Branch
- Approvals Branch
- Project Engineering Branch
- Spills Action Centre

ADM OPERATIONS DIVISION
- Northwestern Region
- Northeastern Region
- Southwestern Region
- West Central Region
- Central Region
- Southeastern Region
- Investigations and Enforcement Branch

ASSOCIATE DM INTERGOVERNMENTAL RELATIONS & STRATEGIC PROJECTS DIVISION
- Hazardous Contaminants Coordination Branch
- Acid Precipitation Office
- Intergovernmental Relations and Strategic Projects
- Niagara River Improvement
- St. Clair/Detroit River Improvement

ADM ENVIRONMENTAL SERVICES DIVISION
- Air Resources Branch
- Water Resources Branch
- Waste Management Branch
- Laboratory Services Branch

MINISTRY OF THE ENVIRONMENT

9.0

Environmental Fate

9.1 WHY BE CONCERNED ABOUT ENVIRONMENTAL FATE?

Just about anyone who deals with environmental issues can benefit from having a basic understanding of the factors that influence the fate of chemicals in the environment. An understanding of environmental fate can be applied to tasks as diverse as responding to recently introduced or proposed legislation, assessing treatment options, developing monitoring programs, and assessing the potential risks from a chemical during its production, use, and disposal.

Recently introduced and proposed legislation, including the Municipal, Industrial Strategy for Abatement (MISA), Clean Air Program (CAP), and Canadian Environmental Protection Act (CEPA), all consider the impacts of chemical releases on the environment. MISA requires water-quality assessments for sensitive receiving water bodies. CAP will utilize the "airshed" concept. CEPA requires a "cradle-to-grave" approach for managing chemicals.

A basic understanding of the environmental fate of a chemical can be used to assess the effectiveness of treatment options. For example, consider two water treatment options, an activated carbon column and air stripping, and two compounds of concern, benzo(a)pyrene and trichloroethylene (TCE). Because benzo(a)pyrene has a relatively high octanol-water partition coefficient and strongly adsorbs to carbon, the carbon column should be effective. Conversely, air stripping would not be expected to be as cost-effective because of the compound's low vapour pressure. For TCE, which has a high vapour pressure and low affinity for carbon, air stripping is the preferred option.

To develop cost-effective monitoring systems, companies and environmental agencies must be able to predict the compartment of the environment where a chemical most likely will be found. The compartments that usually are considered include air, water, soil, sediment, and biota. For example, a decision must be made whether to sample sediment or water for PCBs near an old dump site. Because of its high affinity for sediment the majority of the PCB likely will be found in the sediment. Water column samples would be expected to show non-detectable or very low concentrations.

Understanding the environmental behaviour and fate of a chemical is an essential component of a risk assessment. The behaviour of a chemical will strongly influence which exposure routes or pathways are likely to occur. For example, if a sudden release occurs of a highly volatile compound, it may be necessary to evacuate the area downwind. If the chemical is soluble and could reach a nearby river or water supply, then appropriate interceptors (such as dykes or trenches) may be needed.

The Pesticides Act requires that exhaustive tests be conducted, both in the laboratory and field, prior to the introduction of a new pesticide to the marketplace. These tests are used to assess the environmental fate of a pesticide and determine if it can adversely affect the environment. CEPA will require a similar approach for all new chemicals being produced or imported into Canada. One of the main objectives of CEPA is to avoid the introduction of chemicals that may cause an adverse effect on the environment in the short and long term.

9.2 KEY CHEMICAL PROPERTIES

Every substance possesses a unique set of physico-chemical properties. While many such properties exist, the following five are important determinants of overall environmental behaviour and fate.

Vapour pressure is a measure of the volatility of a chemical in its pure state. Vapour pressure indicates the maximum concentration that a chemical may achieve in the air compartment.

Water-solubility is the maximum concentration of a chemical that dissolves in pure water. Highly soluble chemicals are easily and quickly distributed by the hydrologic cycle. These chemicals tend not to adsorb to soil or sediments and to bioconcentrate only slightly in organisms. Most tend to be biodegradable by microorganisms in soil, surface water, and sewage treatment plants.

Density can indicate how a chemical will move in the environment. For example, dense non-aqueous phase liquids (DNAPL) sink in aquatic environments or if released into the ground water regime. Similarly, a release of dense vapours will follow the contours of the land and may gather in low-lying areas.

Melting point and boiling point determine whether a chemical is a gas, liquid, or solid according to the temperature of the environment of concern.

Molecular weight is important when stoichiometric relationships can be used to estimate various processes such as dissolution, precipitation, and hydrolysis.

9.3 KEY ENVIRONMENTAL PARAMETERS

Several key environmental parameters are presented in Table 9.1. These can influence the behaviour of a chemical in a particular compartment. There are many more parameters that can be used when a finer level of detail is required.

The majority of the parameters associated with the **air compartment** describe the transport, diffusion, and/or convection of a chemical in that compartment. The atmospheric stability class indicates whether a gaseous emission may readily rise and disperse or be trapped by an inversion condition.

In the **water compartment,** the behaviour of a chemical will be influenced by the flow velocity, flow rate, and residence time (or turnover rate) of a water body. Fast-moving streams may promote uniform mixing within a short distance, whereas large lakes can stratify into several layers. The pH and cation/anion balance are useful in determining the precipitation and dissolution of ionic species.

The accumulation of a chemical in the **sediment compartment** is influenced by the rates of sediment deposition and resuspension. It is also influenced by the adsorptive capability and porosity of the sediment.

In the **soil compartment**, the movement of a chemical which has been applied to soil or deposited on the surface can be influenced strongly by hydrological factors (runoff and rainfall), soil type (porosity and adsorption capability), and chemical properties of the soil such as pH and organic carbon content.

The movement of chemicals in the **ground water compartment** is influenced by soil type and flow conditions (hydraulic conductivity and gradient). It is also influenced by the recharge rate to the aquifer (the amount of water flowing into the aquifer).

9.4 PARTITION COEFFICIENTS

Partition coefficients are parameters that describe the transfer of a substance between environmental compartments such as from water to air or soil to air. Table 9.1 presents a list of equilibrium partition coefficients.

For non-equilibrium conditions, the partition coefficients described in Table 9.1 may be used in combination with other parameters such as kinetic rate constants, although the relationships can become mathematically complex. Usually the assumption of equilibrium conditions is valid for a first approximation of the fate of a chemical, especially if several months or years have passed since the chemical was introduced to the environment.

Henry's Law Constant or the air-water partition coefficient relates the concentration of a chemical in the air phase to its concentration in the water phase:

$$H = C_a \div C_w \qquad (9.1)$$

where H = Henry's Law Constant
C_a = concentration in air (g/m³)
C_w = concentration in water (g/m³)

Values of Henry's Law Constant of range from greater than 10 for a highly volatile chemical to less than 10^{-6} for a low-volatility chemical.

The **Octanol/Water Partition Coefficient** is defined as:

$$K_{ow} = C_{oc} \div C_w \qquad (9.2)$$

where K_{ow} = octanol/water partition coefficient
C_{oc} = concentration in octanol (i.e. an alcohol with eight carbons)
C_w = concentration in water

Scientists have found that octanol is a good surrogate for the lipid materials present in the fat portion of fish. Hence, K_{ow} is used to estimate the amount of an organic chemical which can be bioaccumulated by biota. The coefficient is also used in correlations to predict adsorption partition coefficients for organic chemicals in soils and sediments.

K_{ow} values range from 10^{-3} to 10^7 and are usually expressed as logarithms. A chemical with a log K_{ow} greater than 3 is considered to have a high affinity for lipids in biological media and the organic carbon portion of soil and sediment, while a chemical with a log K_{ow} value less than 1 is considered to have a higher affinity for air or water.

The **Organic Adsorption Coefficient,** or K_{oc} value, is a measure of the relative sorption potential of organic chemicals:

$$K_{oc} = S_{org} \div C_w \qquad (9.3)$$

where K_{oc} = organic carbon partition coefficient
S_{org} = ratio of chemical adsorbed per unit weight of organic carbon
C_w = concentration in water compartment

The K_{oc} value indicates the tendency of an organic chemical to be adsorbed, and it can be largely dependent on soil properties. The K_{oc}

parameter may not be as straightforward for ionic organic compounds such as pentachlorophenol.

Several empirical relationships have been developed for estimating K_{oc} using other properties, including octanol/water partition coefficient, solubility, and bioconcentration factors. For example:

$$\log K_{oc} = a \log (S, K_{ow}, \text{ or BCF}) + b \qquad (9.4)$$

where   S   = solubility
$\quad\quad\quad\ K_{ow}$ = octanol/water partition coefficient
$\quad\quad\quad$ BCF = bioconcentration factor
$\quad\quad\quad$ a,b = constants

Two widely used correlations are:

$$\log K_{oc} = 1.00 \log K_{ow} - 0.21 \qquad (9.5)$$

$$\log K_{oc} = 0.544 \log K_{ow} + 1.377 \qquad (9.6)$$

The former is intended for aromatic hydrocarbons, polyaromatic hydrocarbons and some chlorinated aromatic hydrocarbons (Karickhoff *et al.*, 1979). The latter is intended for pesticides (Kenaga and Goring, 1978). Other correlations are available in the literature for other compounds.

Sorption distribution coefficients are used for both organic and inorganic chemicals:

$$C_s \quad = C_w K_d \qquad (9.7)$$

where C_s = soil concentration
$\quad\quad\quad\ C_w$ = aqueous phase concentration
$\quad\quad\quad\ K_d$ = sorption distribution coefficient

For organic chemicals, the K_d value can be determined from:

$$K_d \quad = K_{oc} F_{oc} \qquad (9.8)$$

where K_d = adsorption distribution coefficient for an organic compound
$\quad\quad\quad\ K_{oc}$ = organic sorption partition coefficient
$\quad\quad\quad\ F_{oc}$ = fraction of organic carbon in the soil

For inorganic parameters, no simple correlation exists for sorption, and hence literature K_d values must be sought. The K_d value selected should reflect the inorganic chemical as well as the type of soil and the pH of the soil.

In addition to sorption, solubility-controlled dissolution should be considered when assessing inorganic substances. To estimate the dissolution rate, additional information may be required, such as soil-water pH, ionic balance, concentrations of other ionic species in ground water, and solid phases present.

The **bioconcentration factor,** or BCF, is used to estimate the concentration of the chemical in biotic phases (such as fish). For some chemicals, especially organic compounds, this concentration may be orders of magnitude higher than the water phase. Several correlations have been developed for BCF. The following simple correlation is one of the more widely used ones or organic chemicals (Mackay, 1982a):

$$BCF = L_F K_{OW} \qquad (9.9)$$

where   BCF = Bioconcentration factor
   L_F = lipid content of fish (typically about 0.05)

Some compounds partition into fish very slowly. Hydrophobic chemicals have low solubilities and therefore a large volume of water must passed through the fish to accomplish the necessary transfer. For relatively large molecules, there may be additional resistance to bioconcentration due to the molecule–cell membrane interaction (Mackay and Hughes, 1984).

Equation 9.9 does not take into account biomagnification effects that may be caused by fish feeding on other aquatic organisms, or the ability of fish to metabolically convert a substance. Rates of metabolism for fish are poorly documented. If fish are the organism of interest, consideration also must be given to the migratory nature of the fish.

Plant uptake factors are used to estimate the transfer of substances from soil, water, and air to plants. There are three ways for plants to take up a chemical in the environment: foliar deposition, root uptake, and uptake of vapours via leaves. The first two mechanisms are considered to dominate most scenarios and various equations have been formulated to estimate uptake. For certain compounds (those which are not soluble, persistent, and sparingly volatile), recent studies suggest that the uptake of vapours may be the major long-term uptake route; however, appropriate equations have not yet been published.

One equation developed to estimate the uptake of compounds due to foliar deposition is (Hetrick and McDowell-Boyer, 1984):

$$K_{pf} = R/(Y\,W)\,[1 - e^{(-W\,t)}\,/(W\,t)\,D_p] \qquad (9.10)$$

where K_{pf} = uptake factor due to foliar deposition (on a dry weight basis)
   R   = initial fraction of material intercepted

Y = vegetative productivity or yield
W = weathering constant
t = crop growth period
D_p = deposition rate of particulate matter

A relatively simple equation for estimating root uptake of organic compounds in soil is (DSC, 1989):

$$\log K_{pr} = 0.97 - 0.5 \ (\log K_{ow}) \qquad (9.11)$$

where K_{pr} = root uptake factor for an organic (on a dry weight basis)

Other equations as well as variations of Equations 9.10 and 9.11 have been developed; however, in general, plant uptake is not well understood.

9.5 REACTION RATES AND HALF-LIVES

9.5.1 Reaction Rates

An organic compound in the environment can be subjected to many types of reactions, most of which involve the degradation of the compound and therefore influence its concentration in the environment. The overall effect of the reaction rates often is referred to as a compound's persistence or environmental stability. Various reaction rates are identified in Table 9.1.

Hydrolysis is a chemical transformation process in which an organic molecule reacts with water, forming a new carbon-oxygen bond and cleaving a carbon bond in the original molecule. Typically, the net reaction is the direct displacement of a component of the organic molecule by a hydroxyl ion (Harris, 1982). For example, acetic acid and ethanol are formed by the hydrolysis of ethyl acetate.

Photolysis is the degradation of a chemical due to exposure to light. Degradation typically results via the rupture of covalent bonds. The process is most relevant to chemicals in the atmosphere but also occurs in surface water and on the surface of soils.

Biodegradation involves the breakdown of organic or inorganic materials by organisms, most often microorganisms. Bacterial metabolism alone accounts for 65% of the total metabolism of a soil community because of high bacterial biomass and metabolic rates (Scow, 1982). Biodegradation may occur in the presence of oxygen (aerobic conditions) or absence of oxygen (anaerobic conditions).

Chemical oxidation can involve the addition of oxygen, removal of hydrogen, or the removal of electrons. A chemical that is responsible for oxidizing another is called an oxidizing agent or an oxidant. Examples of oxidizing agents include ozone (O_3) and potassium permanganate ($KMnO_4$).

9.5.2 Overall Rate Constants

In addition to specific reaction rate constants, total compartment rate constants are sometimes used to express the overall rate of loss of a chemical from a compartment. For example, published accounts indicate that the total soil loss rate constant for acetone is about of 1×10^{-7} per second. This value was derived from laboratory studies in which the loss of acetone through soil volatilization, soil leaching, and runoff were measured. A similar value for arsenic would be 2×10^{-10} per second (Environ, 1988).

9.5.3 Half-Lives

An alternative to the use of reaction rates or soil loss rate constants is the half-life which can be calculated, once reaction rate constants (k values) are known, according to the equation:

$$T_{1/2} = \ln 2/k = 0.693/k \qquad (9.12)$$

For each environmental compartment, a persistence half-life can be estimated and used to assess the chemical's fate. The use of half-lives when expressing persistence is sometimes easier to interpret. For example, a half-life of 10 days for toluene in soils following a spill may be easier to understand than a rate constant of 0.069 days^{-1}.

9.6 USING ENVIRONMENTAL FATE TO EVALUATE RELEASES

9.6.1 Overview

The release of a chemical into the environment, even in a small quantity, may be disruptive or lead to adverse effects. A chemical may be transported by several pathways, reaching unsuspecting or non-target organisms (including humans) that may experience subtle and delayed effects (Mackay, 1982b). Such long-range transportation is demonstrated by the presence of trace organic compounds at measurable concentrations in Canadian snow (Gregor and Gummer, 1989).

Wherever chemicals have been released to the environment or a release is being considered, an understanding of environmental fate can be used to ensure that the relevant transport and transformation processes are assessed. The underlying objective of assessing environmental fate is to assist in estimating the exposures that humans and biota may experience and to determine how environmental concentrations of the chemical likely will change with time. This is particularly relevant in light of the environmental policy being advocated by growing numbers of regulatory agencies towards the virtual elimination of persistent toxic chemicals.

9.6.2 Stack and Fugitive Emissions to the Atmosphere

The emission rate and behaviour of a chemical from a stack may be strongly influenced by the type of pollution control equipment used and its operating parameters, production rates, and stack exit gas velocity. In recent years, there has been a shift towards longer residence times (more than two seconds) and higher temperatures (greater than 1000 °C) during the combustion of organic chemicals to ensure complete destruction.

In addition to stack emissions, fugitive emissions can be major sources of releases to the air. Fugitive emissions may result from leaks, storage tanks, vents, open windows near process areas, and waste disposal and treatment site emissions.

Once a chemical is emitted to the atmosphere, it can be transported by turbulent mixing and convection to the surrounding area or even to distant locations. The distance a chemical can travel is a function of several parameters, including the release height, atmospheric stability, wind speed, and prevailing long-range transport phenomena. For example, the Atlantic Ocean appears to be the major sink for PCBs, accounting for 80 to 90% of the PCB burden in the environment (Doskey and Andren, 1981).

The processes that may act upon a chemical in the air compartment are illustrated in Figure 9.1. From the air compartment a chemical may be deposited on water, land, or plants.

Transformation in the form of photochemical degradation or reaction with other compounds is also important for compounds in the atmosphere. An example of the latter is the formation of acidic precipitation from the interaction of water vapour with emissions of sulfur and nitrogen compounds.

9.6.3 Spills onto Water

Whenever a chemical is stored, used, or transported near an aquatic environment, there exists the risk that a spill may occur and the chemical may reach a river, stream, lake, etc. Releases also can result from inadequate effluent treatment at a manufacturing plant, spillage during manufacturing and distribution, losses during transportation, or leakage from disposal sites.

The Exxon *Valdez* incident released approximately 42 million litres of oil into the marine environment. When oil is spilled at sea, various processes act on it, most of which are influenced by the oil's properties. Early behaviour is dominated by the spreading tendency of the oil. The spreading process is very complex, involving unsteady-state transient behaviour of an oil of changing composition as material evaporates on a mobile water surface. The usual behaviour is for the oil to form slicks less than a millimetre thick surrounded by sheens only a few micrometres thick (Mackay *et al.*, 1983).

The oil will also drift and potentially form a heavy water-in-oil emulsion (mousse) which is almost impossible to pump. Eventually, wind and waves may shear the mousse into pieces referred to as "pancakes", which in turn break into tar balls and may wash ashore.

Evaporation is often an important source of loss for chemicals spilled in aquatic environments. The evaporation rate is a function of the chemical's vapour pressure, temperature, and characteristics of the air above the chemical (primarily wind speed). In the case of an oil spill, the most soluble components are also the most volatile and hence will evaporate readily (Mackay *et al.*, 1983).

Other processes that will act upon the chemical are illustrated in Figure 9.2. The chemical may dissolve into the water column resulting in the potential uptake by biota, sorption onto suspended solids or interaction with sediment. The material may undergo oxidation, hydrolysis, and biodegradation in the water column and in the sediment. Oil drops will form by either breaking waves or a local surface convergence which may occur on steep waves. The smaller drops may be conveyed by eddy diffusion currents to depths in the water and become essentially permanently incorporated in the water column (Mackay *et al.*, 1983).

Spilled chemicals that have densities greater than water will sink to the bottom and may interact with sediment. These "sinkers" may become a source of contamination over an extended period of time as components gradually dissolve from the material and enter the water column.

9.6.4 Leaks from Underground Storage Tanks

If a small volume of non-aqueous phase liquid (NAPL) is lost from an underground storage tank into a relatively homogeneous, permeable soil, the liquid will move downward towards the water table. It will pass through the more permeable corridors in the soil. The liquid will continue to move towards the water table as long as the volume is sufficient to offset the absorption of the chemical into the soil void space. Unless the leak is large or ongoing, the leading edge of the liquid plume eventually will become static (Farmer, 1983).

Five potentially damaging conditions may develop (Farmer, 1983):
- light NAPL may migrate along the top of the water table
- residual, but immobile, pockets of chemical, are left as NAPL moves downward
- evaporation of the liquid phase results in vapour dispersing through the unsaturated zone to surface
- NAPL can dissolve into the aquifer and subsequently be transported

by the ground water
- as "lighter" constituents leave the NAPL, "sinkers" may form and move to the bottom of the aquifer; these are difficult to detect and will act as a contaminant source

When contaminants come into contact with a water well or a basement or reach a surface water course, an environmental problem may be created. If the NAPL readily volatilizes, the volatile components will break away and move into the air-filled pores potentially resulting in exposure through inhalation for individuals at the site.

If the density of the NAPL is less than that of water (such as oil) the material will eventually spread out horizontally above the water table. If the material has a density greater than water (often referred to as a dense, non-aqueous phase liquid or DNAPL), it will pass through the aquifer and sink until it reaches a confining or relatively impermeable layer of soil or rock. The direction of the DNAPL movement at that point will be similar to the slope of the confining layer.

9.7 ENVIRONMENTAL FATE MODELS

In recent years, many models have been developed to assess the environmental fate of contaminants. These types of models can be used to assess potential environmental hazards (Cohen, 1986).

Many of the models focus on a specific environmental compartment or fate process. For example, Table 9.2 presents a sampling of models that address vapour transport from soils, chemical movement in both the unsaturated and saturated zones of soil, and chemical fate in surface water environments.

Three of the models that can be used to estimate the loss of chemicals from soil due to volatilization were developed to evaluate the releases of chemicals from landfills. The other two models were developed to assess pesticide movement in soil.

The majority of the unsaturated zone models address the influences of runoff, infiltration and volatilization on chemicals applied to soil. The MINTEQ model (Battelle, 1984) predicts the aqueous speciation, adsorption, and precipitation dissolution of inorganic substances.

The saturated zone models presented on Table 9.2 simulate the movement of a chemical in the saturated zone under the influence of convection, dispersion, adsorption, and reaction processes.

The surface water quality models address the tendency of a substance to distribute itself among the various compartments of aquatic environments. These can include the water column, suspended material, biota, sediment and overlying air.

There are also models that can be used to assess environmental fate in a broader or more general context. Those often are assemblies or combinations of models such as those identified in Table 9.2.

REFERENCES

Baker, L.W. and Mackay, K.P., 1985. "Screening Models for Estimating Toxic Air Pollution Near Hazardous Waste Landfill". J. Air Poll. Control Assn., Vol. 35, pp. 1190-1195.

Battelle Pacific Northwest Labs, 1984. "MINTEQ - A Computer Program for Calculating Aqueous Geochemical Equilibrium". Prepared for the U.S. Environmental Protection Agency, February, PB84-157148.

Burns, L.A., Cline, D.M., and Lassiter, R.R., 1982. "Exposure Analysis Modeling System (EXAMS): User Manual and System Documentation". EPA-600/3-82-023, U.S. EPA, Athens, GA.

Carsel, R.F., Smith, C.N., Mulkey, L.A., Dean, J.D., and Jowise, P.P., 1984. "User's Manual for the Pesticide Root Zone Model (PRZM) - Release 1". U.S. Environmental Protection Agency, Office of Research and Development, EPA-600/3-84-109.

Cohen, Y., 1986. "Organic Pollutant Transport". Environ. Sci. Technol., Vol. 20, No. 6, pp. 538-544.

Dean, J.D., Jowise, P.P., and Donigan, A.S., Jr., 1984. "Leaching Evaluation of Agricultural Chemicals (LEACH) Handbook". U.S. Environmental Protection Agency, Office of Research and Development, EPA-600/3-84-068.

Decommissioning Steering Committee (DSC), 1989. "The Development of Soil Clean-up Criteria in Canada. Volume 2 - Report on the 'Demonstration' Version of the AERIS Model (An Aid for Evaluating the Redevelopment of Industrial Sites)". Prepared for Environment Canada, Conservation and Protection.

Electric Power Research Institute (EPRI), 1981. "Unsaturated Groundwater Flow Model (UNSATD) Computer Code Model". Palo Alto, CA, August, CS-2434-CCM.

Environ Corporation, 1988. "Site Assessment Phase 4B: Risk Assessment-Volume 2, Appendices A Through D". Prepared for the Ontario Waste Management Corporation, January.

Farmer, V.E., 1983. "Behaviour of Petroleum Contaminants in an Underground Environment". Presented at the Seminar on Groundwater and Petroleum Hydrocarbons: Protection, Detection, Restoration, Toronto, 26 to 28 June.

Gregor, D.J., and Gummer, W.D., 1989. "Evidence of Atmospheric Transport and Deposition of Organochlorine Pesticides and Polychlorinated Biphenyls in Canadian Arctic Snow". Environ. Sci. and Technol., Vol. 23, No. 5, pp. 561-565.

Harris, J.C., 1982a. "Rate of Hydrolysis". In Handbook of Chemical Property Estimation Methods, Lyman, W.J., Reehl, W.F., and Rosenblatt, D.H., eds., McGraw-Hill Book Company.

Hetrick, D.M., and McDowell-Boyer, L.M., 1984. "User's Manual for TOX-SCREEN: A Multimedia Screening-Level Program for Assessing the Potential Fate of Chemicals Released to the Environment". Prepared by the Oak Ridge National Laboratory for the U.S. EPA Office of Toxic Substances, EPA Report 560/5-83-024.

Javandel, I.C., Doughty, C., and Tsang, C.F., 1984. "Groundwater Transport: Handbook of Mathematical Models". Water Resources Monograph Series 10, American Geophysical Union, Washington, D.C.

Jury, W.A., Grover, R., Spencer, W.F., and Farmer, W.J., 1980. "Modeling Vapor Losses of Soil-Incorporated Triallate". Soil Soc. Am. J., Vol. 44, pp. 445-450.

Karickhoff, S.W., Brown, D.S., and Scott, T.A., 1979. "Sorption of Hydrophobic Pollutants on Natural Sediments". Water Res., Vol. 13, pp. 241-248.

Kenaga, E.E., and Goring, C.A.I., 1978. "Relationship Between Water Solubility, Soil-Sorption, Octanol-Water Partitioning, and Bioconcentration of Chemicals in Biota". Pre-publication copy of paper dated 13 October 1978 given at the American Society for Testing Materials, Third Aquatic Toxicology Symposium, 17-18 October 1978, New Orleans, LA.

Kincaid, G.T., and Mitchell, P.J., 1986. "Review of Multiphase Flow and Pollutant Transport Models for the Hanford Site". Pacific Northwest Laboratory, PNL-6048.

Mackay, D., 1982a. "Correlation of Bioconcentration Factors". Environ. Sci. Technol., Vol. 16, pp. 274-278.

Mackay, D., 1982b. "Nature and Origin of Micropollutants". Wat. Sci. Tech., Vol. 14, pp. 5-14.

Mackay, D., and Hughes, A. I., 1984. "Three-Parameter Equation Describing the Uptake of Organic Compounds by Fish". Environ. Sci. and Technol., Vol. 18., No. 6, pp. 439-444.

Mackay, D., Stiver, W., and Tebeau, P.A., 1983. "Testing of Crude Oils and Petroleum Products for Environmental Purposes". Proceedings 1983 Oil Spill Conference, San Antonio, TX, Amer. Petrol. Inst., Washington, D.C., pp. 331-337.

Mackay D., Patterson, S., Cheung, B., and Neely, W.B., 1985. "Evaluating the Environmental Behaviour of Chemicals with a Level III Fugacity Model". Chemosphere, Vol. 14, No. 3/4, pp. 335-374.

Mayer, R., Letey, J., and Farmer, W.J., 1974. "Models for Predicting Volatilization of Soil-Incorporated Pesticides". Soil Sci. Soc. Am. Proc., Vol. 38, pp. 563-568.

Scow, K.M., 1982. "Rate of Biodegradation". *In* Handbook of Chemical Property Estimation Methods, Lyman, W.J., Reehl, W.F., and Rosenblatt, D.H., eds., McGraw-Hill Book Company.

Shen, T., 1981. "Estimating Hazardous Air Emissions from Disposal Sites". Pollution Engineering, August.

Short, T.E., 1985. "Mathematical Modeling of Land Treatment Processes". Invited presentation to the National Specialty Conference on Land Treatment, University of Texas, Austin, TX, 16 to 18 April.

Thibodeaux, L.J., 1981. "Estimating the Air Emissions of Chemicals from Hazardous Waste Landfills". J. Haz. Mat., Vol. 4, pp. 235-244.

Table 9.1
KEY ENVIRONMENTAL PARAMETERS

CHEMICAL PARAMETERS
- vapour pressure
- density
- molecular weight
- solubility
- melting point and boiling point

PHYSICAL PARAMETERS

Air
- wind velocity and direction
- physical topography
- temperature and rainfall
- atmospheric stability class

Water
- pH and temperature
- concentration of suspended sediment
- water velocity and flow
- residence time of water
- cation/anion balance

Sediment
- oxygen concentration
- resuspension rate
- porosity
- organic carbon content
- deposition rate

Soil
- pH and temperature
- runoff
- soil type (density and porosity)
- surface vegetation
- rainfall
- organic carbon content
- soil water content
- solid phases present (e.g. carbonate)

Ground Water
- organic carbon content
- hydraulic conductivity/gradient
- dispersion
- aquifer soil type (density and porosity)
- pH and cation/anion balance
- infiltration rate

PARTITION COEFFICIENTS
- Henry's Law constant (H)
- bioconcentration factor (BCF)
- adsorption coefficient (K_d)
- octanol/water partition coefficient (K_{ow})
- organic partition coefficient (K_{oc})
- plant uptake factor (K_p)

REACTION RATES
- hydrolysis
- biodegradation
- reaction with other chemicals
- photolysis
- chemical oxidation

Table 9.2
SELECTED ENVIRONMENTAL FATE MODELS

Volatilization from Soil

Jury, Grover, Spencer and Farmer, 1980
- vapour/non-vapour movement in soil

Shen, 1981
- estimates emissions from landfill

Thibodeaux, 1981
- estimates exposure from landfill emission

Baker and Mackay, 1985
- four models for estimated exposure from landfill emissions

Unsaturated Zone

Electric Power Research Institute, 1981
- Unsaturated Flow Model (UNSAT1D) estimates infiltration, vertical seepage and uptake by water roots

Battelle, 1984
- Metal Speciation Equilibrium Model (MINTEQ) is a thermodynamic equilibrium model for aqueous speciation, adsorption and precipitation dissolution of solid phases

Carsel et al., 1984
- Pesticide Root Zone Model (PRZM) estimates runoff, erosion, plant uptake, leaching, decay, foliar wash-off and volatilization

Dean et al., 1984
- Leaching Evaluation of Agricultural Chemicals (LEACH) is used to assess the leaching potential of pesticides

Short, 1985
- Regulatory and Investigative Treatment Zone Model (RITZ) estimates movement of chemicals following land treatment of oily wastes

Saturated Zone

Yeh and Ward, 1981*
- Finite Element Model of Waste Transport (FEMWASTE) simulates the transport of dissolved constituents in two-dimensional ground water (unsaturated/saturated zones)

Prickett, Naymik and Lonnquist, 1981*
- "RANDOM WALK +" can be used to evaluate one- or two-dimensional flow and solute transport

Garabedian and Konikow, 1983
- "Front-Tracking Model" is a finite difference model for convective transport of a conservative tracer dissolved in ground water under steady or transient flow

Voss, 1984**
- "SUTRA +" simulates two-dimensional, transient, or unsteady state, saturated or unsaturated, transport of energy or chemically reactive single species

UCLA Davis, 1985**
- "GS2" is a two-dimensional horizontal or vertical finite element model to simulate flow and solute movement in ground water (unsaturated/saturated zones)

Surface Water
Mackay *et al.*, 1985
- Fugacity Level III is a steady-state, non-equilibrium chemical fate model; fugacity is a thermodynamic concept that represents the tendency of a chemical to escape from one environmental compartment to another

Burns *et al.*, 1982
- EXAMS (Exposure Analysis Modeling System) estimates chemical fate in various types of aquatic environments including lakes, rivers, and estuaries; has steady-state and non-steady-state options

Notes
*   **Reference:** Javendel *et al.*, 1984
** **Reference:** Kincaid and Mitchell, 1986

Figure 9.1
ATMOSPHERIC TRANSPORT AND
TRANSFORMATION PROCESSES

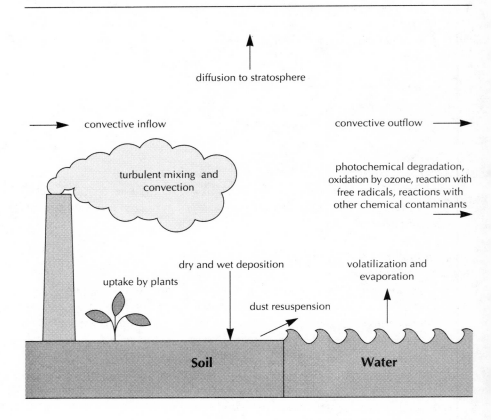

Figure 9.2
TRANSPORT AND TRANSFORMATION OF
CHEMICALS IN WATER

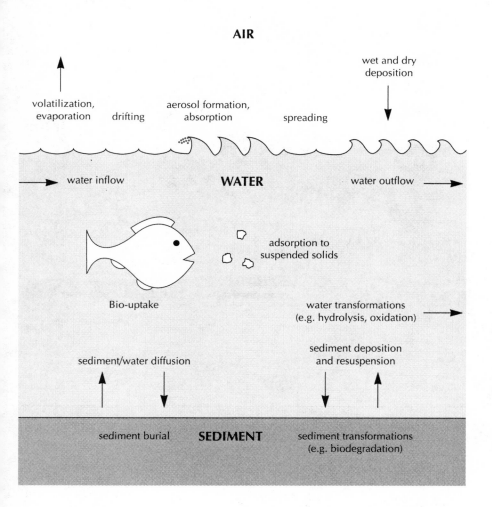

Figure 9.3
LEAKAGE FROM AN UNDERGROUND
STORAGE TANK

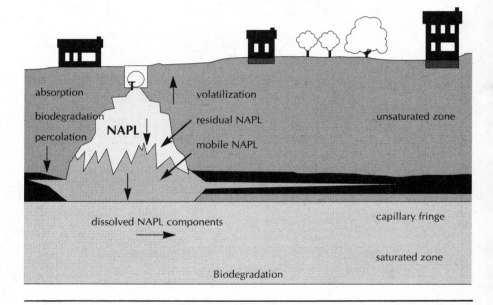

absorption   volatilization

biodegradation   residual NAPL   unsaturated zone

percolation   **NAPL**   mobile NAPL

dissolved NAPL components   capillary fringe

saturated zone

Biodegradation

10.0

Environmental Audits

10.1 WHAT IS AN ENVIRONMENTAL AUDIT?

One of the most important changes in environmental management over the past few years has been the emergence of the environmental audit. While companies may disagree as to the tasks that comprise an audit or when an audit should be undertaken, there is general agreement that an environmental audit is a systematic, objective evaluation of a facility, process, or site from an environmental perspective.

Twenty years ago, no one used the term "environmental audit" and as recently as ten years ago, environmental audits were rarely undertaken and then often in response to a request or directive from a regulatory agency. Within the last five years, many companies have come to regard the environmental audit as a powerful tool for assessing the environmental status well-being of a site or facility. The list of possible applications, which continues to grow, includes:

- assessing compliance with environmental legislation and/or the resources needed to comply with environmental requirements
- verifying the performance of environmental control equipment, programs, and personnel
- identifying potential environmental problems
- protecting companies and employees from potential environmental liabilities
- improving or protecting the environmental reputations of companies
- assigning priorities to capital expenditures on environmental control systems

While environmental auditing is in its early stages of evolution in Canada, there is little doubt that it will become a widespread practice and an essential element of many environmental policies and procedures. Some of the factors that will encourage the use of environmental audits include growing public awareness of environmental issues, increasingly stringent environmental legislation, penalties and liabilities for officers/directors, and the fortified enforcement efforts of regulatory agencies.

The environmental audit is also becoming an essential element in property and business evaluations for potential purchasers, prospective lenders, and investors. Hidden environmental liabilities can render a property or facility virtually unusable or quickly reduce its value. A growing number of companies are requiring that an environmental audit be performed as a condition of offers to purchase facilities and/or properties. (Additional information on the role of audits in real estate transfers is provided in Section 5.7.)

In addition, many regulatory agencies are beginning to undertake environmental audits at industrial facilities. In Ontario, the MOE conducts audits of discharges as part of its Municipal, Industrial Strategy for Abatement (MISA) program.

10.2 PERTINENT REGULATIONS

Table 10.1 lists federal, provincial, and municipal legislation, regulations, and by-laws that can influence the nature and extent of audits. The relative importance of the items listed in Table 10.1 largely will be influenced by the scope of the audit, the type of facility to be audited, and its location.

Individuals who conduct environmental audits need to have a good working knowledge of the environmental legislation that pertains to the situation being evaluated. It also is necessary to use the most recent versions of legislation and regulations. During the past ten years, many regulatory requirements have changed and further widespread change of legislation is expected to continue for several more years. An audit performed without an appreciation of the relevant legislation may fail to identify non-compliance situations or lead to a false sense of security.

The recently introduced Municipal, Industrial Strategy for Abatement (MISA) monitoring program in Ontario is an example of legislation which contains extensive monitoring and reporting requirements. Such requirements increase the likelihood of procedural violations and hence should be considered during an environmental audit of a facility.

10.3 TYPES OF AUDITS

As noted above, the term "environmental audit" is being used to describe a broad range of activities and procedures. Most audits can be assigned to one of three major categories: compliance audits, risk audits, and management system audits.

The **compliance audit** is directed toward determining whether or not a facility meets all of its current environmental requirements. The requirements can include laws, regulations, standards, criteria, guidelines, by-laws, and permits. Failure to comply may result in fines or other penalties such as the revocation of permits and control orders, adversarial relations with regulatory agencies, court injunctions, and even criminal prosecution of corporate officials (Palmisano and Margolis, 1987). This type of audit is often carried out as part of an assessment of a possible acquisition.

The definition of failure to comply has recently been broadened to include failure to notify regulatory agencies of events or conditions. Regulatory reporting requirements have increased dramatically in recent years. In Ontario, the Environmental Protection Act (EPA) and the Ontario Water Resources Act (OWRA) contain extensive reporting requirements. Failure to notify agencies forthwith of an environmental incident (such as a spill or unscheduled release) is becoming one of the most frequently cited violations of non-compliance.

The **risk audit** is used to assess the probability of potential adverse effects that a facility or operation may pose to staff members, neighbours, or the natural environment. All of the routes or pathways by which released substances can move around in the environment or which affect public health need to be considered. Typically these include air, surface water, ground water, and soil pathways.

The release of gases from the Union Carbide facility in Bhopal, India or the warehouse fire at Sandoz Ltd. in Basel, Switzerland and subsequent discharges to the Rhine River illustrate that companies and facilities do not exist in isolation; most often they are located where they may affect nearby residents, community air quality or water supplies, recreational or agricultural activities, adjacent businesses, wildlife, aesthetics, and other features of the local setting. The sorts of risks considered in a risk audit can include direct or indirect health effects, environmental damage, negative publicity, erosion of public confidence, or being named in legal proceedings.

One important way in which risk audits differ from compliance audits is that risk audits usually are not required by law or are not part of a facility's items of compliance. One advantage of risk audits is that they can allow a company to be proactive to existing or potential concerns rather than being reactive.

The **management system audit** is used to review critically the environmental management systems that have been instituted at a facility. An environmental management system may include the company's environmental policies and procedures, organizational structure, assignment of responsibilities, reporting protocols, environmental training, and inspection programs. The management system audit should include a review of environmental departments and personnel, job responsibilities, and accountability (Palmisano and Margolis, 1989). Special attention should be paid to internal training as many companies are finding it increasingly difficult to keep employees informed about new or revised legislation.

This type of audit can draw attention to communication deficiencies, gaps or overlap in responsibilities, schedule delays (especially with regard to obtaining Certificate of Approvals), and unnecessary costs. The identification of problems or situations that appear to pose excessive liability signal the need for improved management systems.

A comprehensive environmental audit program at a facility likely would include all three types of audits. In practice, many companies modify, merge, or otherwise make facility-specific audit programs. Such programs also tend to evolve and become more sophisticated over time.

10.4 PREREQUISITES FOR CONDUCTING AUDITS

Before any audit is conducted, three essential items need to be in place:
1 The reason(s) for conducting the audit must be defined clearly. There should be agreement on the scope of the audit, i.e. the level of detail to be sought.
2 The members of the audit team must have the authority, resources and training to conduct a thorough and accurate job.
3 The audit must have the support of top management.

10.5 STEPS OF AN AUDIT

10.5.1 Selecting the Audit Team

When an audit is to be performed by a company, members of the audit team may include part-time staff, full-time staff, or outside consultants. To ensure objectivity, members of the audit team should not work at the specific facility to be audited as familiarity can lead to certain aspects of the operation being overlooked. A representative from the facility who is familiar with the operations should serve as coordinator for the audit. Using facility personnel also can help promote continuity of compliance and improve the implementation of corrective action.

When an audit is to be performed by a regulatory agency, the auditors may be either government staff or hired consultants. In Ontario, the MOE has designated consultants as Provincial Officers during the course of the audit, thereby allowing them greater access to records. Section 10.7 discusses steps that can be taken when a facility is the subject of an external audit.

In either event, the audit team should include professionals with appropriate engineering and legal expertise. Collectively, the team must understand the operations of the facility or company from a technical perspective and also be familiar with the applicable environmental laws and regulations. The responsibilities of each member of the team must be clearly established. One of the members of the audit team should be appointed leader. The leader should have a general level of familiarity with all aspects of the facility and sufficient authority.

The types of individuals best suited for an audit team will be determined largely by the type of facility to be assessed. Audit teams often include environmental engineers and personnel from similar facilities (particularly those whose jobs directly pertain to environmental control systems or equipment). Team members can also include legal counsel and accountants. Depending on the facility to be evaluated, various types of scientists such as biologists, chemists, toxicologists, or hydrogeologists may be valuable additions to a team.

Environmental engineers should be generally familiar with the types of operations at the facility or be able to understand descriptions provided by operators. They should also be aware of current environmental requirements.

Plant personnel should work at a similar operation and be thoroughly familiar with the facility being audited and its processes, especially the environmental management systems.

Legal counsel should be familiar with all of the legal, environmental requirements of the facility. Counsel also can protect confidential or sensitive material uncovered during the audit from premature disclosure via lawyer-client privilege. Shielding information in this way can lead to confrontation or legal challenges from regulatory agencies and as a result some companies do not favour this approach. (This is discussed further in Section 10.6.)

An accountant can suggest specific "tests" of the system that comply with standard auditing procedures and rules (analogous to those used for financial audits) and address certain tax and financial issues if they arise (Russel, 1985). For example, specific tests may be useful in reviewing Ontario Regulation 309 waste manifests. To review every manifest at some facilities could be excessively time-consuming, and it may be sufficient to review an appropriate number of randomly selected manifests.

10.5.2 Pre-Audit Preparation

A partial checklist of activities that can be performed in preparation for an environmental audit is presented in Table 10.2. This task should be managed by the person assigned the responsibility for the audit program. When organizing the audit team, the availability of team members for the required time period must be unequivocal. The amount of time required to audit a facility will depend on the objective of the audit, the size of the facility and its complexity, as well as the number of people on the audit team. A one-person team may need five to eight days to audit a small or medium-size chemical plant, while a four-member team may require several weeks for a large facility.

Ideally, the audit team should have been provided with various types of information before actually visiting a facility. Foremost among these is a comprehensive **site plan**. The plan should show the locations of all buildings, storage and on-site transportation facilities, waste storage/treatment/disposal facilities, waste discharge or release points, environmental monitoring equipment, sewer connections, site drainage, neighbouring properties, environmentally-sensitive areas, and similar pertinent information (Jolliffe and Gorelle, 1989). Environmentally sensitive areas can include drinking water supplies, streams, wetlands, parks, areas frequented by birds or animals, and any areas used by endangered species.

A **process and emissions block diagram** showing the physical or chemical processes conducted on the site, the handling of raw materials brought onto the site, and all points where waste products (solids, liquids or vapours) leave the facility also should be provided to the team or the team should produce one. A typical block diagram is presented on Figure 10.1. A block diagram is critical since it is impossible to assess compliance if all the emissions or waste streams leaving the facility have not been identified.

All documentation relating to **previous environmental inspection reports** must be collected. Notices of complaints, violations, and prosecutions should also form part of the pre-audit materials. The audit team should be provided with **hazardous materials reports** that identify the locations of materials such as asbestos insulation, equipment that contains PCBs, radioactive materials, or solvents.

Travel arrangements may need to be made along with arranging for **permission to inspect** the facility. In most instances, an initial meeting with plant personnel to discuss the audit and a tour of the facility should be arranged beforehand. Availability of plant personnel must also be established prior to the audit. At many types of facilities, various forms of safety equipment or special security passes are needed. Safety equipment may range from hard hats and safety glasses to respirators and hazard suits. Passes may be required to ensure security and also safety in the event of an accident. Once again, arrangements must be made prior to the site visit.

10.5.3 Using Working Papers or Documents

To ensure that all of the desired facets of an environmental audit are addressed, companies may develop various types of working papers or documents such as manuals, checklists, data outlines, and interview sheets (Russel, 1985). In some companies, working papers or documents may be subject to lawyer-client privilege (in the case of an internal audit), and they may contain revealing and specific comments, notes on legal violations, and other sensitive material.

Some companies use **manuals** of questions to guide the auditor. A manual may be general enough to cover several facilities or it may be necessary to have a separate manual for each facility or operation. Considerable effort can be invested in preparing and updating manuals. Responding to the information requirements in a manual also can impose a heavy paperwork load on the auditor and the facility.

Checklists often take the form of yes/no questions, with explanations provided for negative answers. Generally, the questions are broadly worded, and may be defined broadly or narrowly during the audit, depending on the auditor's judgement.

Outlines and interview sheets can guide the auditor when interviewing plant personnel. The weakness of using an outline/interview approach alone is that it relies solely on opinions and people's recollection. The results of an interview, however, can direct the audit team to areas that warrant further attention, such as past practices that may be improper according to current requirements.

10.5.4 Deciding What to Audit

Almost anything that happens at a facility can be audited. Table 10.3 presents a list of potential areas to address during an environmental audit.

A major component of almost any audit is to **review environmental records**. These can be the records that describe the quantities of all raw materials and finished products (so that a material balance can be derived), all discharges or releases to the environment, the performance logs of environmental control equipment, calibration reports for flow measuring devices, the results of environmental monitoring efforts, Certificate of Approvals (C of As) or control orders issued by regulatory agencies, and reports of unusual or unscheduled events.

The review of environmental records can be very time-consuming. The practices and theory from financial accounting can be used to advantage in some instances. For example, the review of shipping documentation for dangerous goods can be time-consuming if every document must be reviewed. Instead, a representative sample of the documentation can be retrieved from the files and reviewed for compliance. Current legislation requires that environmental records and documentation be retained for up to two years.

When reviewing permits or certificates, special care must be taken to check for any major additions, alterations or modifications that have occurred since the C of A was originally issued. These may require either that an amendment be made to the current approval or that a new approval be obtained.

The audit team should conduct a thorough **site investigation** of all operations, equipment, storage facilities, and all waste discharge, removal, and environmental release routes. Figure 10.2 illustrates the types of information that should be gathered at points where atmospheric emissions or liquid discharges occur as well as solid waste disposal practices. All existing and potential hazards must be noted. All team members should make sure that they have the appropriate safety equipment to enter all parts of a facility.

All procedures used to handle, store, utilize, treat, and dispose of chemicals should be assessed as part of an audit. The adequacy of training received by staff pertaining to the operation of pollution control equipment as well as environmental regulations should be investigated. In addition to evaluating routine or regular events, the training and procedures used to respond to accidents or emergencies also should be checked.

All pollution control equipment, flow measurement devices, and monitoring equipment (on-line and continuous samplers) should be inspected. Examples of items to include on a checklist when assessing a facility involved in the MISA monitoring program may include:

- all samples must be stored in an environment maintained between the freezing point of the sample and 10 °C
- the maximum time interval between sub-samples when using an automatic sampling device (combines equal-volume sub-samples) is 15 minutes
- an automatic flow proportional composite sampling device must collect sub-samples at intervals not exceeding 30 minutes

During the site visit, the auditors should talk to plant staff knowledgeable about conditions. If asbestos is suspected of being present, consideration should be given to taking a sample or having the facility sample the material, as visual inspection of fireproofing and insulating materials is unreliable.

In some cases, **environmental monitoring** may need to be undertaken either to fill in gaps in the available data base or to augment the results of other monitoring efforts. The types of samples gathered can include air emissions, indoor air quality, outdoor air quality on the property, at the property's edge or at the locations of nearby receptors, effluents from liquid treatment facilities, liquids at the point of discharge to the sewer system, water quality in local surface water features such as ditches or streams, local ground water, soils, and noise levels. Solid wastes may need to be analyzed to determine appropriate modes of off-site transport or their suitability for disposal at different types of waste management facilities.

A major focus of many audits is to review the performance of the **environmental management system.** This can highlight recurring compliance problems, malfunctioning equipment, or accidents that may be symptomatic of underlying difficulties (Palmisano and Margolis, 1987).

The reporting structure (the environmental organization chart) should be described. An assessment should be made of whether information is flowing from one level of authority to another and that senior personnel are being made aware of non-compliance and liabilities.

10.5.5 Preparing the Audit Report

The report should be based on the review of the pre-audit materials, the site investigation, the review of environmental records, and any sampling and testing that is done. The report should identify all of the ways that the facility can adversely affect the surrounding environment.

The report should address the existence and severity of any deficiencies on the site. Most audit reports do not make formal recommendations but can lead management in the direction of the appropriate corrective action. Any deficiencies discussed in the audit report should be significant and balanced. Unsupported statements or conclusions should not be included in an audit report. Individuals sometimes make observations outside of their expertise or scope of work which once included in a report become difficult to discredit, especially at a later date.

The report should be marked "preliminary" or "draft" until plant management and legal counsel have had a opportunity to review it and make written comments. The final report should be reviewed by legal counsel. The distribution of the report usually will be determined by plant, divisional, or corporate management, and/or corporate environmental staff with some input from legal counsel.

10.5.6 Post-Audit Procedures

After an audit, the audit team and the facility or plant management should have an **exit interview** to discuss the findings of the audit. Senior management should be made aware of all findings. Ideally a summary table presenting the findings from the audit should be provided to management. The estimated cost and proposed schedule to implement corrective action may be discussed. Some form of response should be produced even if the response merely indicates that the audit report has been reviewed. This will help generate a **positive response paper trail.**

The preparation and implementation of an **action plan** is essential for an effective audit program. In essence, it closes the loop and ensures that all deficiencies are corrected in a timely and cost-effective manner. It represents the due diligence element of the program.

Little good is accomplished if the paper trail of positive responses does not result in specific action, and in some cases inaction on the findings can be damaging. Procedural controls cost little to implement, and large capital projects can be implemented in phases.

10.6 CONFIDENTIALITY

The question of report accessibility by government agencies and by court-directed disclosure is one with which industry and regulators continue to struggle. Environment Canada recognizes that environmental audits are an effective management tool for assessing environmental compliance. Under the Canadian Environmental Protection Act (CEPA), audit reports may be required when inspectors/investigation specialists have reasonable grounds to believe that (Environment Canada, 1988):

- an offence has been committed,
- the audit findings will be relevant to a particular violation, necessary to its inspector/investigation specialist, and required as evidence, or
- the information being sought cannot be obtained from other sources through the exercise of the inspector's/investigation specialist's powers.

Environment Canada has stated that an environmental audit must not be used to shelter monitoring/compliance or other information that would otherwise be accessible to inspection under CEPA. In addition, the demand for access to an environmental audit during an investigation can be made under the authority of a search warrant. An exception can be made when the delay necessary to obtain a warrant would likely result in danger to the environment or human health, or the loss or destruction of evidence (Environment Canada, 1988).

The MOE currently does not automatically and routinely require the production of an audit report. It encourages the use of audits as the best means of ensuring compliance; however, the MOE will review an audit when it may be relevant to investigations or the development of abatement requirements or for some other purpose, where it is in the public interest to do so (McKenney, 1989).

Prior to initiating an audit, the aspect of confidentiality should be discussed with legal counsel. There are currently two schools of thought on the confidentiality of an environmental audit: lawyer-client privilege and due diligence.

Option 1: Lawyer-Client Privilege

Some companies employ "lawyer-client" privilege when conducting an environmental audit and restricting access to the audit report. To be in force, the lawyer must take the lead role and ensure that the following conditions are met:

- the information/study must be requested by the corporation and/or officers and directors
- the request must be in anticipation of litigation
- the information must be delivered by the lawyer to the corporation and/or officers and directors
- the information must be kept confidential

The above conditions allow for an outside consultant and/or corporate staff to assist the lawyer in the preparation of report.

Counsel responsible for an audit should develop procedures for maintaining confidentiality and ensure that those procedures are followed by everyone who participates in the audit.

One disadvantage of the above procedure is that it may deny access to individuals who will implement the corrective action.

Option 2: Due Diligence

Several companies are choosing the due diligence option as opposed to lawyer-client privilege. The benefits flowing from an auditing program may far outweigh any negative concerns associated with disclosure (Villeneuve, 1989). A defense of due diligence based on an active audit program which critically and impartially identifies and corrects environmental deficiencies may be the best defense.

10.7 REACTING TO AN EXTERNAL AUDIT

If an environmental audit is being performed as a result of external actions (i.e. it has originated with a government agency or a potential purchaser), the corporate environmental staff and the legal department should be made aware of the upcoming audit and the scope of the audit should be determined as soon as possible.

Pertinent regulations, certificates of approval, control orders, permits, compliance history, previous audits, and environmental reports should be assembled and reviewed prior to the visit of the external auditors with a critical eye to identifying potential areas of vulnerability.

During the audit, answers should not be volunteered. **Never give misleading or false information**. If a point is raised that has not been considered or the answer is not known, seek clarification of the question and the type of answer being sought. It may indeed be appropriate to respond to the auditor at a later time when more information becomes available. **Do not speculate** for the sake of providing an answer. Be attentive and courteous at all times.

A qualified individual should accompany the auditors throughout the audit, assisting where possible. It is a good idea to carry a notebook and note important questions, and the responses provided.

Record all documents that are provided to the external auditors. All written information provided to the auditors should be formally transmitted (i.e. with a cover letter).

10.8 SUMMARY

Environmental audits are becoming an essential component of environmental management. Some of the reasons for performing audits include assessing compliance with environmental legislation, verifying the performance of environmental control equipment and programs, identifying potential environmental concerns, and protecting companies and employees from potential environmental liabilities.

While environmental auditing is in its early stages of evolution in Canada, there is little doubt that it will become a widespread practice and an essential element of many environmental policies and procedures. Some of the factors that will encourage the use of environmental audits include growing public awareness of environmental issues, increasingly stringent environmental legislation, penalties and liabilities for officers/directors, and the fortified enforcement efforts of regulatory agencies.

As environmental legislation becomes more stringent, the complexity of the audits will change dramatically, especially with respect to assessing procedural non-compliance (i.e. reporting requirements, sampling and analysis techniques). Changes to legislation should be incorporated into audit programs. For example, audits in Ontario should address the recently introduced Municipal, Industrial Strategy for Abatement (MISA) program.

Prior to the implementation of an auditing program the scope of work must be developed and agreed upon, auditors must be properly trained, and management support obtained. Once an audit is completed, senior management at the facility being audited should be fully informed of the findings. An action plan should then be developed to "close the loop" and ensure that all deficiencies are corrected in a timely and cost-effective manner.

REFERENCES

Environment Canada, 1988, "Canadian Environmental Protection Act: Enforcement and Compliance Policy". May.

Environmental Protection Act (EPA), 1989. "Ontario Regulation 695/88 as amended to Ontario Regulation 533/89 Under the Environmental Protection Act: Effluent Monitoring—General".

Jolliffe, R.S. and Gorelle, L., 1989. "The Environmental Audit: An Ounce of Prevention". Engineering Dimensions, July/August, pp. 34-36.

McKenney, M.G., 1989. "Environmental Enforcement in Ontario". Presented at the Environmental Auditing Workshop, 10 and 11 October, University of Toronto.

Palmisano, J. and Margolis, J., 1987. "Environmental Audits as the Core of a Risk Management Program". *In* Managing Environmental Risks, proceedings of an APCA International Specialty Conference, Washington D.C.

Russel, D., 1985. "Managing Your Environmental Audit". Chemical Engineering, June 24, pp. 37-43.

Villeneuve, E., 1989. "Overview of an Environmental Auditing Program". Presented at the Environmental Auditing Workshop, 10 and 11 October, University of Toronto.

Table 10.1
REGULATIONS RELEVANT TO
ENVIRONMENTAL AUDITS

EXAMPLES OF ONTARIO LEGISLATION

A—ENVIRONMENTAL PROTECTION ACT (EPA)

Part II   **General Provisions**
Section 1   —Definition of Adverse Effect
Section 5   —Prohibition of Exceeding Regulatory Limits
Section 6   —Control Orders Related to Emissions/Discharges
Section 8   —Approvals to Construct, Alter, Extend or Replace
Section 12   —Notification of Section 5
Section 13   —Prohibition of Discharging a Contaminant Which Causes an
                Adverse Effect
Section 14   —Notification of Section 13
Section 17   —Study and Reporting of Preventative Measures

Part V   **Waste Management**
Section 27   —Approvals for Waste Management System or Disposal Site
Section 39   —Prohibition of Depositing Waste Except at Approved Sites
Section 40   —Prohibition on Using Waste Management System Unless
                Approved
Section 45   —Prohibition of Using Former Waste Disposal Site

Part IX   **Spills**
Section 80   —Notification of Spills
Section 81   —Restoration of the Environment

PART X   **Control Orders and Stop Orders**
Section 114   —Control Orders
Section 119   —Stop Orders

PART XII   **Provincial Officers**
Section 126   —Inspection by Provincial Officer
Section 127   —Seizure of Files/Samples
Section 129   —Hinder/Obstruct Provincial Officer

Part XIV   Miscellaneous
Section 147A —Duty to Take Reasonable Care to Prevent Unlawful
              Discharges

Regulations Within EPA:

Air Regulations
REG. 308   —Air Pollution
REG. 349/89   —Ozone Depleting Substances
REG. 295   —Emissions, Ferrous Foundries
REG. 16/86   —Boilers

Waste/Spills Regulations
REG. 309   —Waste Management
REG. 11/82   —PCB Wastes
REG. 148/86   —PCB Mobile Destruction
REG. 618/85   —Spills

MISA Monitoring Regulations
REG. 695/88   —General Effluent Monitoring (as amended by REG. 533/89)
REG. 359/88   —Petroleum Refining Sector
REG. 209/89   —Organic Chemicals Sector
REG. 321/89   —Iron/Steel Sector
REG. 359/89   —Inorganic Chemicals Sector
REG. 91/90   —Industrial Minerals Sector

B—Ontario Water Resources Act (OWRA)
Section 14   —Definition of Impaired
Section 16(1) —Prohibition of Discharges that Cause Adverse Impact
Section 16(2) —Notification of Discharges
Section 17   —Prohibition of Discharges
Section 18   —Equipment to Alleviate Impairment
Section 19   —Protection of Public Water Supplies
Section 24   —Approvals for Sewage Works
Section 32   —Maintenance of Sewage Works
Section 75   —Duty to Take Reasonable Care to Prevent Unlawful
              Discharges

C—GASOLINE HANDLING ACT
Section 6   —Requirements for aboveground storage tanks
Section 7   —Requirements for underground storage tanks
Bill 133   —Revision to requirements for underground storage tanks

D—PESTICIDES ACT

EXAMPLES OF FEDERAL LEGISLATION

A—CANADIAN ENVIRONMENTAL PROTECTION ACT (CEPA)
Interim Orders Respecting PCBs
Federal Mobile PCB Treatment & Destruction Regulation

B—TRANSPORTATION OF DANGEROUS GOODS ACT (TDGA)

C—FISHERIES ACT

EXAMPLES OF MUNICIPAL BYLAWS

A—MODEL SEWER USE BY-LAW

B—NOISE BY-LAW

Table 10.2
CHECKLIST FOR PREPARING FOR AN
ENVIRONMENTAL AUDIT

- Determine the objective, scope and type of audit
- Organize audit team and schedule
- Compile and review pertinent regulations
- Obtain copies of permits, certificates of approval, and incident reports
- Obtain site plan and process flow sheets
- Compile descriptions of pollution control equipment and waste treatment systems
- Obtain descriptions of pollution control equipment and waste treatment systems
- Obtain documents that describe waste types, volumes, and classifications
- Obtain procedures for handling, transporting and disposing of waste and dangerous goods
- Obtain descriptions of emergency response plans and reporting procedures
- Documentation on previous environmental audits and/or inspections, both internal and external
- Notices of violations and prosecutions
- Obtain information on the environmental management system
- Obtain descriptions of environmental reporting requirements
- Ensure appropriate safety equipment and passes are available

---

Table 10.3
WHAT GETS AUDITED

LIQUID EFFLUENTS OR DISCHARGES

Assemble and Review the Documentation Concerning:
1) Files concerning discharges to surface waters, storm sewers, and sanitary sewers
2) Maintenance records and operation logs for wastewater treatment systems, samplers, and flow measurement devices
3) Unscheduled releases/incident reports and sampling equipment malfunction reports
4) Certificates of approval for recent construction, alterations, extensions or replacement
5) Integrity tests and maintenance record for above- and below-ground storage tanks
6) Control orders or violation notices
7) Previous environment reports dealing with effluents
8) Reporting and monitoring requirements
9) MISA monitoring reports, updates and non-compliance reports
10) Calibration records for flow measuring devices (primary/secondary)
11) Sampling procedures, schedule and list of chemicals

Inspect During the Site Visit:
1) The physical condition and operation of process equipment where liquids are used
2) The physical condition of all elements of wastewater treatment systems including any lagoons
3) All effluent samplers and flow measurement devices
4) All above- and below-ground storage tanks
5) Dykes and berms around aboveground storage tanks
6) Record keeping including backing-up of computer disks

ATMOSPHERIC EMISSIONS

Assemble and Review the Documentation Concerning:
1) Files concerning emissions from stacks, vents, etc.
2) Maintenance records for air pollution control systems, monitors
3) Unscheduled releases/incident reports
4) Operation logs of control equipment systems
5) Certificates of approval for recent construction, alterations, extensions or replacements

6) Previous environmental reports dealing with emissions or air quality
7) Notices of violations, complaints from neighbours on odours, dust, etc.
8) Reporting and monitoring requirements

Inspect During the Site Visit:
1) All stacks, vents, etc.
2) Dust from plant operation on building roofs, pavement and surrounding property
3) All air quality monitors
4) The behaviour of emissions from stacks (i.e. initial opacity, plume rise, etc.)

NOISE

Assemble and Review the Documentation Concerning:
1) Review of data on noise emissions and levels
2) Noise complaint records

SOLID WASTES

Assemble and Review the Documentation Concerning:
1) Data on waste analysis as per Reg. 309 classification
2) Shipment manifests as per Reg. 309
3) Certificates of approval for recently established waste disposal systems or site
4) Inventory of waste stored on-site and registration
5) PCB storage facility specifications

Inspect During the Site Visit:
1) Types and integrity of waste storage vessels
2) Housekeeping in storage areas
3) Labelling of containers and designation of waste storage areas
4) PCB storage facility

TRANSPORTATION OF DANGEROUS GOODS

Assemble and Review the Documentation Concerning:
1) TDG manifests
2) TDG emergency procedures
3) Proper registrations of carriers

Inspect During the Site Visit:
1) Labels on containers and trucks

MANAGEMENT SYSTEM

Assemble and Review the Documentation Concerning:
1) Defined responsibilities of environmental staff
2) Internal environmental inspection and reporting procedures
3) History of compliance
4) Qualifications of environmental management

LABORATORY FACILITIES

Assemble and Review the Documentation Concernimg:
1) Laboratory QA/QC procedures
2) Analytical test methods, protocols, and method detection limits
3) Sample labels and chain-of-custody tracking system
4) MISA monitoring reports and updates

PROCEDURES/TRAINING PROGRAMS

Assemble and Review the Documentation Concerning:
1) Incident reporting procedures
2) Emergency response procedures
3) Wastewater treatment operator training
4) Training of shippers in TDG classification and registration
5) Environmental legislation and updating
6) Hazardous chemical handling and storage procedures

Figure 10.1
TYPICAL BLOCK DIAGRAM OF EMISSIONS, DISCHARGES AND WASTE STREAMS

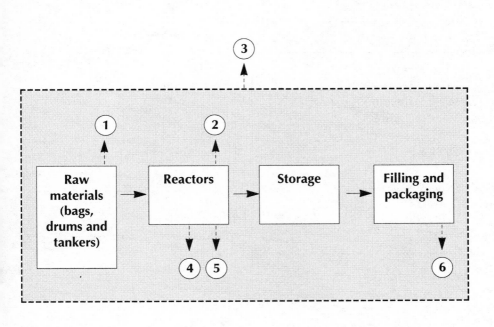

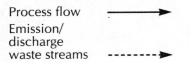

Process flow ⟶

Emission/
discharge
waste streams ----►

1. Duct from raw material storage
2. Stack for reactor discharge
3. Fugitive emission to atmosphere
4. Water discharge to sanitary sewer
5. Solid waste
6. Spoiled product for off-site disposal

Figure 10.2
AUDIT INFORMATION GATHERED AT
THREE TYPES OF RELEASE POINTS

Air Emissions

Stream Identifier:_____

Description:_____
Control Device:_____
Stack Height (m):_____
Stack Dia. (m):_____
Stack Temp. (°C):_____
Stack Exit Vel. (m/s): _____
C of A No.:_____
Emissions (g/s): _____
   benzene_____
   xylene _____
   etc._____

Water Discharges

Stream Identifier:_____

Description:_____
Treatment: _____
Flow (m^3/h):_____
Temperature (°C): _____
Toxicity (LC_{50}): _____
C of A No.:_____
Concentration (mg/L):_____
   TSS_____
   iron _____
   lead _____
   etc._____

Waste Disposal/Treatment

Stream Identifier:_____

Classification: _____
Solid Fraction (mg/kg):
   zinc _____
   lead _____
   etc._____
Leachate Conc. (mg/L):
   zinc _____
   lead _____
   etc._____
Volume Stored (L): _____
Storage Duration (days):_____
Hauler:
   Registration No. _____
   Company_____
Treatment System:
   C of A No._____
   Company_____
Ultimate Disposal:
   C of A No._____
   Company_____

11.0

Risk Assessment and Management

11.1 OVERVIEW

Risk often is defined as the probability or likelihood that an adverse outcome will be caused by an action or condition. In the context of environmental issues, the action or condition of concern usually can be associated with the exposure to a chemical or physical agent such as noise, heat, or radiation.

Risk assessment is the process of determining the adverse outcomes that can occur. This can include evaluating the types of potential effects (also referred to as hazards), the probability of an effect occurring, and the numbers of people, animals, and plants that might be exposed and/or suffer the consequences of exposure. **Risk management** is the process of evaluating the possible courses of action and selecting among them. In this framework, risk assessment is the vital precursor to risk management. Figure 11.1 shows one interpretation of the steps that make up risk assessment and risk management and how these two processes are related.

During the last two decades, there has been a growing trend to incorporate risk assessment and management into various decision-making processes including the setting of environmental policies and regulations. These efforts have often proven to be cumbersome and onerous. Like most new technologies, there are differences of opinion as to how risk management should be used and what its role should be. There are also uncertainties as to its value and a lack of consensus on the terminology that should be used. As a result, a certain amount of scepticism and caution has been directed toward the risk assessment and management processes.

In part, these shortcomings may be the natural outcome of expecting too much too soon from a relatively new aid for decision-making. Risk assessment and risk management often are expected to bring order to large pools of information and resolve conflicting interests and uncertainties en route to identifying appropriate options. Some of the factors with which a risk manager often must contend include situation-specific economic, social, political, and legal considerations. The complexity of such situations can be overwhelming.

Despite the difficulties that have been experienced (and no doubt will continue to be experienced), risk assessment and management are likely to play increasingly important roles in decision-making processes. Factors that will continue to support the need for risk assessment and management include:

- the realization that there are insufficient resources to address all concerns (and therefore priorities need to be set),
- the need to compare the relative importance of an ever-increasing number of environmental concerns,
- government agencies being asked to regulate more risks than ever before, and
- the increasing number of issues, such as acidic precipitation, global warming, or exposure to carcinogens, which are relatively insidious, complex, and require careful assessment.

11.2 RISK ASSESSMENT

11.2.1 Purpose and Elements

Risk assessment is directed toward determining the types and probabilities of adverse effects occurring as a result of some activity or condition. Consider the example of a proposed stack which will emit vapours that may be inhaled by downwind residents and cause adverse health effects. To assess the potential risks, it first is necessary to determine the characteristics of release (how much? when? at what exit velocity and temperature?). It then is necessary to determine how the release will behave in the atmosphere (how much dilution will occur? will the substance degrade while airborne?). Various characteristics of the person(s) who could inhale the vapours need to determined (how much air do they breathe? will they breathe the vapours all day? every day?). Of obvious importance is the toxicological nature of the substance (what kinds of adverse effect can it cause? how much does a person need to inhale to experience an adverse effect?). Finally, the estimated doses need to be described in terms of the risk or the probability of adverse effects occurring.

Many descriptions of these elements or steps have been prepared and there is considerable variability in the terminology used and the number of steps involved. The remainder of this section uses the steps and terminology suggested by the U.S. Environmental Protection Agency, which considers risk assessment as consisting of four steps (U.S. EPA, 1986):

- hazard identification
- exposure assessment
- dose-response assessment
- risk characterization

11.2.2 Hazard Identification

The first step in a risk assessment is the identification of potential hazards, which in environmental management usually involves identifying where and how chemicals are being released (or have been released) into the environment. Examples of release points include:

- **air emissions** from stacks and vents, open storage tanks, pressure relief valves, waste ponds and lagoons, fugitive sources, land farms, open process tanks and vessels, tank and drum loading/unloading operations
- **liquid discharges** from point sources to surface water, discharges to municipal sewers, releases to ground water, leaky storage tanks and ponds
- **hazardous waste** shipments to off-site disposal, transfer to on-site disposal, on-site disposal/treatment facilities

The types of activities that are likely to identify hazards include environmental inspections or audits (see Chapter 10), or gathering information to comply with regulatory requirements. Examples of regulatory requirements include completing a Waste Inventory Survey as required by the Ontario Municipal Model Sewer Use By-Law, and preparing a chemical inventory or toxic chemical release inventory report like that being considered by the Clean Air Program (see Section 2.8.4).

11.2.3 Exposure Assessment

When a **receptor** (usually a person but the term can also be used to refer to an animal or plant) comes into contact with a chemical that has been released into the environment, **exposure** occurs. For example, a person may be exposed to a chemical in the air by inhaling it. Exposure assessment involves determining the environmental fate of the chemicals released from each release point (see Chapter 9) and the ways in which a individual can be exposed to those chemicals. Exposure **pathways** can include:

- ingestion of water
- ingestion of soil
- inhalation of vapours
- inhalation of particulate matter
- ingestion of fish
- ingestion of milk and dairy products
- ingestion of produce

- ingestion of dust
- dermal absorption

In many situations, one or two pathways are the major contributors to exposures. For example, the ingestion of meat and milk accounts for 99% of human exposure to 2,3,7,8-TCDD, one of the more toxic forms of dioxin (Travis and Hattemer-Frey, 1987). The factors that determine which pathways predominate is a function of the physicochemical properties of the substance, characteristics of the receptor, the receptor's behaviour in the environment where contact occurs, and characteristics of the environment. Determining which substances and pathways are of greatest concern is a major step in the process of determining the form that remedial measures may need to take.

For compounds with established provincial or federal guidelines such as ambient air and water quality guidelines or criteria, the estimated or measured concentration of a substance at the point where a receptor makes contact can be compared to the guidelines as a measure of relative hazard.

The **dose** is the amount or mass of chemical taken up by the receptor via the pathways noted above. Dose and exposure often are used incorrectly as synonyms. For example, a receptor may be exposed to a substance present at a concentration of 3 mg/L in water. Upon drinking 2 L of the water, the receptor's intake is 6 mg of the substance. If the receptor weighs 30 kg, their dose is 0.2 mg/kg of body weight (bw). If they drink 2 L of the water every day, the dose is 0.2 mg/kg-bw/d. Dose is a function of several parameters:

- quantity of material taken into the receptor's body
- characteristics of the receptor, for example body weight
- concentration of chemical in the material taken in by the receptor
- frequency of occurrence of exposure
- bioavailability factor(s) specific to the chemical and exposure route

The bioavailability factor refers to the percentage of material taken into the body that actually enters the body tissue or blood. It is the dose at the target tissue that determines the response, not the level of external exposure. Some researchers have suggested that the term "dose" be replaced by "potential dose" if bioavailability is ignored or assumed to be 100%, and that the term "internal dose" be used once bioavailability is taken into account (Lioy, 1990). It has also been suggested that that fraction of the internal dose which actually leads to a specific effect or physiologic change be called the "biologically effective dose".

It is important to state all of the assumptions employed to derive doses as the results can vary widely depending upon the assumptions made. There are at least two basic philosophies that have been used to estimate dose:

1 Calculate a maximum or upper extreme dose using conservative

assumptions (those deliberately made to avoid underestimating risks) to arrive at a so-called upper bound estimate of the risk.

2 Make assumptions about receptors and pathways that are consistent with what the evidence and the best current scientific information suggest are probable or typical (as opposed to extreme). At the end of the process, apply a final safety factor to ensure public protection.

The first method puts the onus on the risk assessor to make inferences about conservative safety factors as opposed to leaving these assumptions to the judgement of the risk manager. Taken to extremes, the first "conservative" approach can lead to gross overestimations of exposures or portray receptors with unrealistic behaviours or characteristics. As a result, the second method is beginning to gain favour (Deisler, 1988).

In evaluations that use the first approach, it often is assumed that the receptor is a hypothetical individual who spends all of his time (24 hours a day, 365 days a year) for 70 years, outdoors at the location of highest contaminant concentration attributable to the source of the substance. In addition, it is often assumed that the source continuously emits the chemical for 70 years. Information about the behaviour of people indicates that it would be more realistic to assume that the receptor spends one-third of their time indoors at the site, one-third outdoors, and one-third off-site for a period of 30 to 40 years.

In the conservative approach, the maximum level of exposure is assumed to occur for the duration of the exposure. This requires a constant or infinite source of the substance, which seldom is the case. For example, soil containing organic compounds may be the source of vapours that a receptor can inhale. The vapour emissions of a compound, especially one that volatilizes rapidly, will deplete the amount of the compound in the soil, especially from the top soil layer. In turn, this will lead to a steady decrease in the exposures and doses with time.

In the conservative approach, it often is assumed that 100% of a substance is bioavailable for each pathway (i.e. all the chemical is absorbed or metabolized by body tissue or the bloodstream). In many cases, this assumption is made because there is insufficient evidence to support the use of a different value; however, there is a growing amount of data indicating that **bioavailability** often is substantially less than 100%. This likely is the case for the bioavailability of many organic substances that are ingested in the diet and the bioavailability of substances associated with inhaled particles.

To facilitate the calculation of exposures and doses, mathematical **models** can be used. Such models should take into account the emission or discharge rate of a chemical, its behaviour or fate in the environment, and the conditions under which receptors come into contact with the chemicals. Many such models exist. Some are highly specialized and may be limited to specific types of release points (for example, point sources such as factories), particular risk agents, or specific types of environmental settings such as watersheds or lakes (Cohrssen and Covello, 1989).

By their very nature, these models are only partial representations of real systems and contain a number of parameters which are either imperfectly known or inherently variable by nature. Uncertainties also arise when these models are used to predict effects over conditions and periods of time different from those for which the models and model parameters were developed. As a result, the outcomes generated by models, or for that matter any other exposure/risk assessment approach, contain a degree of **uncertainty.**

Until recently, uncertainty has been addressed in models indirectly. The traditional approach has been to run a model with conservative values of the parameters, typically near the upper or lower extreme of the expected range of the probability distributions for the parameters. The result of such an approach is generally a very conservative estimate of the effects.

An alternative approach is to use some form of **probabilistic analysis**. This approach attempts to take uncertainty into account explicitly by specifying probability distributions rather than single values for parameters that are model inputs. The model is run many times with new values selected for the input parameters on each run. The parameter values used in each run are randomly selected from the appropriate distributions. The model output is a probabilistic distribution of possible effects.

Output data from the uncertainty analysis can be used to assess the relative importance of the various model parameters by assessing their relative contribution to overall uncertainty in model predictions and determining how sensitive the predicted values are to small changes in model input parameters.

The benefits of this approach are that more realistic estimates of exposure and risk can be made, and the reliance on worst-case assumptions is reduced.

11.2.4 Dose-Response Assessment

The relationship between dose and response is based upon a thorough analysis of relevant data which may include epidemiological, clinical, environmental, animal toxicological, biochemical, structure-activity, and exposure data. Figure 11.2 presents a schematic plot of various levels of response (lethal, sublethal and behavioral) versus exposure (environmental and laboratory).

The exposure levels of interest associated with most environmental issues are often orders of magnitude less than those which cause obvious adverse effects (such as lethality). As a result, it is often necessary to extrapolate the response data into regions which are experimentally impossible for statistical reasons (i.e. natural variation exceeds the effect), and in which the knowledge about the extent or existence of the toxic event may be simply inaccessible (Mackay, 1982).

In terms of response, chemicals can be broken into two groups: carcinogens and non-carcinogens. **Carcinogens** are defined as chemicals that produce self-propagating lesions. It is commonly assumed that there is some risk associated with any exposure to carcinogens, no matter how small the dose. Similarly, it has become common practice to assume that the relationship between dose and response for carcinogens is linear; however, there is considerable scientific debate regarding the linearity of dose-response relationships, whether or not there may be thresholds below which adverse effects do not occur, and whether the linear models currently used are unduly or inadequately conservative.

Non-carcinogens are substances for which the information indicates that there is a dose below which measurable adverse effects should not occur even if there is a lifetime of exposure. The threshold below which no observable response occurs is defined as the no-observable-adverse-effect-level (NOAEL).

11.2.5 Risk Characterization

Risk characterization should include a description of the qualitative factors that help to establish the existence of a hazard and a risk; descriptions of the human population subject to risk and the possible responses; and estimates of the background or natural rates at which the responses occur and of their upper and lower statistical bounds (Deisler, 1988).

Once a dose has been calculated for a given situation and set of conditions, it may be compared to an **acceptable** level based solely on human health. Establishing acceptability of a dose is a complex process influenced by economic, social, political, and technical factors as well as scientific factors and therefore is not part of the risk characterization but is part of risk management.

For **carcinogens**, acceptability in terms of human health usually is expressed in terms of the lifetime risk levels that doses present. Until recently, one of the most commonly used approaches was to establish "virtually safe dose" (or VSD) values for carcinogens. A VSD often was set as the dose which presented a lifetime cancer risk probability of one in a million. Such a risk was thought to be acceptable and "virtually safe" because it represented a level of risk that most individuals willingly accept. To avoid the possible implications or misunderstanding of using the term "virtually safe", many agencies are now using the term **"risk-specific dose" (RSD)** for carcinogens. This terminology clearly indicates that there is a risk level (i.e. a probability of developing cancer given a lifetime of exposure) associated with the dose. Whether that risk level should be one in a million or a higher or lower value is an issue that regulatory agencies must address.

An RSD value is usually calculated by extrapolating from health effects observed (at relatively high doses) in laboratory test to low doses using one of several mathematical models which have been developed for this purpose. The dose-response models employed are simplistic probabilistic representations of highly complex biological phenomena.

Non-carcinogens are substances for which measurable adverse effects should not occur below a specified dose. Until recently, such a dose was called an "acceptable daily intake" (ADI). Because of the possible implications of using the term "acceptable" to describe such doses, agencies are now using the term **"reference dose" (RfD)**. An RfD value is calculated by dividing the lowest no-observable-adverse-effect-level (NOAEL) by an extrapolation or safety factor (values of 10, 100, 1000 or more are used). The magnitude of the extrapolation factor depends on the confidence that can be placed in the allowable data, judging the relevance of the data to humans, the severity and the type of effects observed, and the types of test systems studied. Unlike RSD values, there is no risk level associated with RfD values.

Another approach that some agencies use to judge acceptability is to compare exposures or doses to **background conditions**. Nuclear scientists have led the way in using natural background exposures as a baseline from which to assess acceptability. The background approach is also one option for setting clean-up levels noted in the MOE publication for decommissioning sites in Ontario (see Chapter 5). This approach cannot be used when the substance in question is man-made and therefore should not be present in "uncontaminated" environments or when there is uncertainty as to how background conditions are to be defined. For example, it is unclear as to whether clean-up levels for an urban site should be based on background concentrations measured at a rural site.

Because RSD values have an associated risk level while RfD values do not, it is difficult to assess the risks posed when a receptor is being exposed to both types of substances. One potential way to assess the risks from both carcinogens and non-carcinogens is the use of **Relative Margin of Safety (RMOS)** values:

RMOS = observed dose ÷ acceptable dose   (11.1)

The "acceptable" dose can be either an RSD or an RfD.

An RMOS value greater than 1 indicates that the estimated dose exceeds the acceptable dose and indicates potentially unacceptable health hazard. RMOS values between 0.1 and 1.0 indicate a situation of potential concern, although not necessarily unacceptable. Such values can be used to identify situations where additional assessment of releases, exposure parameters, and/or health evaluation criteria likely are warranted.

The RMOS approach is used in the California Air Pollution Control Districts reference manual for non-carcinogens. The manual provides a step-by-step approach to estimating and assessing the public health impacts of sources of air contaminants (CAPCD, 1987).

For carcinogens, the RMOS value is also termed the individual lifetime cancer risk. It represents the probability of an individual contracting cancer. The individual **cancer incidence rate** can be multiplied by the population residing within a predefined area to estimate the annual cancer incidence rate for that area. Estimates of annual cancer incidence rates have been used by regulators in the United States to assess control options for toxic chemicals.

Individuals seldom are exposed to a single chemical; most exposures are to complex mixtures of assorted compounds. Assessing human exposure to such mixtures is a formidable task. Firstly, it is generally impractical or impossible to measure the concentration of all constituents contained in a complex mixture. Secondly, even if all constituents were known, their respective toxicities are often unknown. Thirdly, even if the toxicities of individual components are known, the toxicity of a mixture can be substantially different from the composite of the toxicities of its constituents.

Chemicals can interact synergistically or antagonistically to form a mixture that is more or less toxic than expected. Many such interactions are reported in the toxicological literature. For example, cigarette smoke and asbestos are known to interact synergistically, thereby increasing the incidence of lung cancer in asbestos workers. Benzene and toluene interact antagonistically to decrease damage resulting from benzene exposure. While direct exposure of experimental animals to complex mixtures in the laboratory is one way to overcome these limitations of information, it is difficult to duplicate complex environmental conditions in a laboratory setting. The exact composition of environmental mixtures can be unknown and may change over time.

11.3 RISK MANAGEMENT

11.3.1 The Need for Risk Management

While there are uncertainties associated with virtually every aspect of assessing risks, there also are ways that the uncertainties can either be overcome or at least highlighted so that assessors are aware of them. There also is a certain commonality throughout risk assessment in that it largely is the purview of scientific disciplines that have developed various mathematical ways to express conditions. Risk management, on the other hand, is not so restricted in scope and often must try to balance factors that are not easily compared or quantified.

Risk management is generally portrayed as an interactive process of identifying the options available for abating unacceptable risks, evaluating the cost-effectiveness of those options, and identifying the preferred course of action for achieving the desired risk reductions.

The management process may need to consider both actual and perceived risks. The conclusions often will not be satisfactory to all parties concerned but should allow for their input in a managed manner. The preferable outcome of risk management is the abatement of an actual risk in a cost-effective manner. The reduction of risks for reduction sake alone has little long-term benefit and may be detrimental if it consumes resources that could be used more effectively to reduce other sources of risk.

As noted in Section 11.2.5, regulatory agencies must decide how to define acceptable risks and recognize that there is little merit or economic justification in striving for lower levels. For example, chasing analytical detection limits is not considered a viable method of defining acceptable exposure, dose, or risk levels. The search for hazardous micropollutants has on occasion been compared to a "witch hunt" in which the hunters will never be fully satisfied because there is no clear proof of innocence (Mackay, 1982).

11.3.2 Factors That Often Need to Be Considered

As indicated in Figure 11.1, there are many non-technical factors that need to be incorporated into the risk management process. While it may be imperative that they be included, these factors add layers of complexity to risk management and can make the process become rather "messy" (Fischhoff, 1985).

Benefit to Society—All other factors (e.g. size of exposed population, potency) being similar, a chemical that makes vegetables more colourful ought not to be subject to the same standard of "acceptable risk" as one that is released from the processing of raw materials for important industries. Society's willingness to forgo some of those benefits in the course of reducing the risks to the public are vastly different (Dwyer and Ricci, 1989).

Litigation—The possibility of litigation by one or more parties makes the task of risk management much more difficult. Litigation may introduce delays and the possibility of additional financial risks into the process (Deisler, 1988).

Economics—The expenditures required to clean up a site, decommission a facility, or comply with air and water emission criteria can be substantial to both the company and the economy as a whole. Both the Municipal, Industrial for Abatement (MISA) program and the Clean Air Program (CAP) require that for certain types of discharges and emissions, the best technology that is "economically achievable" be used.

11.3.3 Possible Applications for Risk Management

Risk management can be used to address several types of issues:

* Is remedial action required?
* What level of risk is acceptable?
* What is the optimum remedial action?
* What priorities should be assigned to action items?

The first two issues can arise when evaluating situations such as the decommissioning of a property or during the assessment of air emissions or liquid discharges. Once a decision has been made that remediation is required an assessment of options must be conducted. A preliminary risk assessment of each option can assist in the identification of the optimal alternative.

Assigning priorities to action items is critical if resources such as funding, manpower, technical equipment, and technical expertise are scarce. No government agency or company can immediately implement activities for all actual or potential situations which require remediation. Some of the activities must wait until additional resources can be made available.

An example of a need for prioritization is the clean-up of hazardous waste sites in Canada and the United States which for various reasons have become the responsibility of federal and/or provincial agencies. The average cost of cleaning up such sites is likely several million dollars. In the United States, there now are more than 1000 sites on the National Priority List (NPL) of the Superfund Program.

A recent assessment of the decision process used at the NPL sites suggests that the Superfund program lacks clear priorities (Travis and Doty, 1989). The current goal of the program to restore every site on the NPL to a pristine state is not realistic, given the costs involved and the unavailability of effective and permanent remedial technologies. Those authors indicate that the highest priority of the Superfund program should be to identify sites that pose a clear and immediate threat to human health and the environment and to remediate them using proven and effective technologies.

11.4 RISK COMMUNICATION

11.4.1 Overview

Risk communication must be an integral part of risk management. It cannot merely be passed along to the public relations staff or community affairs department, especially if most of the inquiries will be handled by the plant or environmental manager. These individuals also must be able to communicate effectively to avoid damaging the company's reputation (Sandman, 1986).

11.4.2 The Media

Most managers would probably prefer that the media and the public go away and leave them to do their jobs. Since it is highly likely that the media and public will persist, it is imperative that the managers understand how to communicate effectively with the media and the public and to anticipate the sorts of information that are likely to be of greatest interest. While communications often becomes a source of confusion, the risks of avoiding the media may be far greater than the risks of working with them (Sandman, 1986).

Preparation—It is important to remember that a reporter's job is news, not education: events, not issues or principles. The news is the "risky" thing that has happened, not the difficult determination of the numerical risk value. A reporter may seek answers to simple direct questions such as: What happened? How did it happen? Who's to blame? and What are the authorities/company doing? The media focuses on the politics of risk rather than the science of risk (Sandman, 1986).

Response—It is important that a company makes its position known and realizes that a story will be covered, whether or not it arranges to be included. Environmental risk stories often turn into political stories in part because political content is more readily available and understood than technical content.

In responding to questions from the media or members of the public, keep the following points in mind (Sandman, 1986):

- provide facts; never guess or lie
- if you do not know, say so but get back to the reporter
- remember that journalists, deadlines are measured in minutes not months
- decide in advance main points
- stress points consistently and repetitively
- leave out technical qualifiers
- leave in important qualifiers
- do not use technical jargon
- explain technical terms if considered essential

The journalists will want the response to be on one side or another of a situation; i.e. safe versus unsafe, legal versus illegal. They do not want to dwell on the complex nuances of intermediate positions as the length of their news story seldom allows for a lengthy response. Managers, scientists, and technical staff often resent the pressure from journalist to dichotomize and simplify an issue.

11.4.3 Members of the Public

Whether through regulatory requirement or as a result of voluntary programs, information on facilities toxic chemicals may have to be presented to the public. In Ontario, the Canadian Chemical Producers' Association (CCPA) has taken the bold step of establishing a "Community Right to Know Policy" in its "Responsible Care" document. The policy recognizes the need and the right of the public to know the risks associated with the operations and products present in or transported through communities (CCPA, not dated).

Successful communication begins with the realization that risk perception is predictable, that the public overreacts to certain sorts of risks and ignores others, and that you cannot know in advance whether the communication problem will be panic or apathy (Sandman, 1986). There is no way to present risk data which is neutral, only ways that are alarming or reassuring in varying degrees.

It is important to remember when communicating to the public that society has reached a near-consensus that pollution is morally wrong. Some agencies are quick to realize this and to deal with environmental risk in terms of "good-and-evil" instead of "costs-and-benefits".

The use of quantitative risk assessments, risk-benefit calculations, risk-cost ratios, and risk comparisons are difficult for individuals to accept when they are being asked to bear the risks and someone else makes the decision. The process of who decides can be a key factor, in most cases much more that the substantive issues. Consider the example of a town being selected as the future site of a hazardous waste treatment facility. The community, offended at this infringement of local autonomy, prepares to stop the facility by collecting information on the unacceptability of the site and initiates litigation. Both their anger and the legal process itself encourage community members to overestimate the risk of the proposed facility and to resist any argument that some package of mitigation, compensation, and incentives might actually yield a net gain in the community's health and safety, as well as its prosperity (Sandman, 1986).

People will participate more if they exercise some real control over an ultimate decision. In response to this need, regulatory agencies are trying to encourage public participation on various issues. Many previous public participation exercises have been perceived as being too little too late, and often involving only draft decisions. As a result, many members of the public believe that they will not be taken seriously.

Table 11.1 presents rules and guidelines published by the U.S. Environmental Protection Agencies for effective risk communication. Rules and guidelines like these can be used as a foundation for a company's risk communication program and lead to a constructive interaction with the community.

In Ontario, the Environmental Assessment Act (EAA) and Environmental Protection Act (EPA) both allow for input from the public. For example, there is a requirement to conduct a public hearing before issuing a certificate of approval for the use, operation, establishment, alteration, enlargement or extension of a waste disposal site for the disposal of hauled liquid waste or hazardous wastes (see Section 4.6.4). For areas of concern on the Great Lakes, Remedial Action Plan (RAP) teams have been formed consisting of stakeholders from various governments, industry, environmental groups and concerned citizens. It is anticipated that this approach will be employed in the future by the MOE to resolve other areas of environmental concern.

11.5 SUMMARY

Risk assessment and risk management are likely to play an increasingly important role in environmental decision-making. The ever-increasing number of environmental issues and the realization that there are insufficient resources to address all concerns will continue to support the need for risk assessment and management.

The process of assessing risks often consists of four parts: hazard identification, exposure assessment, dose-response assessment and risk characterization. The information obtained from a risk assessment is only one part of the overall package needed to conduct risk management. Risk management is an interactive process of identifying the options available for abating unacceptable risks, evaluating the cost-effectiveness of those options, and identifying the preferred course of action for achieving the desired risk reductions.

An integral part of risk management is risk communication. It is imperative that managers understand how to communicate effectively with the media and the public and to anticipate the sorts of information that are likely to be of greatest interest. Whether through regulatory requirements or voluntary programs, information concerning the toxic chemicals used at a facility may have to be presented to the public. It is important that the information be communicated effectively.

REFERENCES

California Air Pollution Control Districts, 1987. "Toxic Air Pollutant Source Assessment Manual for California Air Pollution Applications for Air Pollutant Control District Permits". Prepared by the Inter-Agency Working Group, October.

Canadian Chemical Producers' Association (CCPA), not dated. "Responsible Care: A Total Commitment".

Cohrssen, J.J., and Covello, V.T., 1989. "Risk Analysis: A Guide to Principles and Methods for Analyzing Health and Environmental Risks". United States Council on Environmental Quality, Executive Office of the President, ISBN 0-934213-20-8.

Deisler, P.F., 1988. "The Risk Management-Risk Assessment Interface". Environ. Sci. and Technol., Vol. 22, No. 1., pp. 15-19.

Dwyer, J.P., and Ricci, P.F., 1989. "Coming to Terms with Acceptable Risks". Environ. Sci. and Technol., Vol. 23, No. 2, pp. 145-146.

Fischhoff, B., 1985. Issues in Science and Technol., Vol 2(1), pp. 83-96.

Lioy, P.J., 1990. "Assessing Total Human Exposure to Contaminants—A Multidisciplinary Approach". Environ. Sci. and Technol., Vol. 24, No. 7, pp. 938-945.

Mackay, D., 1982. "Nature and Origin of Micropollutants". Wat. Sci. Tech., Vol. 14, pp. 5-14.

Sandman, P.M., 1986. "Explaining Environmental Risk". U.S. Environmental Protection Agency, Office of Toxic Substances, Washington, D.C., November.

Travis, C.C., and Doty, C.B., 1989. "Superfund: A Program Without Priorities". Environ. Sci. and Technol., Vol. 23, No. 11, pp. 1333-1334.

Travis, C.C., and Hattemer-Frey, H.A., 1987. "Human Exposure to 2,3,7,8-TCDD". Chemosphere, Vol. 16., pp. 2331-2342.

U.S. Environmental Protection Agency (EPA), 1986. Fed. Register, 51, 33992-34003.

SUGGESTED FURTHER READING

The Conservation Foundation, 1985. "Risk Assessment and Risk Control". Washington, D.C.

Covello, V.T. and Allen, F., 1988. "Seven Cardinal Rules of Risk Communication". Washington, D.C., U.S. Environmental Protection Agency, Office of Policy Analysis.

Covello, V.T., Sandman, P.M., and Slovic, P., 1988. "Risk Communication, Risk Statistics, and Risk Comparisons: A Manual for Plant Managers". Chemical Manufacturers' Association, Washington, D.C.

Paustenbach, D.J. (ed.), 1989. "The Risk Assessment Of Environmental and Human Health Hazards: A Textbook of Case Studies". J. Wiley & Sons.

United States Environmental Protection Agency (EPA), 1986. "Superfund Public Health Evaluation Manual". Office of Emergency and Remedial Response, Office of Solid Waste and Emergency Response, U.S. EPA, EPA 540/1-86/060.

Table 11.1
EPA RULES AND GUIDELINES FOR EFFECTIVE RISK COMMUNICATION

Rule 1. ACCEPT AND INVOLVE THE PUBLIC AS A LEGITIMATE PARTNER
Guideline: Demonstrate your respect for the public and your sincerity by involving the community early, before important decisions are made. Make it clear that you understand the appropriateness of basing decisions about risks on factors other than the magnitude of the risk. Involve all parties that have an interest or a stake in the particular risk in question.

Rule 2. PLAN CAREFULLY AND EVALUATE PERFORMANCE
Guideline: Begin with clear, explicit objectives such as providing information to the public, motivating individuals to act, stimulating emergency response, or contributing to conflict resolution. Classify the different subgroups among your audience. Aim your communication at specific subgroups. Recruit spokespersons who are good at presentation and interaction. Train your staff, including technical staff, in communication skills, rewarding outstanding performance. Whenever possible, pretest your messages. Carefully evaluate your efforts and learn from your mistakes.

Rule 3. LISTEN TO YOUR AUDIENCE
Guideline: Do not make assumptions about what people know, think, or want done about risks. Take the time to find out what people are thinking: use techniques such as interviews, focus groups, and surveys. Let all parties that have an interest or a stake in the issue be heard. Recognize people's emotions. Let people know that you understand what they said. Recognize the "hidden agendas", symbolic meanings, and broader economic or political considerations that often underlie and complicate the task of risk communication.

Rule 4. BE HONEST, FRANK AND OPEN
Guideline: State your credentials; but do not ask or expect to be trusted by the public. If you do not know an answer or are uncertain, say so. Get back to people with answers. Admit mistakes. Disclose risk information as soon as possible (emphasizing any appropriate reservations about reliability). If in doubt, lean toward sharing more information, not less—or people may think you are hiding something. Discuss data uncertainties, strengths and weaknesses—including the ones identified by other credible sources. Identify worst-case estimates as such, and cite ranges of risk estimates when appropriate.

Rule 5. COORDINATE AND COLLABORATE WITH OTHER CREDIBLE SOURCES

Guideline: Closely coordinate all inter- and intraorganizational communications. Devote effort and resources to the slow, hard work of building bridges with other organizations. Use credible intermediates. Try to issue communications jointly with other trustworthy sources such as credible university scientists, physicians, trusted local officials, and opinion leaders.

Rule 6. MEET THE NEEDS OF THE MEDIA

Guideline: Be open with and accessible to reporters. Respect their deadlines. Provide information tailored to the needs of each type of media, such as graphics and other visual aids for television. Provide background material for the media on complex risk issues. Follow up on stories with praise or criticism, as warranted. Try to establish long-term relationships of trust with editors and reporters.

Figure 11.1
RISK ASSESSMENT AND RISK
MANAGEMENT PROCESSES

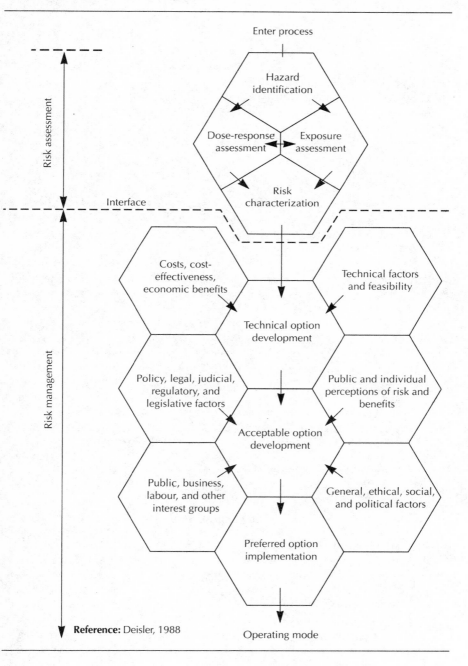

Reference: Deisler, 1988

Figure 11.2
SCHEMATIC PLOT OF RESPONSE AS A
FUNCTION OF EXPOSURE

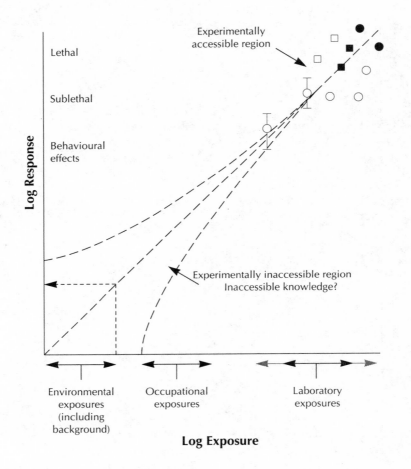

Reference: MacKay, 1982

12.0

Emergency Planning and Spills

12.1 BACKGROUND

Despite the training, procedures, and other precautions that may be taken, spills still occur as a result of equipment failure, transportation accidents, third-party involvement, and human error. Current legislation in Ontario places far-reaching obligations on companies and individuals to report and clean up spills. It is a corporation's responsibility to show reasonable care by ensuring that records of inspection and maintenance of equipment are kept, employees receive adequate spill training, and equipment and procedures are available to respond to spills.

12.2 LEGAL REQUIREMENTS FOR NOTIFICATION

12.2.1 Environmental Protection Act

Section 14(1) of the EPA requires every person who discharges a contaminant or causes the discharge into the natural environment out of the normal course of events that may cause an adverse effect to "forthwith notify" the MOE.

Part IX of the EPA (commonly known as the "Spills Bill") deals specifically with spills of pollutants. Section 80(1) of Part IX requires that a person having control of the pollutant or every person who spills or causes a spill which is likely to cause an adverse effect should immediately notify:

- the MOE
- the municipality/regional municipality
- the "owner" of the pollutant
- the person who has control of the pollutant

In addition, employees of a public authority who know of a spill are also required to notify the MOE.

Section 79(1)(j) defines a **spill** as a discharge into the natural environment from or out of a structure, vehicle or other container that is abnormal in quantity or quality in light of all circumstances of the discharge.

Several types of events are exempt under Part IX. These include:

- disposal of animal wastes as per normal farming practice
- air emissions which do not contravene any of the conditions of an MOE approval
- discharges to water or land, provided such discharges do not contravene any of the conditions of MOE approvals, licences or permits
- spills of water from reservoirs formed by dams
- spills of pollutants from fires equivalent to those from fires of ten or fewer households.

Several types of discharges are exempt from the notification requirements of the Spills Bill; however, other provisions such as clean-up are required under Regulation 618/85:

- Planned spills such as would be generated by some industry start-up or shut-down procedures and for spill training exercises. This exemption is on condition that a MOE director be notified in advance and consents, and that the release is monitored.
- Spills of less than 100 litres of vehicular fuels, lubricants, and coolants from a motor vehicle if the liquids have not entered and are not likely to enter any surface water or well and on the condition that notification under the Highway Traffic Act, if required, has been made.
- Water discharges from broken municipal water mains where there is no personal injury and no damage to buildings. (These incidents are also exempt from the reporting of Section 14 of the EPA.)
- Sewer bypass overflows through approved bypass systems if the bypass was caused by precipitation or runoff.

A sewer discharge through a bypass must be reported if an adverse effect is likely, or if water quality impairment may occur.

12.2.2 Ontario Water Resources Act

The OWRA has similar notification requirements to those of the EPA. For example, Section 16(2) requires every person that discharges or causes or permits the discharge of any material of any kind, and such discharge is not in the normal course of events, or that lets material of any kind escape into any waters or on any shore or bank or into any place that may impair the quality of any waters, to immediately notify the Minister.

The main difference between the EPA and OWRA reporting requirements is the use of the term "may" in the OWRA versus "likely" in the EPA with respect to adverse effects or impairment. It is more difficult to prove that a pollutant is likely to impair (the OWRA phrase) than it is to prove that a contaminant may impair (the EPA wording).

12.2.3 Gasoline Handling Act

Section 8 of the Gasoline Handling Act (GHA) requires the owner of above- or underground storage tank or lines to arrange for tests which are acceptable to the Director and to report all leaks to the nearest inspector or Fire Prevention Authority within twelve hours of discovering a leak.

Section 10 requires that the owner and the operator of the facility must notify the Director verbally or in writing as quickly as possible (and not longer than 24 hours) if it appears that a fire or explosion has occurred due to the handling or use of gasoline or any associated product.

An important precedent set by Ontario courts is the concept of "one door" incident reporting. It has been ruled that when a spill is reported to the Ministry of Consumer and Commercial Relations (MCCR) under the GHA, the requirement for reporting to the MOE for "sister" legislation also is met.

12.2.4 Transportation of Dangerous Goods Act

If a **dangerous occurrence** happens, such as a spill of dangerous goods or wastes regulated by the Transportation of Dangerous Goods Act (TDGA), the person in charge at the time must immediately notify certain government offices (see Section 4.5.6). Table 12.1 presents the quantities or levels for which immediate reporting is required. In Ontario, the local police must be called to satisfy the immediate reporting requirements. The TDGA Regulations list various reporting centres throughout Canada for immediate reporting requirements.

A written report must be made to Transport Canada for some dangerous goods occurrences as specified in Section 9.14 of the TDGA regulation. In addition, shipping documents for chemicals listed in Schedule XII of the regulations must carry 24-hour emergency phone numbers to comply with TDGA regulations. Many dangerous goods occurrences are also spills under the EPA and carry requirements for reporting to several agencies.

Examples of other reportable events include the loss, theft or misplacement of a consignment of product for certain classes of dangerous goods, and the discharge, emission or escape of dangerous goods from any packaging or means of transport.

12.2.5 Canadian Environmental Protection Act

A release of a toxic substance (as defined by Schedule 1) into the environment, or the reasonable likelihood of a release, is in contravention of the Canadian Environmental Protection Act (CEPA). Section 36 requires that a person who owns or has charge of a substance immediately before its initial release or its likely initial release into the environment, or who causes or contributes to the initial release or increases the likelihood of the initial release, must report the incident as soon as possible in the circumstances and make a reasonable effort to notify any member of the public who may be adversely affected by the release or likely release.

12.2.6 Ontario Spills Action Centre

The MOE has a **Spills Action Centre** (SAC) which can be reached by dialling the following 24-hour toll-free number:

1-800-268-6060

The SAC staff will determine whether the report is to be handled as a spill or an environmental complaint. If it is a spill, the staff may ask for the following information:

- name and address
- telephone number/call-back number
- circumstances of the spill
- material spilled (including chemical composition)
- source of spill
- quantity spilled
- weather conditions
- action being taken to clean up the spill
- involvement of other agencies

The SAC works closely with response agencies such as police, fire departments, the Canadian Coast Guard, and other reporting or information centres such as the National Environmental Emergencies Centre (CANUTEC). SAC and CANUTEC can provide technical advice on emergency response and clean-ups.

All telephone conversations are recorded by SAC for future reference and potentially as a basis for prosecution. Upon receipt of the notification, SAC may take the following steps (MOE, 1988):

- contact suspected pollution source in an attempt to verify and resolve the problem
- contact local MOE personnel to initiate the field response
- contact other agencies or potentially affected parties as needed such as police, fire departments, ambulance, local municipalities, Coast Guard and/or U.S. authorities, etc.
- notify senior MOE management if the incident is considered serious and coordinate information flow to the public
- for a major incident, contact the Minister's office and convey orders or directions from the Minister where necessary
- maintain liaison with the agencies in charge of public safety in an emergency and coordinate MOE supporting efforts
- provide information on chemicals and clean-up techniques

12.2.7 Aspects of Uncertainty

There are several less-than-clear aspects that concern the reporting of spills. Two such areas are the ways and terms used to define spills and the obligations and procedures of forthwith notification.

Words like "adverse effect", "impair", "deleterious substance" are used to define spill scenarios in the EPA, OWRA, and Fisheries Act. All of these phrases having some reliance on the quantity spilled and properties (chemical/physical and toxicological) of the particular material.

The EPA definition of adverse effect covers everything from the impairment (damage and/or rendering unfit) of any part of the environment to the loss of enjoyment of the property (Part I, Section 1(a)).

Questions which emerge from these definitions are related to small quantities of material. For example, is it necessary to report the spillage of a gallon of paint on bare ground inside a facility because of the small potential for vapour emissions and contamination of soil or to report a broken mercury thermometer because of the release of mercury vapours into the surrounding air? In principle, the MOE requires that a spill be reported if there is contamination of the environment.

The strict interpretation of the law can lead to two extremes. One company may report all spills and discharges regardless of the adverse effect/impairment clause while a second company only reports what it feels are substantial spills. The first company feels it is being a good "corporate citizen" by reporting everything but the associated effort may tie up a large portion of the environmental staff's time. It also may gain a reputation of being a company that has frequent incidents. The latter point can be very important if the number of spills are reported to the public without corresponding text indicating that this company takes a rigorous approach to reporting. It also can be important if the information is presented during a court trial involving the company to illustrate deficiencies in past environmental performance.

The second type of company, while potentially not generating negative publicity, is putting itself and its directors into a position of potential litigation.

Both the OWRA and the EPA require the **forthwith notification** of a spill. This gives rise to questions as to what action should be taken and, more importantly, the time period spent on that action prior to notification.

In an ideal world, sufficient personnel would be present to initiate action to stop and/or mitigate the effect of the spill and notify the appropriate parties. Unfortunately, in most cases there are insufficient personnel to perform both tasks.

It is usually during the first few minutes of a spill that the greatest mitigation, such as turning off valves or laying down adsorbent material, can be performed. Accordingly, priority should be placed on performing short-duration tasks. During the first "break" in the action, the MOE and other parties should be notified. It is important to avoid the mentality that "If I did a little bit more, I would not have to report it".

12.3 LEGAL REQUIREMENTS FOR RESTORATION

12.3.1 Environmental Protection Act

Section 81(1) of the Spills Bill portion of the EPA requires the owner of a pollutant and the person having control of a pollutant that is spilled and that causes or is likely to cause adverse effects to do everything practicable to prevent, eliminate, and ameliorate the adverse effects and to restore the natural environment.

The scope and duty to clean up and restore the environment is restricted to what is considered "practicable". Section 79 of the EPA indicates that for determining what practicable means, attention should be paid to the technical, physical and financial resources that are at hand or that can be made reasonably available.

The restoration of the environment is defined in Section 79(1)(i) of the EPA to include all forms of life, physical conditions, the natural environment and things existing immediately before the spill of the pollutant that are affected or that may reasonably be expected to be affected by the pollutant.

Section 87(2) of the EPA indicates that the owner of the pollutant or the person having control is responsible for the costs of cleaning up a spill and may be legally responsible for loss and damage as a direct result of the spill.

The MOE staff sent to investigate a spill site will:

- determine nature and extent of environmental damage
- evaluate the adequacy of the clean-up and restoration efforts and recommend appropriate procedures where applicable
- help to enforce the legislated responsibilities imposed on the discharger
- recommend spill prevention measures
- document all findings, actions and recommendations
- transfer documents to the Investigation and Enforcement Branch of the Ministry where appropriate

The involvement of the MOE Investigation and Enforcement Branch will depend on the circumstances involved in the incident (refer to Chapter 8).

12.3.2 Gasoline Handling Act

When a leak is suspected at an underground storage tank, Section 8 of the GHA obliges the owner to arrange for pressure tests and the immediate repair or replacement of any leaking systems. The owner also must take steps to recover the escaped product and remove any contaminated soil before installing a replacement tank.

12.3.3 Environmental Compensation Corporation

The Environmental Compensation Corporation is a Crown corporation established to compensate any person, including an owner or person having control of the pollutant, for loss or damage incurred as a direct result of the spill of a pollutant or neglect or fault in carrying out an order or direction under the EPA.

The EEC may pay compensation to an owner or person having control, if such individuals have had to pay compensation to spill victims but were not themselves at fault for the spill.

The ECC does not replace the role of insurance companies, nor does it lessen the illegal responsibilities of those involved in a spill.

12.4 SPILL PREVENTION

Spill prevention is a cornerstone of environmental protection. Several steps can be taken to ensure the prevention of releases into the environment. Human error, whether in the form of improper procedures, lack of training, or poor engineering, has shown to be the cause of approximately 75% of all hazardous chemical spills (Shrives, 1987).

There are several types of programs that a facility may undertake to improve spill prevention capabilities and ensure "due diligence".

An important part of spill prevention is the **training** of employees on spill prevention and response. Regular updates of spill notification and response procedures as well as hazardous chemical handling, storage and disposal are important.

Testing of a response system is critical, as one can never be sure that the plan will work unless one tests it. At some facilities "spill drills" analogous to fire drills are practised to ensure that all parties know their responsibilities and can carry them out in a professional manner.

The key to any prevention program is **planned maintenance**. Equipment failure often contributes to spills, whether directly or indirectly. The MOE no longer entertains the defense of equipment failure if planned maintenance was not being carried out in a scheduled manner.

Because many spills result from the failure of equipment, **backup equipment** is being seen as the only way in which spills can be prevented. It also is looked upon by the MOE as an integral part of spill prevention.

Procedures must be in place for the handling, storage and transportation of hazardous materials such as chlorine, asbestos, and ammonia. A first step in establishing procedures may be to obtain copies of government reference books on spill response—for example, "Environmental and Technical Information for Problem Spills (EnviroTIPS)" and "Manual for Spills of Hazardous Materials" (Environment Canada, 1984a and 1984b). Both publications are produced by Environment Canada to assist in the design of countermeasures for spills and to assess their impact on the environment. Currently there are 50 EnviroTIPS manuals which cover common and widely used hazardous compounds. The Manual for Spills of Hazardous Materials provides qualitative and quantitative information on 220 chemicals for those responding to or planning for hazardous material spills.

The Centre for Occupational Health and Safety provides information on 27,000 substances as part of its "CCINFO disc". The CCINFO data base includes information on the substances, physical and chemical properties, and toxicological hazards. Additional lists of references may be obtained from the MOE SAC office and CANUTEC.

Environmental audits can be used to ensure that appropriate procedures have been developed and are being followed. Chapter 10 presents a more detailed discussion of environmental audits. **Hazard assessments** can identify areas of potential vulnerability, deficiencies in scheduled maintenance, etc.

A critical part of prevention is the **containment** of a potential hazardous material by using berms, dykes, or storage ponds. Containment allows for the collection and potential treatment or disposal of a substance in a controlled manner. It may also allow a facility to continue discharges from process areas and thus continue operations, thereby reducing expensive down-time.

There is a growing trend towards the **elimination** of hazardous chemicals **substitution** with non-hazardous chemicals. If it is at all practical, chemicals that are spilled more frequently or in large volumes should be substituted with products that pose lesser environmental concerns.

Important environmental parameters to review when assessing the material the degree of safety are aquatic toxicity (e.g. the lethal concentration at which 50% of fish are killed), persistence (the ability of the substance to degrade) and bioaccumulation (the ability of the substance to accumulate in humans and wildlife). For example, prior to selecting a hydraulic oil, data could be a collected concerning operational specifications, aquatic toxicity, persistence, and costs (both purchase and disposal). If more than one product was able to meet the operational specifications, the next two criteria would be assessed with the goal of reducing the environmental impact of a potential spill.

The **modification of processes/systems** may, in the long run, be the most cost-effective way to achieve compliance as various pieces of legislation place more and more responsibility on a discharger to mitigate losses. An example of a system modification would be the use of recirculating cooling water as opposed to once-through cooling water. A leak of a chemical into the cooling water would stay within the system and provide an opportunity for corrective action.

12.5 TYPES OF EMERGENCY PROCEDURES AND PLANS

12.5.1 Emergency Response Plans

Emergency response plans should be developed for any facility where hazardous materials are used. A response plan for on-site emergencies should include:

- maps showing evacuation route(s)
- maps indicating location of potential hazards accompanied by brief description of each
- descriptions of alarm systems and locations
- shutdown procedures and valves/switches locations
- list of individuals responsible for shut down
- "call-out" procedure for employees and visitors
- names, addresses and phone numbers of neighbours
- contact number for police, fire, MOE, municipality, etc.
- contact number for up-to-date meteorological data

Some facilities require that an up-to-date, operational emergency plan be developed based on a site-specific risk assessment.

In the event of an off-site spill or a spill at a place with off-site effects, a company representative should be dispatched to the site immediately to ensure that all action is being taken to mitigate the effect of the spill and that the clean-up and restoration is being done properly and in compliance with MOE and TDGA requirements.

For certain dangerous substances, specified in Schedule XII of the TDGA (such as infectious waste, explosives, certain gases, and radioactive wastes) the generator or consignor of the waste must file an emergency response plan with the Director General of the TDGA. Documents for each shipment of the dangerous goods must show the emergency response plan number and the telephone number for actuating the plan. The plan should allow for a qualified person to be dispatched to the accident to deal with the emergency.

Currently, the MOE has no legal requirement for spill contingency plans to be in place at a facility although it is strongly encouraged. The MOE has the legal authority, however, to request a contingency plan under Section 17 of the EPA. In the United States, emergency response plans are required under Title III of the Superfund Amendments and

Reauthorization act (SARA) of 1988.

The Canadian Manufacturers' Association (CMA) has published an informative guide to emergency planning. The guide was prepared as a basic resource for the development and implementation of emergency response plan at the facilities of CMA members (CMA, 1989).

12.5.2 Incident Reporting and Clean-up Procedures

Incident reporting and clean-up procedures are essential to ensure proper notification and clean-up action. Many facilities have incident procedures which only cover reporting. This situation may result in confusion if easy-to-follow clean-up procedures are not available which have been reviewed by experienced personnel prior to the incident.

The procedures should provide step-by-step instructions for several types of actions:

- classification of spill
- individuals to notify
- emergency equipment and storage location
- monitoring, e.g. aquatic toxicity
- clean-up contractors and registered haulers

Every incident must be classified (using the MOE definitions) as to whether or not it will result in an adverse effect or impairment. This includes adverse effects or impairment as well as the likelihood of same to the natural environment within the plant property and the threat to the safety of any worker. If the release is classified as a spill, the requirements of EPA Part IX must be acted upon immediately. If the consensus is that the release is not a spill, internal procedures should be followed.

Individuals to be notified should include both internal and external parties. Names, titles, and telephone number(s) (including home numbers for employees) should be included in the procedure. It is essential that this portion of the procedure be updated frequently.

Monitoring of the environment is essential after a release or spill has occurred to assess the potential "adverse effect" on the environment and to assist in identifying further remedial actions. The monitoring may include fish toxicity tests and testing for appropriate physical and chemical characteristics.

The MOE may require monitoring of the area during and following the clean-up. A short-term assessment may include fish toxicity testing and organic/inorganic chemical analysis. A long-term assessment may include biomonitoring for changes in the benthic community (bottom dwellers), levels in sediment and vegetation, bioaccumulation in aquatic organisms, residual toxicity, and contamination of food resources (Laughton, 1989).

It is important that background information on the area be obtained to determine if an adverse effect has truly occurred. Some monitoring should be performed as a proactive step.

A list of clean-up contractors should be kept and updated frequently. Some facilities have clean-up contractors on retainer to ensure a better response time. In addition, a list of registered haulers (see Chapter 4) should also be kept. It does little good to do a great clean-up job only to have the waste taken off-site by an unregistered hauler and face the possibility of receiving a violation notice.

Table 12.2 presents equipment which may be stored on-site to assist in spill containment and clean-up. The equipment includes spill protection and foul-weather gear for workers, equipment to contain and clean-up the spill and monitoring paraphernalia. The availability of plywood sheets has been found in the past to prove very useful in the containment of a spill. A totally encapsulated suit and self-contained breathing apparatus should be available for situations where there is the possibility of hazardous or unknown vapours.

Even if all of the above steps or more are followed, a company may still be liable if the same type of spill occurs on a frequent basis. It is imperative that a positive paper trail of investigation into the spill, development of recommendations, and implementation of the recommendations be undertaken to eliminate or at least mitigate future spills. The "tallying" of spills with no further action leaves a company in an awkward position with regards to its "due diligence".

12.6 BEST MANAGEMENT PRACTICE PLANS

Best Management Practice (BMP) plans may be generally defined as the processes, procedures, human actions or actual construction activities that prevent toxic pollutants or hazardous substances from damaging the aquatic environment. They include any actions or procedures that anyone from the plant manager to a consultant can identify as a means of pollution abatement.

It is anticipated that the MOE will require some form of BMP plans at industrial facilities as part of the Municipal, Industrial Strategy for Abatement (MISA) program for both direct and indirect dischargers (see Chapter 3). The concept of BMP is included in the MOE Model Sewer Use By-Law which, in turn, has been incorporated into municipal sewer by-laws. It is also anticipated that similar programs soon will be used in other provinces.

BMP plans, as defined by MISA, will be used to control on-site spills, leaks and run-off from raw materials storage and handling areas. In many instances, the first step towards developing a BMP will be to create a BMP Committee and assign it the responsibility of preparing the BMP plan and assisting in its implementation, maintenance, and updating. Plant management is responsible and accountable for the plan's quality.

The activities and responsibilities of the BMP Committee should include:

- identify toxic and hazardous materials to be addressed
- identify potential spill sources
- develop incident reporting procedures
- establish inspections and records procedures
- periodically review BMP for possible changes
- coordinate incident notification, response and clean-up procedures
- establish training programs for personnel
- assist in the interdepartmental coordination of plan implementation

The BMP committee should use **risk identification/assessment** to identify those plant areas requiring BMP to the plant engineering group, environmental engineer, and others. All ancillary sources need to be examined to determine the potential risk of toxic pollutant or hazardous substances being discharged to receiving waters.

A **materials inventory** listing all hazardous substances and toxic chemicals contained on-site should be prepared. Details of this inventory will be commensurate with quantities present and potential access to receiving waters. Records of any spills, leaks, runoff or other improper discharges must be kept by means of an **incident reporting system**. Such a system will minimize recurrence, expedite mitigation or clean-ups and comply with legal requirements.

The BMP plan must provide procedures for ensuring the **material compatibility** of toxic or hazardous substances with container materials and mixtures. Containers must also be compatible with the surrounding environment. Such procedures will consider the design and operation of all equipment storing and transferring of these materials for possible non-compatibility.

The overall facility's pollution control can be enhanced when staff maintain a clean, orderly work environment. This can be accomplished by providing staff with periodic training in **good housekeeping** techniques in those areas of potential risk. Good housekeeping techniques can include:

- neat and orderly storage of bags and drums of chemicals,
- prompt spill clean-up to prevent significant runoff, and
- sweeping, vacuuming, etc. of dry chemical accumulations.

Preventive maintenance (PM) involves the inspection and testing of a facility's equipment and systems to uncover conditions leading to possible breakdowns or failures, resulting in discharges. Prevention occurs through adjustment, repair or replacement.

A part of the PM program involves the maintenance of a record system to schedule tests and inspections, record results and to facilitate any required corrective actions. This BMP element is intended to evaluate the current PM program by qualified plant personnel to recommend any changes to bring it in line with other BMP requirements.

The recommended PM program should include the identification of equipment and systems to which the program will apply. It also involves periodic inspections and tests of these systems and equipment as well as the maintenance of complete PM records.

A **record system** should be developed to document all incidents and to track the responses and corrective actions. In addition, inspections should be made to ensure appropriate spill protection and procedures are in place.

The accidental or intentional entry to a facility resulting in sabotage, theft, etc. can be prevented by incorporating a **security** system. Security systems should be detailed in the BMP plan along with any necessary improvements to ensure no toxic chemical discharges from unauthorized entry.

Any **training program** must ensure that all employees understand the BMP plan. The program should emphasize plant processes and materials, safety hazards, discharge prevention practices, as well as proper and rapid response procedures. Information meetings should be held at least once a year to highlight individual responsibilities. In addition, any incidents, equipment programs, or changes to the BMP plan should be reviewed. Spill or environmental incident drills are encouraged to improve employees' reactions to situations and incidents. These drills, held at least semi-annually, must form a fundamental part of any training program.

12.7 SHARING EMERGENCY RESPONSE INFORMATION

12.7.1 Response Organizations and Associations

The Province of Ontario has a contingency for spills of oils and other hazardous materials that is designed to deal with spills where:

- the incident is beyond the capabilities of the party responsible,
- the responsible party fails to respond,
- the source of a major spill cannot be established easily, or
- upon request for assistance.

The plan complements the Joint Canada-United States Marine Pollution Contingency Plan and the National Marine Emergency Plan (MOE, 1989). As part of MOE efforts to foster spill readiness, various training films and reports are available via the MOE Spill Action Centre.

Several industrial associations and local industries have formed spill response groups to share resources and costs so that a cost-efficient and timely response capability can be achieved.

The Transportation Emergency Assistance Plan (TEAP) was developed by the Canadian Chemical Producers' Association as a Canada-wide emergency response program. TEAP allows for companies to share resources by pooling data, equipment and expertise. The TEAP program includes procedure manuals and training. Currently there are eleven sites across Canada which have response teams that are available 24 hours a day. In addition, there are 20 voluntary response centres.

The Hamilton Harbour Spill Control Group is an example of a cooperative venture undertaken by a group of companies. It provides funding and assistance in the advent of a spill to the Hamilton Harbour. The group is coordinated by the Hamilton Harbour Commission.

12.7.2 The Role of the Community

A spill contingency plan should be developed with community involvement. The Canadian Chemical Producers' Association (CCPA) document entitled "Community Awareness and Emergency Response Code of Practice" outlines various forms that community involvement can take. It encourages each member to develop an emergency response plan which:

- identifies situations where company materials or processes can have an impact upon the community in the event of an emergency
- is based upon emergency plan frameworks developed by site management to address emergency situations and assist other authorities in emergency response planning for neighbouring industry and the community
- integrates the company's emergency response planning and organization with those of industrial neighbours and the community into a community emergency response plan
- is communicated regularly, in its key elements, to the community, and in a manner which recognizes their right to know, to gain their cooperation and support
- requires active participation, cooperation and coordination by company people with local officials and the media during the planning and communication stages

Under the Emergency Planning Act of 1983, municipalities may develop emergency disaster plans which deal with large-scale emergencies and disasters. Most incidents, however, are not of a sufficient magnitude to require the implementation of an emergency disaster plan, and therefore usually involve the traditional essential services such as fire departments, ambulance services, local police departments and, occasionally, the municipal public works department (Lesnicki, 1989).

In recent years, many municipalities have recognized that public works departments may play a more active role in responding to spills. Hence, municipal emergency response teams have been formed by some municipalities, such as the Emergency Spill Response team of the Regional Municipality of Halton. Established in 1986, the team is made up of staff from the Waste Management Division of the Public Works Department. The team receives additional training in spill response and has at its disposal a specially equipped van to deal with incidents (Lesnicki, 1989).

12.8 SUMMARY

Spill prevention is a critical component of environmental protection. Steps that should be undertaken include training, planned maintenance, backup equipment, procedures, environmental audits, containment, substitution of chemicals, and modification of processes/systems. Only by having a system in place to prevent spills can due diligence be assured.

In the event of a spill, individuals and companies are responsible for the prompt notification of the discharge to the MOE, the municipality, the owner of the pollutant, and the person who has control of the pollutant. In addition, the "Spills Bill" requires the owner of a pollutant and the person having control of the pollutant that is spilled to do everything practicable to prevent, eliminate and ameliorate the adverse effect and to restore the natural environment.

REFERENCES

Canadian Chemical Producers' Association (CCPA), not dated. "Responsible Care: A Total Commitment".

Canadian Manufacturers' Association (CMA), 1989. "A Simplified Guide to Emergency Response".

Environment Canada, 1984a. "Enviro—Technical Information for Environmental Spills: Toluene". Environmental Protection Service, March.

Environment Canada, 1984b. "Manual for Spills of Hazardous Materials". Environmental Protection Service, March.

Lesnicki, V., 1989. "Handling Spills—Technical Issues". Presented at the Spills Response and Regulation Seminar, 1 December, Toronto.

Makuch, S.M., 1989. "Environmental Liability for Spills and How to Avoid It". Presented at the Spills Response and Regulation Seminar, 1 December, Toronto.

Ontario Ministry of the Environment (MOE), 1988. "Spills—Response Program". ISBN 0-7729-3210-7.

Ontario Ministry of the Environment (MOE), 1989. "Province of Ontario Contingency Plan for Spills of Oil and Other Hazardous Materials". April.

Shrives, J.S., 1987. "Best Management Practices (BMPs) and Their Application to Ontario MISA Program". Draft Version, May 12.

Table 12.1
QUANTITIES OR LEVELS FOR IMMEDIATE REPORTING UNDER TDGA

Class and Division	Quantities or Levels
1	All
2.1 and 2.2	At least 100 L*
2.3 and 2.4	All
3	At least 200 L
4	At least 25 kg
5.1	At least 50 kg or 50 L
5.2	At least 1 kg or 1 L
6.1	At least 5 kg or 5 L
6.2	All
7	Any discharge or a radiation level exceeding 10 mSv/h at the package surface and 200 uSv/h at 1 m from the package surface
8	At least 5 kg or 5 L
9.1	At least 50 kg
9.2	At least 1 kg
9.3	At least 5 kg or 5 L

Note
* container capacity

Table 12.2
POTENTIAL EQUIPMENT FOR SPILL CONTAINMENT AND CLEAN-UP

- booms and oil skimming devices

- shovels and brooms

- pumps and vacuum equipment

- adsorbent materials

- neutralizers

- protective clothing such as respirators, gloves, etc.

- foul-weather gear

- Material Safety Data Sheets (MSDS) for all chemicals used on-site

- portable air or water monitoring devices/kits

- sample bottles and sample buckets (i.e. for fish toxicity test)

- sand, earth or vermiculite

- plywood sheets

13.0

The Role of Aquatic Toxicity in Environmental Management

13.1 BACKGROUND

Most environmental regulations are directed toward prohibiting releases of substances that can cause adverse environmental effects. The wording used in these regulations often is somewhat vague. For example, some regulations prohibit the release of "deleterious substances", others prohibit the discharge of substances in "toxic amounts", yet others prohibit releases that create "toxic conditions". The federal Fisheries Act has been used to convict persons for discharging a "toxic substance" based only on the presence of the substance. The amount of substance involved has historically been used to assess the level of damage and extent of fines.

Regulations concerning water quality were among the first to use concepts based on toxicity, no doubt because a large fish kill is an obvious sign of environmental distress or damage. As a result, the control of effluent toxicity has been incorporated into regulations, orders, approvals and guidelines for many types of commercial and industrial operations.

An extensive array of toxicity test methods have been developed that use many different test organisms and techniques for interpreting data. Some of the tests have withstood the rigours of litigation and have been incorporated into the regulation of liquid effluents and the management of aquatic environments.

13.2 TYPES OF TOXICITY TESTS

13.2.1 Acute Lethality Tests

The most common use of toxicity tests is to measure acute lethality of an effluent to an aquatic organism. This involves placing a fish or invertebrate into a series of containers each holding a different dilution of the effluent or toxicant to be evaluated. One of the containers, the control, contains only dilution water. The test organisms are observed at predetermined time intervals over a relatively short period (typically less than four days). The numbers of organisms that die in each of the dilutions provides the data used to estimate the dilution required for the effluent to be non-lethal. These tests are intended to quantify the overall toxicity of an effluent. They do not identify the substance(s) that cause the toxicity.

Several variations of this procedure have been developed to evaluate various aspects of acute lethality. Most test procedures can be described or categorized according to three characteristics: test duration, test method, and the organisms tested. The most commonly used test duration is 96 hours but shorter (typically 24-hour or 48-hour) or longer durations are also used.

Test methods largely concern how the water-effluent dilutions are managed during a test. **Static** test solutions are not renewed for the duration of the test. **Semi-static** or "static replacement" tests incorporate renewal of the test solution once every 24 hours. **Continuous flow** (or "flow-through") tests, involve replacement of the solution by the use of a device (diluter) that provides a continuous flow of effluent or toxicant dilution to the test containers. A fourth type of test, the *in situ* or "ambient water" bioassay test, requires cages to be set in a receiving river or stream at different locations to develop an effluent dilution gradient.

The organism most frequently used in static regulatory tests is the rainbow trout (*Salmo gairdneri*). The water flea (*Daphnia magna*) is becoming a frequently used organism in Ontario and will be required as a routine test organism under both the Municipal, Industrial Strategy for Abatement (MISA) program and the Fisheries Act. The fathead minnow (*Pimphales promelas*) and bluegill sunfish (*Lepomis macrochirus*) are also used but primarily in assessments of warm-water environments. Many other species of fish as well as crustaceans, aquatic plants, and algae are used for laboratory-based toxicity testing.

The **rainbow trout** has become the standard cool-water fish for freshwater pollution studies and research in aquatic toxicology. A large data bank of toxicological data has been assembled for this species over the last 20 years. Culturing of rainbow trout is well established in Canada and many hatcheries will provide eggs or young fish of appropriate size and quality for toxicity test purposes. The fish must be certified as being free of specific pathogens by Fisheries and Oceans Canada (Environment Canada, 1989).

The essential elements of the MOE protocol for trout lethal test are summarized in Table 13.1. The protocol specifies the fish requirements and specific test conditions and is virtually identical to the methods required by other provinces, Environment Canada, many U.S. states, the U.S. Environmental Protection Agency (U.S. EPA), and the American Society for Testing and Materials protocols. Under the MISA monitoring program, the toxicity testing protocol for rainbow trout requires that six effluent concentrations and a control be used. Previous toxicity testing in Ontario required only five effluent concentrations and a control.

Daphnia magna has a short life cycle capable of producing young at about two weeks of age and is relatively easy to culture in the laboratory. It is widely distributed in ponds and lakes of intermediate water hardness in Canada and the United States and has been found to be sensitive to a broad range of aquatic contaminants. One advantage of using *Daphnia magna* is that its small size (about the diameter of a large pencil head) requires less than 1% of the volume of test solution required by trout. This greatly reduces the physical requirements for sampling and transporting of effluent samples. *Daphnia magna* are generally more sensitive and respond more rapidly to some toxicants than do fish (Johnson and Finley, 1980) and are easily raised in the lab in large numbers. The toxicity test conditions of the MOE protocol for *Daphnia magna* are summarized in Table 13.1 and are similar to those of many other jurisdictions.

The results of acute lethality tests are expressed in terms of the concentration of the effluent estimated to cause the death of 50% of the test organisms. This is referred to as the 50% Lethal Concentration (or the LC_{50} value). The LC_{50} value and its 95% confidence limits are calculated graphically by plotting percentage mortality against effluent concentration or with the aid of a calculator or computer program. In the past, the term median tolerance limit (often was abbreviated as TL50 or TLm) often was used. It is synonymous with LC_{50}.

If no test organisms die after exposure to undiluted effluent, the result is reported as "non-lethal". If less than 50% of the test organisms die in undiluted effluent, the LC_{50} of the effluent is reported as greater than 100% (> 100%). If 50% or more organisms die in undiluted effluent, a statistically valid LC_{50} is calculated from the mortality data. Some jurisdictions also require that the 95% confidence limits be reported.

The highest concentration of a test substance in which no changes are observed is referred to as the "No Observed Effect Concentration" (or NOEC).

A useful expression that uses LC_{50} data is toxic units (TU), which are calculated according to the equation:

$$TU = 100 \div LC_{50} \qquad\qquad (13.1)$$

This expression is an estimate of the amount of dilution required to make the effluent non-lethal (LC_{50} >100%). For example, if an effluent has an LC_{50} of 5%, it has a TU value of 20 and requires a 19:1 dilution to become non-lethal. More toxic effluents have higher numbers of toxic units or require greater dilution than less toxic effluents.

The toxic unit value can be used to quantify the amount of toxicity being discharged per unit of time as the Toxicity Emission Rate (TER) using the equation:

$$TER = TU \times Flow \qquad\qquad (13.2)$$

The TER can be used to compare quantities of toxicity being discharged from different sewers within a single plant or to compare final discharges among plants. The TER concept places equal weight on the toxicity and the flow of the effluent.

13.2.2 Acute Sublethal Tests

While most acute tests are directed toward observing lethal effects, sublethal effects such as organism immobilization and lethargy may be observed and measured. For example, immobilization often is reported in tests with *Daphnia magna*. The numbers of immobilized organisms can be used to calculate the median effective concentration (EC_{50}) value in the same way that LC_{50} is calculated.

A number of sublethal tests have recently been developed that use bacteria as the test organism. One of these assays, known as the "Microtox", has been used to evaluate various types of effluents. The test establishes an EC_{50} value on the basis of the amount of light produced by the luminescent bacterium *Photobacterium phosphoreum*. The test requires less than one hour to conduct and less than 5 mL of solution. The test has been reported to be less sensitive than tests that use rainbow trout or water fleas (McLeay and Associates Limited, 1987). Environment Canada has discarded this test for routine monitoring because of its lack of sensitivity (Craig, 1990).

13.2.3 Sublethal Toxicity Tests

Ultimately, it will be important to estimate the extent of long-term, sublethal or chronic effects that an effluent has in the receiving environment. Chronic tests may be required under the MISA program once a discharge is shown to be non-lethal during acute toxicity testing. Several chronic tests are being used routinely to estimate the impact zone of a discharge. The test organisms are exposed over as much of the life cycle as possible or sensitive life stages are exposed that would have a chronic effect on the organism's success. The types of effects that may be observed in sublethal tests include growth, maturation, spawning, hatching, behaviour, and sensitive life stage survival.

The following are a few examples of sublethal toxicity tests (U.S. EPA, 1989):

***Ceriodaphnia Dubia* Survival and Growth:** Ten animals are exposed to different concentrations, each animal being placed in a separate exposure vessel. Each surviving organism is transferred daily into a new test vessel with freshly prepared test solution and food suspension. Once the *C. dubia* has matured and produced young (on about the third day) only the adult is transferred to fresh effluent solution and fed. After seven days, the cumulative number of young produced per female are counted. The Chronic Value is calculated as the geometric mean of the No Observed Effect Concentration (NOEC) and the Lowest Observed Effect Concentrations (LOEC).

***Daphnia Sp.* Life Cycle Toxicity Tests:** Using *Daphnia sp.* which are less than 24 hours old, ten animals are exposed to different concentrations, each animal being placed in a separate exposure vessel. The test organisms are transferred into fresh test solutions and fed every day. Once the individual daphnids have matured and produced offspring (approximately 8 to 14 days), only the adults are transferred to a fresh test solution and fed. The remaining young are examined, counted and recorded. After 21 days, all surviving first-generation daphnids are thoroughly examined, sacrificed and weighed. The Chronic LC_{50}, daphnid growth, and reproduction are then evaluated statistically.

Fathead Minnow Larval Survival and Growth: Ten newly hatched fathead minnow larvae are placed into each test vessel. The larvae are fed and after seven days of exposure are sacrificed and weighed. The Chronic LC_{50} and larval growth are evaluated using statistical methods.

Fathead Minnow Embryo Larval Survival and Teratogenicity: Fifteen eggs fertilized within 24 hours are removed from spawning substrates, washed and placed into test vessels. The test solutions are renewed daily with freshly prepared concentrations. The number of surviving, dead, and deformed larvae are recorded over a seven-day period. Seven-day embryo and larvae LC_{50} values, as well as teratogenicity endpoints, are calculated using statistical methods.

For marine environments, oysters, mussels, or other shellfish are being used for sublethal toxicity tests. In many instances, corroborative field studies and monitoring of indigenous species are required before the relevance of these tests are appreciated.

Because of the duration and costs involved, chronic toxicity tests often are not widely used for routine assessments of effluents. The State of California has incorporated sublethal toxicity tests into regulations that use fathead minnows and *Ceriodaphnia magna.*

13.3 ONTARIO REQUIREMENTS

Several provincial acts allude to aquatic toxicity as a way of evaluating effluents. The Ontario Water Resources Act (Chapter 361, Section 16(1)) prohibits persons from discharging any material into any water that "may impair water quality". The Environmental Protection Act (Chapter 141, Section 13) states that "no person shall discharge a contaminant or cause or permit the discharge of a contaminant" into the natural environment that causes or may cause an adverse effect. In addition, under the terms of the Canada-Ontario accord, Ontario has agreed to establish and enforce effluent requirements at least as stringent as federal requirements.

Acute lethality testing is a requirement of the recently introduced Municipal, Industrial Strategy for Abatement (MISA) program in Ontario (refer to Section 3.3 for additional information on MISA). Under the MISA program, most dischargers are required to perform acute toxicity testing using rainbow trout and *Daphnia magna*. The MISA program will require that the Best Available Technology - Economically Achievable (BATEA) be implemented to control all discharges in Ontario. One of the principal criteria when determining what is the Best Available Technology (BAT) will be the achievement of a non-lethal discharge.

The MISA program may also require that a Toxicity Identification Evaluation/Toxicity Reduction Evaluation (TIE/TRE) be performed if a discharge is observed to be lethal after the BATEA has been installed. The TIE/TRE approach is discussed in Section 13.5.

The MOE document entitled "Water Management Goals, Policies, Objectives and Implementation Procedures" (commonly referred to as the "Blue Book") states that one of the overall goals of the MOE is to ensure that surface waters are of a quality which is satisfactory for aquatic life (MOE, 1984). Policy 3 of that document addresses effluent regulations and indicates that bioassay tests may be required to identify discharges deleterious to aquatic organisms. Discharges which produce 96-hour LC_{50} values under static test conditions may require more rigorous biological testing to determine if additional treatment is needed to afford adequate protection to the environment. The testing may include biological responses other than mortality to demonstrate impairment.

The Blue Book recognizes the concept of a mixing zone around a discharge point; however, mixing zones should not be rapidly lethal to important aquatic life or result in conditions which cause sudden fish kills or mortality of organisms passing through the mixing zone or create barriers to the migration of fish and aquatic life (MOE, 1984). Under the MISA program, the mixing zone concept may be allowed for chronic toxicity only and not for acute toxicity.

13.4   FEDERAL REQUIREMENTS

The federal government has incorporated aquatic toxicity testing into effluent regulations and guidelines for several commercial and industrial sectors. For metal mining (excluding gold), meat and poultry product plants, potato processors, and petroleum refineries, undiluted effluent must not be fatal to more than 50% of rainbow trout in a 96-hour, flow-through test. Since the promulgation of these regulations, relatively few flow-through tests have been conducted due to the excessive logistical demands of the protocol.

The proposed national effluent regulations for pulp and paper mills may require acute lethality testing using rainbow trout and *Daphnia magna*. The regulations may also require that if a discharger fails the toxicity tests for rainbow trout three times, a Toxicity Reduction Evaluation (TRE) must be performed (see Section 13.5.2).

Environment Canada has embarked upon a multi-year development program for acute lethality tests, acute sublethality tests, and sublethal toxicity tests. The first two standardized biological test methods to be developed are for rainbow trout and *Daphnia magna* (Environment Canada, 1990a and 1990b). The new reference methods have been designed primarily to meet the needs of proposed national effluent regulations, and hence are very explicit to suit the legal framework in which they must be employed.

13.5   DETERMINING THE CAUSES OF EFFLUENT TOXICITY

13.5.1   Conventional Approach

Traditionally, when an effluent is identified as toxic to aquatic organisms, a sample of the wastewater is analyzed for certain pollutants such as those in the MISA Analytical Test Groups (ATGs) of substances or the U.S. EPA priority pollutants. The concentration of each pollutant present in a sample subsequently is compared to toxicity data for the pollutant in the published literature or the rationales for the Provincial Water Quality Objectives and the surface water guidelines of Environment Canada (Figure 13.1). Unfortunately, determining the source of an effluent's toxicity rarely is so straightforward.

The first problem encountered is one of effluent variability. There is no way to determine whether the toxicity observed over time is consistently caused by a single pollutant or combination of pollutants or a number of different pollutants, each periodically being the cause of the toxicity. Experience has shown that the latter scenario occurs frequently. Further complicating the problem is that the variability in conventional effluent monitoring parameters may not coincide with variability in the effluent of the causative toxicant (Mount and Anderson-Carnahan, 1988).

A second limitation with the conventional approach is the assumption that one or more of the ATGs or priority pollutants is the cause of the toxicity. While some of those pollutants are regulated largely due to their toxicity to aquatic organism and/or a high frequency of occurrence in discharges, the ATGs or the priority pollutants list by no means represent the universe of toxic chemicals present in wastewater. Artificially limiting the search to these compounds also limits the chances for successfully identifying the causative toxicant.

A third problem may result if a broad scan analytical technique approach is used (i.e. higher detection limits are used to reduce the costs of analyzing for a large number of chemicals). The higher detection limits may result in missing the causative chemical(s).

13.5.2 U.S. EPA Approach to Toxicant Identification

In the United States, the National Pollutant Discharge Elimination System (NPDES) includes toxicity testing requirements. Chemistry and toxicity data pertaining to the discharge are provided by the discharger, the U.S. EPA, and/or the state. The lowest one-week average flow that will likely occur once every ten years is also provided. Depending upon the data, it is then decided if toxicity limits should be incorporated into the permit.

Where toxicity limits have been imposed, the in-stream concentration of the effluent in the receiving water must not exceed the lowest observable effect concentration of the most sensitive test species. For dischargers with greater than a 100:1 dilution at low flow, there must not be acute lethality at the end of the pipe (i.e. the LC_{50} must be greater than 100%). For dischargers with less than 100:1 dilution, the dischargers also must comply with a chronic toxicity limit and the effluent concentration which occurs at the edge of the mixing zone at low flow must not cause a chronic effect.

When a discharger is not in compliance, a stepwise investigative process termed a **Toxicity Reduction Evaluation** (TRE) can be used to determine the measures needed to maintain toxicity at an acceptable level. A key part of a TRE is the **Toxicity Identification Evaluation** (TIE). Procedures for performing TIEs have recently been developed by the U.S. EPA National Effluent Toxicity Assessment Centre (NETAC). The NETAC approach is divided into three phases (Burkhard and Ankley, 1989):

Phase I   - identification of physical and chemical nature of toxicant(s)
Phase II - identify toxicant(s)
Phase III - confirm suspected toxicant(s)

Figure 13.2 shows the relationships of the NETAC approach to TIE with the overall TRE process.

Phase I of the TIE is used to characterize certain physical and chemical properties of the toxicant(s) using a series of relatively simple, low-cost chemical and biological analyses. Each test is designed to remove or render biologically unavailable a specific group of toxicants such as oxidants, cationic metals, volatile compounds, non-polar organic compounds and metal chelates (Mount and Anderson-Carnahan, 1988). Figure 13.3 presents the various Phase I tests.

The **oxidation reduction test** is designed to determine whether oxidants and other electrophiles are responsible for effluent toxicity. Examples of oxidants include chlorine, bromine, iodine, ozone, and chlorine dioxide. Sodium thiosulfate ($Na_2S_2O_3$) is added in varying ratios to produce reducing agent/total electrophiles solutions and thus reduces any toxicity due to the above compounds.

The **aeration test** is designed to determine whether the toxicants present are volatile. Sparging of samples using air and nitrogen gas are used to remove the volatile substances from solution. Examples of chemicals which may be detected using this method include benzene and hydrogen sulfide.

The **filtration test** involves passing samples of the test solution at three pH values (pH of 3, 7, and 11) through glass fibre filters. The test identifies which groups of compounds can be precipitated under acidic or alkaline conditions. Data from this test can help define treatment strategies.

The **pH adjustment test** is used to identify the presence of cationic and anionic toxicants. Changing the pH changes the ratio of ionized to unionized chemical species and since the later is the more toxic form, the toxicity of the solution will change as the pH is shifted.

In the **graduated pH test**, the pH of the effluent is adjusted within the tolerable range of 6.0 to 8.0 before retesting with aquatic organisms. This test is designed primarily to identify ammonia, hydrogen sulfide, and cyanide but some ionizable pesticides and heavy metals also can be identified.

The **Solid Phase Extraction (SPE) test** is designed to determine the effluent toxicity caused by non-polar organic compounds and metal chelates. The effluent is passed through a small column, which removes non-polar organic compounds. Toxicity reduction suggests the presence of toxic organic compounds.

The **chelation test** is used to determine if the toxicity is caused by cationic toxicants such as heavy metals. Ethylenediaminetetraacetate ligand (EDTA) is a strong chelating (binding) agent that produces non-toxic complexes with many metals and can reduce the toxicity of solutions containing metal ions.

Aquatic organism toxicity tests, performed on the effluent prior to and after treatment, indicate the effectiveness of the treatment and thus provide information on the nature of the toxicant(s). By repeating the series of toxicity characterization tests using samples of a particular effluent collected over a period of time, these screening tests can provide valuable information on the variability associated with the type of compounds causing the toxicity (Mount and Anderson-Carnahan, 1988).

Phase II of the TIE is directed toward identifying toxicants. Various chemical fractionation techniques such as high-performance liquid chromatography, mass spectroscopy, and further SPE tests may be used. The results obtained in Phase I can provide a guide to selecting appropriate techniques for Phase II.

For each toxicant that is identified in Phase II, the published literature is searched for LC_{50} values. Concentrations of the toxicant in effluent can be compared with the LC_{50} values. A list of suspected toxicants is then compiled.

Phase III of the TIE is used to confirm the suspected toxicants identified in Phase II. Techniques that can be used in Phase III include correlations, relative species sensitivity, spiking, and removal of one toxicant at a time from the effluent. In most instances, several tests are needed to confirm the toxicants. Research is continuing at the U.S. EPA to refine this phase of the overall approach.

Once a TIE is completed, it may be necessary to enter the next step of the TRE process control. In some cases, it is possible that Phase I of the TIE can indicate which treatment methods should remove the causative toxicant(s) from the effluent. Bench scale studies can be used to evaluate the feasibility of treating effluent toxicity on a large scale. The actual identity of the causative toxicant(s) may not be required, it is only necessary that enough information be available on the toxicant physical/chemical characteristics to predict which treatment options should be studied (Mount and Anderson-Carnahan, 1988). This is analogous to designing a treatment system to handle a specified biochemical oxygen demand (BOD) loading with little or no knowledge of the actual chemicals that comprise the BOD.

In other cases, Phases II and III may be needed to identify the toxicants. If a causative toxicant can be identified in an effluent, it can be tracked through the process line or effluent collection system to its source using chemical analysis (provided that it is not a by-product of other chemicals in the system). Once the source is identified a source investigation can be conducted. The source control may be in the form of improved spill control, process modification, substitution of raw materials, pretreatment and/or treatment.

13.6 SUMMARY

Current regulatory requirements of the MISA program specify acute lethality toxicity tests using rainbow trout and *Daphnia magna*. Within the next few years, facilities with lethal effluents will be required to control toxicity by employing Best Available Technology - Economically Achievable (BATEA).

Facilities that fail to achieve a non-lethal discharge may be required to perform a Toxicity Identification Evaluation/Toxicity Reduction Evaluation. A well-documented, stepwise investigative process for toxicant identification has been proposed recently by the U.S. EPA. The approach focuses first on identifying the physical and chemical nature of the toxicant(s), followed by the identification of the toxicant(s) and development of control alternatives. The approach may result in product substitution, process modifications and/or additional treatment.

Proposed regulations under both the MISA program and Environment Canada's new national effluent regulations may also require chronic sublethal toxicity tests placing increased emphasis on the impact of the discharge on the receiving water body. The types of effects that may be observed in sublethal tests include growth, maturation, spawning, and sensitive life stage survival.

REFERENCES

Burkhard, L. P. and Ankley, G. T., 1989. "Identifying Toxicants: NETAC's Toxicity-Based Approach". Environmental Science and Technology, 12(12):1438-43.

Craig, G., 1990. Persona communications. April 10.

Craig, G., Flood, K., Lee, J., and Thomson, M., 1983. "Protocol to Determine the Acute Lethality of Liquid Effluents to Fish". Aquatic Toxicity Unit, Quality Protection Section, Water Resources Branch.

Environmental Protection Act (EPA), 1989. "Ontario Regulation 695/88 as Amended to Ontario Regulation 533/89 Under the Environmental Protection Act: Effluent Monitoring—General". Schedule 4 —Toxicity Test Requirements.

Environment Canada, 1989. "Acute Lethality Test Using Daphnia Sp. Final Draft". Unpublished report of Conservation and Protection, Environment Canada.

Environment Canada, 1990a. "Draft Acute Lethality Test Using Rainbow Trout". Conservation and Protection, April.

Environment Canada, 1990b. "Draft Acute Lethality Test Using Daphnia Sp.". Conservation and Protection, April.

Johnson, W.W., and Finley, M.T., 1980. "Handbook of Acute Toxicity of Chemicals to Fish and Aquatic Invertebrates". U.S. Fish and Wildlife Service, Publication No. 137.

McLeay and Associates Limited, 1987. "Aquatic Toxicity of Pulp and Paper Mill Effluents: A Review". Environment Canada Report EPS 4/PF/1.

Mount, D.I., and Anderson-Carnahan, L., 1988. "Methods for Aquatic Organism Toxicity Reduction Evaluations: Phase I Toxicity Characterization Procedures, Second Draft—February 1988". U.S. Environmental Protection Agency, February.

Ontario Ministry of the Environment (MOE), 1984. "Water Management Goals, Policies, Objectives and Implementation Procedures of the Ministry of the Environment". May.

Poirier, D.G., Westlake, G.F., and Abernathy, S.G., 1988. "*Daphnia Magna* Acute Lethality Toxicity Test Protocol". Aquatic Toxicity Unit, Aquatic Biology Section, Water Resources Branch, MOE.

United States Environmental Protection Agency (U.S. EPA), 1989. "Short Term Method for Estimating the Chronic Toxicity of Effluents and Receiving Water to Fresh Water Organisms". Second edition, U.S. EPA 600/4-89/001, February.

Table 13.1
ACUTE LETHALITY TEST PROTOCOLS

Test Organism: Rainbow Trout (Salmo Gairdneri)
- 96-hour duration
- individual fish should weigh between 0.5 and 5 g
- the longest fish should not be twice the length of the shortest fish
- 10 fish per test container
- maintain dissolved oxygen concentration of 7 mg/L
- pH between 5.0 and 9.0 (prefer 6.0 and 8.5)
- temperature 15 ± 1 °C
- dilution water must be capable of maintaining healthy fish stocks for at least 10 days
- fish should not be fed within 24-h period prior to the test or during the test
- observations mandatory at 0.5, 1, 2, 4, 24 hours and every 24 hours thereafter (should be made as often as possible)
- five test concentrations (e.g. 100, 50, 25, 12.5 and 6.3%) and a control solution (100% dilution water)

Reference: MOE protocols, as described in Craig *et al.*, 1983

- six test concentrations (i.e. 10, 20, 30, 40, 65, 100%) and a control solution (100% dilution controls)

Reference: MISA monitoring program as described in, EPA, 1989

Test Organism: Water Flea (*Daphnia Magna*)
- 48-hour duration
- minimum of 10 organisms per chamber
- only used when water hardness is greater than 80 mg/L
- pH between 6.0 and 9.0 (prefer 6.5 and 8.5)
- temperature 20 ± 1 °C
- five test concentrations (e.g. 100, 50, 25, 12.5 and 6.3%) and a control solution (100% dilution water)
- observations mandatory at 1, 2, 4, 24, and 48 hours
- dissolved oxygen, pH, hardness, and conductivity must be measured immediately before and after the test is completed

Reference: MOE protocol, as described in Poirier *et al.*, 1988

Figure 13.1
CONVENTIONAL APPROACH TO IDENTIFYING EFFLUENT TOXICANTS

Step 1 Toxicity test of effluent

Step 2 Priority pollutant analysis

Step 3 Comparison of analysis results to literature values for aquatic organism toxicity

Step 4 Toxicant(s) identified—reduction, substitution and/or treatment of toxicant(s)

Toxicant(s) not identified—perform additional monitoring of parameters, in terms of both frequency and number of parameters

Figure 13.2
FLOW CHART FOR TOXICITY REDUCTION EVALUATIONS

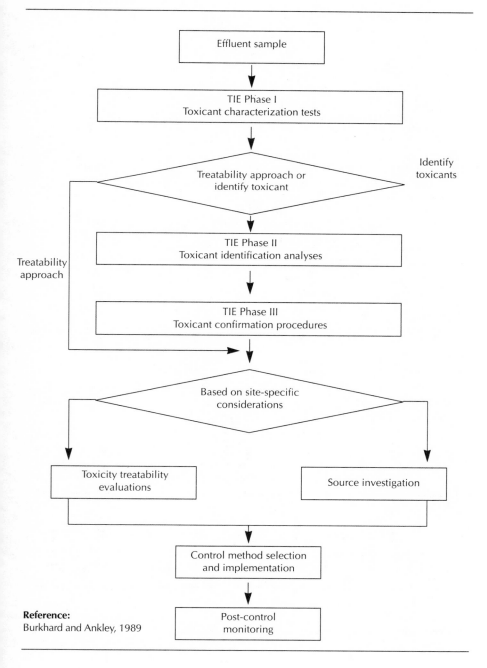

Reference:
Burkhard and Ankley, 1989

Figure 13.3
TOXICITY INVESTIGATION EVALUATIONS—
PHASE I TESTS

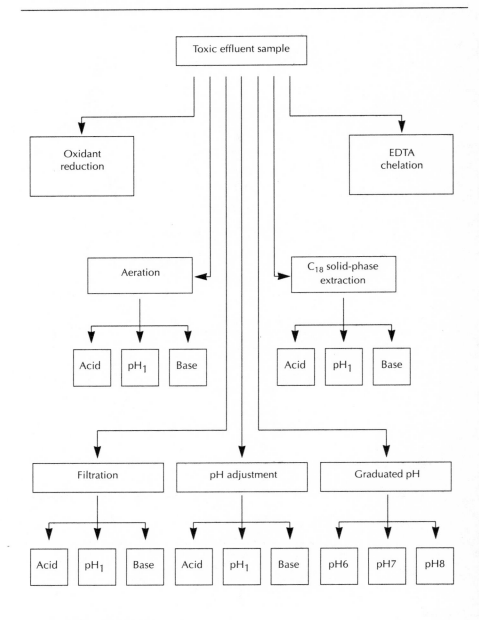

Reference: Burkhard and Ankley, 1989